RUTGERS UNIVERSITY-CAMDEN

StoryQuarterly, founded in 1975, is a literary journal published by Rutgers University in Camden, New Jersey. We welcome submissions only through our submissions portal, which is available at http://storyquarterly.camden.rutgers.edu. We no longer accept hard copy submissions. Any opinions expressed in this magazine are not necessarily the opinions of the staff. For subscriptions, please visit us online. For all other correspondence, email the editors at storyquarterlyeditors@gmail.com.

StoryQuarterly
Department of English
311 North Fifth Street
Armitage Hall
Rutgers University
Camden, NJ 08102

Book design by Jaime Watson
Cover design by Kevin Klinskidorn

Contents

NONFICTION

~~Letter From the Editor~~

A bricolaged Welcome from the SQ Staff in our writers' words...

We came here because we don't know why. To embody a role and not be able to escape it, together in a jumble like a necklace knotted at the bottom of a pocketbook. As soon as anyone writes anything, or wants to, they stop being normal. Wandering into a stranger's yard. I'm never lonesome when I go there. Is it me or is the city falling?

You tell me a place that is for us. We drifted for many years, watching our own faces change. The city became thick with stillness, a gem, gleaming before a backdrop of what was essentially silence. Been writing to an illusion and part of the illusion was my own age, my own body, an equation I didn't even know how to solve.

I was already writing eulogies on the ledger of my heart. Our mother told us to treat her like pottery, to not ask questions, to creep around the house like ants before their queen. Then she died. Her spirit slipped out of her body along with their beliefs.

In between two tall mountains is a terrible liar, people dressed as various shadow to leach some of her assured energy. They'll also tear your throat out, malodorous and frightening, subsequent pinched-faced, taut and tender.

Outside, it was somehow still light. We were with the dog out on the road walking toward the grave. We sat quietly, grinning at each other, making strange faces, mouths and eyebrows and tongues parading. Everyone laughed but everyone was not happy. It seemed like we were being sucked inside by a force we couldn't see.

We slammed the gate behind us and raced for what felt like blocks.

See Page 323 for Bricolage Source List

Bryan Washington

Cousin

I.

She'd turned 26 and I'd hit high school. Gloria blew through our lives on a Wednesday, and our mother told us to treat her like pottery, to not ask questions, to creep around the house like ants before their queen. Our mother, who returned grape bushels over single sourings; who'd shipped my sister Jenna to Tech with a knife in her pillowcase; who'd slipped into this country, this home, her life, on the whim of a fortune-teller, from the markets of Tank Hill, along the western coast of Negril, after she'd told her, peasant to peasant, that good things came to women who looked to the shore. This premonition cost her four American dollars, and if you asked my mother now you'd think she was still pissed off about it. So Gloria (thought my mother) was following a manifest destiny, universal to her people, ubiquitous to her heritage—although she may not have said this in so many words, or even at all if I'm honest.

II.

We'd heard about our cousin. It was the usual family circus. We knew she was coming from Kingston, after bouncing from Mandeville to Ochi to Portmore. She'd fled to South Beach, I think, after the island became inhospitable, back when the last thing you could hope for in Miami was hospitality. She'd been a student, once, and then a mother, briefly, and then (most scandalously) a prostitute, one of those women who open their legs for soursop (my mother's words again). We heard she'd had a baby, a little boy named Dylan, and they'd had to cut him out, which island doctors are loath to do; but then the baby died, from sepsis, or pneumonia, one of those things that occasionally happens to babies in some countries but never in others; and this, above all, was why she was coming to see us; for a change of scenery, some time away, a chance to slow things down.

III.

Our family moved, again, after my father landed the promotion. He translated transcripts for an oil mogul downtown, and the mogul had finally struck oil. Our new place sat on Knollwood and Willowick, in the middle of River Oaks, Houston's oasis for new money, but the only differences I could pick out were the paint, the veranda, the sofas choked in shrink wrap. Which made me ungrateful. Which my mother called another reason to welcome Gloria home—as a woman who'd been through *It*, someone who *appreciated* a rough time.

Jenna said that's all Jamaica was: a rough time. Four months upstate had made my sister sharp. Now she smoked kush with the windows open; she read *Les Fleurs du Mal* unabridged; she wore tight red pants and Sonic Youth tees, but never around our mother and always after dark. She fucked white boys from the corner store and left them in her bed. I caught one, once, checking his phone on the comforter, and when he finally saw me peeking I did my best to look indifferent.

You wouldn't know a rough time if it pissed on you, said my mother, nodding toward our father, who raised an empty Shiner as he nodded toward the television. He'd been to Jamaica twice. Pale, and graying, and broad-shouldered, even then, the second time around he made it back to the States with a wife.

Grow up and have babies, said my mother. Then you'll see.

Let one of them quit on you, she said. Then you'll see.

And she looked to me for confirmation, which I gave.

IV.

Gloria's dress glowed a shade of margarita. Her sandals smacked. You could see the tops of her ankles as she hovered toward baggage claim. She hugged the aunt she'd heard so much about, slid into the arms of her handsome white uncle. Jenna had opted out of the airport, promising a meal when we made it back home—but, really, I knew she was roasting a bowl, yakking on the phone with one of her tricks around the block.

When Gloria reached me, she bent to squeeze my ears.

And your name is, she said, in patois thick enough to knock on.

VIII.

I remember my father puckering.

And I remember my mother's face.

And Gloria waved to the rest of us, starting her long limp upstairs.

And we sat unspeaking, with the refrigerator's hum in the foreground, until Jenna reared back, slowly, and laughed.

IX.

Gloria grew up in Kingston, and she lived there until she couldn't, until it became something like a warzone, when it turned into what it is now. Her parents passed for intellectuals on the island—teaching literature at UWI—and my cousin grew up on wood floors, with Ravel and Mahler conducting the apartment. She took her first steps on paperbacks lining the rugs—on the face of Javier Marias, on the back of Derek Walcott, and even as Jamaica's knees began to buckle, under narcotics, under voodoo politics, and the sidewalks began to choke with the homeless, the drugged, and the cracked out, her parents held her close, they filled her ears with what comfort they could. She grew up loved. She never forgot that.

But, eventually, her folks got caught up too. Slowly at first. And then all of a sudden. The money for the coke came from money for their clothes, and then the money for their bills, and then the money for their apartment.

Later on, Gloria told me she hadn't been upset—she'd always been a dilettante, didn't need anyone telling her who to look at—but even walking to the library became a burden, it became a needless risk. Kingston had begun to swallow itself. She was risking her life for poems. And she felt herself sinking, whether or not she was in the house, parents prone on the floor, noses crusty from yesterday's binge.

Even still, they had to eat. So Gloria became the breadwinner. She was 15, with nothing like a marketable skill, but there are always ways to make some bank in the Caribbean if you're young and beautiful and willing.

She knew some girls who worked the resorts. They knew some girls who weren't opposed to another player.

Gloria started working the cruise ports. Businessmen and bachelors and newlyweds, mostly, but occasionally she'd find herself an islander, a big man with a little extra cash, and these were the ones she passed on to the next girl, because they reminded her of something she didn't want to think about. But, despite everything, she found time to read—she spent the money she was saving for a lifeline on books. She hit the resorts; she discovered Milton; she worked the coast; she discovered Rimbaud; she bought some heels; she discovered Babel; she took care of her skin; she discovered Rumi; she tried not to catch the clap; she discovered Borges; she caught the clap; she discovered Allende; she waited it out; she discovered Plath; she tried not to catch anything else. There'd been a baby named Dylan, she'd named him after the poet; but one day Dylan died, and of course she couldn't find the father. She couldn't even have guessed what he looked like.

X.

Our mother didn't retaliate after the kiss. This confused me. It disrupted a logical sequence of events. I remember when she spat on the grocer in Sharpstown, because he'd refused to accept an expired coupon for bananas. I remember when my father failed to replace the bedroom's air filters, and she'd stuffed them in herself, and he'd had to phone a repairman. I remember when Jenna first left for college, after the crying and the hugging and the promise of weekly visits; and how, after she hadn't called, for the second Sunday in a row, my mother rode the nine-hour bus to Lubbock to ask what, specifically, was the problem. But on that evening, and every other night for the next few months, all she did was grin.

Gloria's still smelling the sand, she said.

I was wild when I was her age too, she said.

All it takes is a little time, she said; but my father stayed out of her way—he'd jump a little when she slipped in the room.

XI.

But Gloria's presence wasn't a burden. My cousin was on bedrest—that was the point of her stay. And since she didn't ask for much at all, sometimes I even forgot about her. She slept in the guest room, although my mattress was what she'd been promised, but she never called me out on it. Gloria said it didn't matter. She could fit just about anywhere. And Jenna didn't doubt it, she said that vermin would always adapt.

In fact, Gloria said, I should sleep at the foot of her bed, or I should at least bring in a sleeping bag, she wouldn't mind the company.

My father was skeptical. He simply frowned when she brought it up. But my mother called this a Good Idea: I could act as a runner, I could keep her off her feet.

So I shook the cobwebs off some blankets from the attic, and after my first night on the floor Gloria told me she didn't need a runner, or an aide, or assistance, or whatever, because she just wanted company, she needed someone else to talk to, it made her think less of her son.

XII.

Going into the summer, I'd had my own plans: we'd entered that part of July where the days begin to swallow themselves. The houses in our neighborhood fit together like box tops, with their pastel reds and blues and whites, and I rode bikes with Ben Owens and Jeff Tan and Kyle Okri, blazing past porch stoops manned by the daughters we deified. Every once in a while, one of us got bold, asking if they had any ice water inside. We'd already talked about making it past the porch. What we'd do if they let us in, if they asked us to pull it out. This was the summer we were going to get laid, to touch and to suck and to fuck, if they let us. Eventually Ben snagged some condoms from his brother, but of course we had nowhere to put them; and we tried our hand at a dime of weed—courtesy of Jeff's older sisters downtown—but I spent that evening lost inside of myself, marveling at all of the space in my head no one had taken the time to tell me about.

XIII.

With my father negotiating Arabic downtown, and my mother scouring the museums for bargains, we mostly had the house to ourselves. Jenna and Gloria struck up a truce: if one shared her books, then the other would shut her mouth. Jenna holed up in her room with Bobby from the supermarket, and Rafa from the gas station, and Jacob from the pool, surfacing from time to time to ask why I was so useless. And despite clear instructions from her island doctor to stay in one place, to stop moving so goddamn much, Gloria found ways to get out and about, from the porch, to the living room, to the sidewalks lining the cul-de-sac. No one knew she was gone until she finally came back.

XIV.

Some days Gloria told me stories. She told me about the red-light district in Kingston. About the palms in Ocho Rios, which bent inwards like arches. About how roads sank in the hill country, how she'd found rabbit ears in the mud. She told me about trips to London, to São Paulo, to New York, and how the World Trade Center had made her feel mortal, like she didn't matter at all. She told me about beaches in Antigua where babies drank the water. About the seagulls in Haiti, how she'd fed them, how they'd thanked her.

In the mornings she brewed coffee and read. It was the only time that she glowed. She'd start with my father's *Business Affairs,* and my mother's outdated *Oprahs*; after lunch, she'd slip into Jenna's shelves, with the Bolaño and the Woolf and the Calvino and the Foucault. She flipped through Chekhov. She nosed through Tanikawa. She threw a long-lost copy of Huck Finn at the wall.

She asked me for highlighters and underlined everything. She read beautifully, deeply. I don't know how else to describe it.

One day, she was roaming through Rilke, she'd found something lovely, she'd had to tell someone about it; something about perception and confinement, how one must be something or other in order to represent something or other; and I finally asked her what she got out of it, what the words on the page had anything to do with her. The kind of question an idiot asks. But she took it seriously, she pursed her lips.

It's just another way to talk to the dead, she said.

It's another way to make a way, she said.

XV.

She finally brought up Dylan on a walk. Okri had skittered away on his bike, down the road and into the skyline, because Ben and Jeff had made it past the porch. We hadn't seen much of them lately. Gloria asked me who Okri was, and I called him a friend, my friend, and Gloria smiled, nodding, and in a tone of voice that I will never forget she insisted that she understood, even if I didn't yet, and then she squeezed my knuckles.

Dylan was underweight, she explained, but the doctor told me he'd grow.

Light like you (and here she prodded my stomach), or maybe more like your father.

Like his dad, I asked, and she agreed, but more like me.

His fingers were this big, she said.

I pushed my thumb through the circle she'd made, pointing toward the road and the city it led to.

The nurse said he cried too much, she said, but really he was laughing. That's it. All he ever did was laugh.

I told her she could have another baby, and she frowned—the first one I'd ever actually seen on her face. She said it probably wouldn't happen. She said her body couldn't take it (or, maybe, that she couldn't take it).

I knew I'd lost her, so I tried to backtrack: I said her son would've been a real man, the kind I would've looked up to, and she said, Yes, he would've been, and I knew that I'd done something Good.

XVI.

July was on its way out when my father got the second raise. The mogul had struck gold, again, and his profits trickled down to the lowest rung. We braced ourselves for another move; but my father said no, what we ought to do was wait; the neighborhood was nice, or at least nice enough; and besides, we had a house guest, supposedly on bed rest, and what were we as a family if not considerate of others. My mother made vague noises of taking a trip, swooping through Jamaica for the first time in years, but these were just words, we knew that they wouldn't, she hadn't touched its soil since she'd taken off from the tarmac.

One day, Okri and I spent an afternoon in the bayou. We walked the length of the neighborhood to reach it, until we crossed the freeway, where we had to wade through the muck in our sneakers. He suggested we take our shoes off, because of course they were getting filthy, the water was full of shit, and then we were stepping through it, soaking the rest of our clothes, we were sopping, really; so slowly, categorically, we began to strip; first our pants, as we stepped through the stream; our shirts, once we'd found ourselves tangled in vines; until we were wading through the water in our shorts, with the highway above us, where we reached a clearing beneath an overpass, and Okri and I laughed, just at the sight of each other, our clothes were irreparable, we smelled like shit; and we decided, or we came to the conclusion that we should grope one another, tenderly, and then furiously; and we did this, wordlessly, touching without kissing; and when he'd finished, and I'd finished, he made a joke about the cars, something banal, but necessary, if we were to survive the walk back.

And that's what we did. We picked up our shit and we walked back.

We made it to the neighborhood, and we slipped into the sneakers, and it isn't something we talked about then, or since.

XVII.

Obviously this upset me. I spent the next few days in a funk. My mood was indistinguishable to my parents—I was quiet most days; compounding that silence meant nothing whatsoever—and Jenna didn't care much one way or the other. One morning, eating an egg sandwich at the table, I began to shake, my toes first, my legs, until the chills made their way to my fingers, and Jenna watched me from the counter, said I'd never get any ass if I stayed so fucking weird.

Gloria noticed. She was starting to get better. She'd mentioned buying her return ticket soon. She'd make a go of it, she said, it was time to start planning ahead; but my mother told her not to think anything of it—she really wasn't a burden. When Gloria asked me what was wrong, I told her nothing, nothing at all, but in a way that implied that everything was, in fact, very wrong, that the most wrong thing had occurred, that wrong had become my reality.

XVIII.

One evening, or many evenings later, I knew what I had to do. Gloria and I slept in the guest room, on the other side of the house. She slept late and she read, and sometimes she told stories, and other times she just cried herself to sleep, but on this particular night I asked her to tell me about her work.

She looked at me as if I were joking, or maybe it was because she hoped I was joking, but I wasn't. I wasn't. I told her I wanted to know.

She said she wasn't sure if she knew what I was asking. I really should go back to bed.

I said that my mother had called her a whore. A prostitute. A soursop woman.

I told her that she was all of those things.

That if they were true, then the least she could do was prove it.

We wore the same look on our faces, one of disbelief; that these words that were forming in my mind; that they were leaving my mouth; that they were in the air between us, the air we'd come to think of as our own.

But it wasn't, and they were; and I kept talking, I said terrible things.

I said the things she thought were her escape were no escape at all.

I said she felt like she had to escape because she had no escape.

I said her son was better off without her, that she was better off without a son.

When I'd finished she asked me if that was all. If it was, she said, then she was tired. She'd like to go to sleep. She said I should go to my room, my real room, and when I stood up to leave she said to shut the door behind me.

XIX.

From that evening on, I was ashamed.

I'd revealed more of myself than I'd meant to. There really was no excuse. And I did the only thing that I could, I treated my cousin like a ghost.

I no longer slept on the floor. I left every room that she entered, sat silently at every table. My mother slapped me, once, for ignoring her at dinner, and my father didn't acknowledge it, although he asked me, twice, if anything was wrong (I don't remember my response). Jenna didn't broach it, because I wasn't Jenna's problem, and even when I'd considered clueing her in I ended up changing my mind.

And then, one evening, Gloria slipped into my room. I wasn't sure what time it was, it could've been one or four, one of those hours when it no longer makes a difference. She asked me what was wrong, and I didn't reply. She asked me what was wrong, and I pretended to snore. She asked me what was wrong, and she touched my shoulder, and I told her I was broken. She asked me what that meant, and I didn't say anything to that, I opened my eyes and looked right at her, or I looked right past her, because I couldn't see anything at all.

We sat there in silence, with her holding my shoulder and me looking past her, and then she told me that she understood. Or that she didn't understand, not really, but she understood enough.

She placed her hand on my knee, and I watched it sit there, not moving, until it began to rise, until it reached my thigh, and then it rose higher, until she was touching my cheek, and she was looking at my face, and then we were kissing, and then it was both of her hands, and we looked through each other, deeply, because she was no longer on the edge of the mattress, she'd maneuvered herself on top of me, she'd slipped some of me inside of her, and she told me to look up, to look into her eyes, and I couldn't do it, it wouldn't work, I started crying, my god, until she finally set her ear on my shoulder and told me everything would be fine, everything would be okay, it would all turn out alright.

XX.

About a month later, Gloria flew back to Kingston. Jenna didn't see her off this time either. My sister was packing for her own return, and she gave Gloria the roughest of nods, and my cousin wished her well in all of her future endeavors. I didn't show my face—I told everyone I was sick. My mother told me this didn't matter, I didn't know when I'd see her again, but my father told her to leave me alone, it wouldn't make anything better, and besides, I only felt that way because I loved her. This, he said, was obvious.

I remember watching Gloria step into the van from the driveway, and she waved from inside the car, and eventually I waved back. She'd left a book for me on her bed, she'd written something in it, she told me I'd know when to read it. But I didn't read it then. And then the book was lost. And I left home, and I came back, and when it was finally time or when I thought it was finally time, it wasn't there to open, whatever she'd written had disappeared. I asked my mother where she'd put it, where the fuck it could've gone, and she said there were so many books in the house she had no way of knowing for sure. She told me to calm down. It couldn't have been that important. And, if it was, then surely I could just buy another one.

XXI.

One day, years later, I thought I would find her. I'd been living abroad, in an unpainted building, living as if I had no family, because at the time I liked to think that I didn't. I knew my father wouldn't have it, so I called my mother from the States, and she was quick to tell me that she hadn't kept up with Gloria. She had no idea where my cousin was staying. And why the hell did I care now. What should've happened then was I should've given up, I should've chalked it up to something that'd happened in my life, one of those doors you close before you've realized doors can close.

But Jenna called me, from her home in Lubbock, with her yard and her kids and her white boy in accounting, a few months later, and asked why I needed it. I told her it didn't matter. She gave me a number anyways.

No one answered the first time I called. I called back again. I knew how the phone lines in Jamaica work. I called back again.

And another day, months later, I called, and a boy answered, and I said, hello, and he said, hello, and I said nothing, and he said, hello. We stood on either side of the line, him listening to me breathe and not hanging up, and me breathing, listening to him listen to me. And then I hung up.

ALIX OHLIN

THE UNIVERSAL PARTICULAR

Of course she'll never admit it to anybody but the first thing she feels, seeing the girl, is relief: how awkward and homely she is, acne-splattered, not to mention overweight, bent under jet lag and luggage, coming down the escalator at the airport with a glazed look in her eyes. She might even be a little cross-eyed. Tamar's holding a sign with her name–AZIZA–written in black marker, but the girl walks right past her. Maybe she's not familiar with the convention of sign-holding. Maybe she's illiterate. That's unkind, and also impossible. Aziza and Albert have been messaging for months; obviously she can read. Many's the time, late at night, Tamar has watched her husband hunch over his phone, thumbing long responses to this girl who just marched by, a dirty green backpack strapped to her shoulders, like a soldier in a shabby army.

Tamar has to jog to catch up. The girl disappears into a restroom, and Tamar waits outside. She throws the sign in the trash. When Aziza comes out, Tamar, ready with a brilliant smile, calls her name.

The girl startles. Her first reaction is a kind of horrified grimace, which she smooths away slowly, without complete success. Tamar leans in, offers a hug. Aziza is stiff and Tamar's palms meet the backpack instead of her body.

"Welcome," she says. "Welcome."

"Where is Albert?" says the girl.

"He had to work, he's so sorry, his hours are super intense lately, he'll tell you all about it," Tamar prattles. She's trying to tug the backpack off the girl's shoulders but Aziza's fingers are curled tight around the straps as if she fears being robbed. Giving up, Tamar grabs an elbow instead, guiding the girl outside to the parking lot while keeping up commentary on the weather, the traffic, the nuisances of travel.

Aziza says nothing. She smells of sweat and plane air. There's a scratch on her arm that looks infected. They find the Honda.

Tamar says, "We're going to take good care of you."

As they drive, Aziza stares out the window at the airport terminals, the planes lifting and landing. It's a grubby airport, outdated and partially under renovation, and the car moves sluggishly past traffic cones and construction machines. On the steering wheel, Tamar's nails gleam fluorescent orange, like a warning. Her black hair is streaked with blue; on her right bicep is a tattoo of a tomato plant, faded red circles with green tendrils that swirl toward her armpit. Aziza can't imagine loving any vegetable enough to ink it on her arm. She wishes to be elsewhere, while knowing there is no elsewhere for her to be. Mainly what she feels is embarrassment. Why did she tell Albert so much, why did she beg for his help? In truth, a lot of the time she forgot she was writing to an actual person. She treated the messages like a diary, and into them she poured all her hatred of her mother, her anger, her fears. Her loneliness. She and her mother fought constantly, right up to the day of her death, and then all of a sudden Aziza realized that she had no one, no place to go. From a continent away, Albert's words bobbed into her inbox like a life-raft on a stormy sea. *We're your family,* he wrote. *Why don't you come stay with us for a while? A change will do you good.*

A change will do you good. It seemed so optimistic, so North American. Aziza's life had consisted of nothing but changes, of which her experience had been less good or bad than crushingly inevitable. First her childhood in Somalia, where her birth father vanished before she could even begin to remember him, and then her mother meeting Alvin, who worked for a technology company with interests in Africa, and latching on to him with a desperation that was transparent to Aziza even as a child. But not, apparently, to Alvin. Or maybe he didn't care. In any case he took Aziza and her mother home with him to Stockholm, and settled them in a quiet, boxy apartment in Djursholm. At the wedding she was introduced to Albert, her new father's cousin, although the day was a blur to her now. She learned Swedish and English. When she was twelve Alvin died of heat exhaustion on a business trip to Uganda. Abandoned, she and her mother turned on each other. Aziza stayed out late, got in trouble at school. Her mother threatened to send her back to Somalia, which made Aziza laugh bitterly and say, "Go ahead." Her mother was a terrible liar. She lied the day she told Aziza she was sick but it wasn't serious, that everything would be fine. She lied when she said, at the very end, trying to make up for all their fights, that Aziza had made her proud. She wanted to stage some scene of kindness that would linger in Aziza's memory, even if it was a fiction. Then she died.

Aziza, eighteen years old, three times orphaned, responded to Albert's gentle inquiries with messages she spent hours composing. He told her about himself and Tamar, how they had longed for children of their own but weren't able to have any. Then: the invitation. Now: a car speeding along the highway as fat raindrops splash against the windows and Tamar hums a tuneless song.

Albert hits the garage opener with one hand while turning the steering wheel with the other. He has it down to a science, knowing exactly how close he has to be to the house for the opener to work, how much he has to slow down to bring the car in. It's dumb but it makes him feel a little like Batman, driving his car into the bat cave. Also a perfectly coordinated docking in the garage, with zero lag time, saves him from conversation with his next door neighbor, Oszkar, an underemployed "consultant" who seems to spend all day in his "home office," watching out the window for Albert to come home. Any time he catches Albert lingering in the driveway he's there instantly, with a hearty handshake and some pronounced opinions about the news of the day. Oszkar thinks we need to hit back hard against the terrorists. He thinks climate change is a myth—"The weather's always been changing, since the dinosaurs, no?"—and that immigration needs to be curtailed. "It's too much!" he says, clapping Albert on the back. "There are no more jobs!"

Albert usually nods and smiles, mumbles something about dinner. But every once in a while he has to disagree, for his own moral peace of mind or whatever, and then there goes half an hour, as they stand in the driveway and hash it out, knowing neither of them will change their minds. Oszkar loves to argue. "Good talk!" he always says at the end, after having yelled explosively at Albert for a while.

"Why do you even engage with him?" Tamar wants to know when he finally comes inside, and Albert says, "Some statements you can't let pass," and Tamar says, "The curry is cold," and Albert sighs and says, "We do have a microwave," and then they both start drinking.

Tonight's evasive manoeuvers are successful, but still he sits for a minute in the darkened garage, door closed, before he goes in. He's nervous to meet Aziza. The last time he saw her she was a bright-eyed child of—what, seven? Now, he knows from Facebook, she's a young woman with long dark hair and her mother's scowl. It's possible he wrote her too much, and too often. It's certain he did. And he had a few too many the night he invited her to stay—*we'll get you a student visa, you can take classes for a while, have a great time!*—and when he woke up the next morning, furry-tongued and regretful, she'd already begun making plans. Tamar was not pleased; but Tamar is rarely pleased.

Inside, he smells the tofu lasagna she always makes for guests. Aziza is asleep on the couch in front of the TV, which is showing news about a bombing in Europe. He frowns and turns it off, and the silence wakes her; she moves upright, wiping drool from her mouth, and sees him. She's both younger than he thought, and older.

"Hello, hello," he says.

Aziza struggles to get up off the couch, which appears to fight to keep her down. The couch wins. He sits down beside her instead and gives her a semi-hug, trying not to make contact with her surprisingly large breasts. What does he know of teenagers, especially girls? Not a thing. He'd been writing to an illusion, and part of the illusion was himself as a father figure, dispensing wisdom and care. "How are you?"

"Tired," she says. Her accent is straight up British, as his cousin's had been.

"Did Tamar show you your room?"

"It's very nice, thank you." In truth the room intimidated her; it was enormous and carpeted in white, with a bed twice the size of the one she had at home. The posters on the walls were of rock bands she didn't recognize. She'd placed her suitcase against the wall and fled.

Tamar enters clapping her hands, saying "Dinner's ready," then frowns as they both flinch at the sound. She is irritated by social awkwardness, despite often being the cause of it. They eat quickly and with little conversation, and then Aziza is released to the big, white room.

*

Several days later, Tamar and Albert host a party and invite the neighbors. Cindy and Mike, from down the block, bring their two kids, who are close to Aziza's age. Linda and Rafael bring their rambunctious ten-year old twin boys, who will go through the bedroom, ransacking closets and medicine cabinets if given the chance (Tamar has learned this the hard way). And Oszkar—you might as well invite him, because he'll come over either way—brings his girlfriend Tilda, who is from the Philippines and never says anything, though she seems to understand English just fine. They carry a platter of beautifully arranged tropical fruit and a large bouquet, presenting it to Aziza with ceremony.

"Thank you," she says woodenly, and stands there with the flowers gripped in her hands, clearly not knowing what to do with them. So far, saying "thank you" and standing still is how she handles most situations.

"Let's put those in water!" Tamar says cheerily, guiding her to the kitchen. Under Tamar's care, Aziza already looks better than when she arrived. She's wearing a well-cut sundress that flatters her hourglass figure, and the salicylic acid face wash is clearing up her skin. On their trips to the mall, the drugstore, the spa where Tamar works as a massage therapist and where she gets her friend Miriam to give Aziza a facial, Aziza has said next to nothing. She keeps her eyes down, though more than once Tamar has caught the girl studying her, her gaze fixed on Tamar's tattoos, her nose piercing, her hair. Surely they have piercings and tattoos in Sweden; for godssakes, she and Albert live in the suburbs and people here don't look twice.

Tamar is losing patience. Albert was the one who invited her, and of course Albert is now busy at work, monetizing his inexplicably successful blog, and the only time Aziza perks up is when he comes home. Sometimes they sit on the couch together late at night, whispering, looking up guiltily if Tamar comes in.

Albert, at her direction, is grilling veggie kabobs in the backyard. He knows nothing about grilling and doesn't care about it either, just turns the things over and over until Tamar tells him they're done. Mike lingers near him, drinking beer after beer.

"So she's, what, a refugee?"

"No, not at all. She's my cousin."

Mike belches discreetly. "But she's like African?"

"Somalian." Albert has to go through the whole thing, how his father moved here from Sweden, but Alvin was his Swedish cousin, who married Aziza's mother, and even though the story is clear and succinct he can tell he has lost Mike's attention, that all he heard was *Somalian*.

"She must be psyched to be *here*," Mike says, "after Africa."

Albert sighs. All the neighbors are idiots. He and Tamar bought this house years ago, for almost nothing, at a foreclosure sale. The schools were good and they were planning a family that never came. It had seemed like a joke, a role-playing exercise. *We're moving to the suburbs!* Albert at the time was still playing with his band and had started his website, *Beards of North America,* as a pastime during long bus rides. When he was on tour he would interview men about their soul patches and Van Dykes and take their pictures, and he'd post the interviews in a serious, white-paletted layout, as if these dudes were talking about national security or famine or something. Then all of a sudden he had thousands of clicks a day and advertisers were all over him. He had meetings with venture capitalists. Boxes of sample grooming products kept showing up at the house. Now he has an office and contracted photographers who sell him images for the subsidiary sites–*Beards of Japan, Beards of New Zealand, Beards of Scandinavia*–and a twenty-four-year-old assistant who handles the social media accounts and flirts with him aggressively, enjoying how it makes him uncomfortable, which he actually finds pretty insulting. He and Tamar should have moved away a long time ago, but instead they slid into a static, low-grade misery that made planning for a different future impossible. Now somehow all he can do is keep rushing headlong into the days, no matter how stupid the days are.

He should slow down and focus, though, on Aziza. She's standing across the yard getting harangued by Oszkar about God only knows what, and he lifts a hand in her direction, then turns it on himself and pretends to shoot himself in the head. She looks alarmed, then laughs. When she laughs she's beautiful, with a wide, gorgeous smile that makes you wish it didn't disappear so quickly. She is a girl whose life has offered her almost no reason to smile like that, and still it's the moment when she seems most herself.

Tamar is dragging Tim, Cindy and Mike's son, across the yard by force. He's nineteen and shy, with dark hair that falls over his eyes. From what Mike says, Tim spends all his time in the basement, obsessed with some online multiplayer game set in apocalyptic New Mexico. It's based on an ancient civilization with its own language, in which Tim, though he barely graduated high school, is fluent. Aziza nods at Tim, and he nods back. Tamar abandons them, a look of satisfaction on her face. Then she scowls at Albert and makes a gesture he understands too late. He has burned the kabobs.

*

In the Taymors' dark basement, Aziza and Tim sit with consoles in their hands. They don't talk, but Aziza doesn't mind. She has played the game before. People don't expect it from a girl—Tim, who invited her under duress, clearly didn't expect it—and she uses this to her advantage, playing timidly at first as she susses out his skill level, then venturing into a side canyon and stealing his stone weaponry when he least expects it. Some guys would freak out but Tim only glances at her with respect.

They break for soda and chips, which his mother brings downstairs on a tray. The look she gives Aziza broadcasts sharp betrayal; she wanted Aziza to lure Tim outside, instead of joining him here in artificial reality. But Aziza can imagine nothing more artificial than the reality outside, the hum of vehicles disappearing into garages, the angry wheeze of leaf blowers operated by men in masks, like a gardening militia. Here in the basement, her thumbs bent and ready, she feels invisible. Sweat gathers under her arms; she has to pee. She's more comfortable than she has been in weeks.

Only when Tim's mother comes back and tells her it's time to go does she understand that hours have passed.

"Bye."

"Bye."

Outside, it's somehow still light. The walk home is only three minutes long but Aziza drags it out as long as she can, scuffing her new running shoes against the curb until the rubber frays at the tip. She dreads Tamar's cheerful cruelty and the long hours until Albert comes home. She's been treated worse—at school, when she first came to Sweden, girls asked if they could touch her hair and then whispered about it afterwards. Once a boy in her class told her excitedly that he'd found a picture of her family in a magazine. It was a pack of dogs. But there is something particularly painful about Tamar's sugary care, her wide smile and flat dead eyes, her constant, unstated insistence that Aziza should be and look and act different than she does.

Can she dash straight from the front door to her room without seeing Tamar? She can only try.

But Tamar isn't home. No one is home. It's the first time Aziza has been alone all summer. Set free, she drifts around the house, snooping. Vaguely now she remembers Tamar saying she'd be working late, and that Aziza should help herself to the cashew nut casserole in the fridge. All the food Tamar makes is vegan and gluey, and anyway Aziza is pleasantly full of chips. She wanders into Tamar and Albert's bedroom. They have a bed with controls on the side, that each person can raise or lower as they wish. Tamar's half is propped higher than Albert's. It makes Aziza think of her mother's bed at the hospital, and she averts her eyes from it. Instead she runs her hands across Albert's shirts—he owns a ton of them, in endless variations of blue and white. She doesn't know what he does, something online; she pictures him in a loft office, cracking jokes with his employees, casual but business-like with his sleeves rolled. He looks like a nicer version of the Alvin she remembers. He's younger and fitter and also not bald, and his eyes are kinder and more wrinkled from smiling. She wishes he would put his arm around her sometime. She wishes she could curl up next to him like a cat and be petted, her body tiny like a cat's is tiny, tucked into itself. She would purr.

She runs her fingers through Tamar's jewelry, opens her bedside drawer: magazines, costume jewelry, lipstick. On Albert's side, the nightstand is covered with coins and crumpled dollar bills. She takes nothing. She knows she'd be suspected. She knows Albert and Tamar's carelessness is just a show they put on for themselves; they pay more attention to little things than they let on.

There had been some talk, over email, about her enrolling in summer classes, maybe something with computers, that might help her in an eventual career. But deadlines were missed and paperwork unfiled. "I don't *know* what kids around here do," she hears Tamar telling Albert one night. Her tone is exasperated. "How am I *supposed* to know?" Albert's answer is low and unintelligible, as always.

Aziza decides to try babysitting. At the market with Tamar, she has seen flyers on the bulletin board, so she puts up her own, listing the number of the cell phone Tamar got her. Soon she has more work than she can handle; the parents are desperate, even willing to overlook the fact that she doesn't drive. She takes the bus all over, drags kids away from flat screen televisions, makes them play in their lush backyards. She has no particular affection for children, but isn't scared of them either. "You're no nonsense," a mother says to her, "I like that." Aziza repeats this term whenever she meets a new parent, despite not entirely understanding what it means. "I'm no nonsense," she says. "Understandable, given where you're from," a father muses, and she doesn't answer. She has found that not answering is usually the best answer.

Soon her own nightstand drawer is filled with bills, which she keeps tied in a rubber band; she has nothing to spend the money on except candy, which she buys from the convenience store and eats on the bus, the cheap American chocolate dissolving fast on her tongue.

One evening, trudging home from the bus stop, she is accosted by Oszkar, who is out front spraying his flower beds with a hose. "My lady," he says to her, and she says nothing. It sounds sarcastic. He's a short hairy man wearing what look like pyjama pants, striped and floppy, and a T-shirt that hangs over his jutting belly like an awning over a porch.

"How's it going over there? You surviving the dungeon masters?"

She nods. He's trying to get her to admit something or confess something. She has seen him, at night, standing at his bedroom window, trying to see into Tamar and Albert's house.

"If it gets too much, feel free to come over and hang with me and Tilda. Pop a beer or whatever. Let off some steam."

"Okay," she says.

"You making any friends? Meeting any boys?"

"I'm quite busy," she says, and something about this—her accent? her gravity?—makes him laugh. His eyes graze her body hungrily. She's been flirted with before, but never quite so brazenly as this. It wouldn't be true to say she likes it, indeed she finds him disgusting. But she would like somebody else to look at her like Oszkar is, ravenous and direct. She'd like to hold somebody's attention so tightly that they can't look away.

As if sensing her desire a car speeds fast around the curb and hurtles into the open maw of the garage. Albert gets out and heads straight for them, his face red and furious.

"Hey neighbor!" Oszkar waves.

Albert ignores him. "You all right?" he asks Aziza.

She nods. Albert puts his arm around her, a pressure on her shoulders turning her towards the house. Oszkar is unperturbed. He flicks the water across the heads of his pansies and grins at Albert.

"Don't forget what I said," Oszkar calls after them, and when Albert asks her what it was, Aziza tells him she can't remember, which only makes him scowl more.

*

Albert is drunk. He's brushing his teeth too hard, which always sets Tamar on edge. He'd killed most of a bottle of wine over dinner and Tamar watched Albert quiz Aziza about the creepy neighbor, what he'd said and done, while the girl grew first flustered, then sullen. Albert never knows when he's gone too far, doesn't understand that he's acting less like a protective patriarch than his own brand of creep.

"Let it go," she told him, only to have him turn on her.

"Like you care," he said, and she could tell from Aziza's brief, crumpled smile that she agreed. An army of two, massed against her. Tamar stood up, carried her plate to the sink, and left.

Now Albert sways as he gets into bed, lying on his side away from her. She places a hand on his shoulder and he doesn't stiffen, but he doesn't move either. He's numb to her. She lies on her back, looking at the red curtains, the dark blue wallpaper. They'd picked these things out together, years ago, when they'd still shared the same taste. In this bed she'd lain after the third miscarriage and told Albert she was done trying. *No more*. He'd nodded and held her hand, and she'd thought he understood, that he would not be angry. But she was wrong. In this bed, before that, she'd lain after sex, when they first married, astonished that he was her husband, and she was his wife. She'd wanted him so badly, had in fact stolen him from her roommate Brenda and burned up that friendship with zero regrets. *I got what I wanted.* Even after the wedding, she was still amazed. Now in this bed she lies still and feels him revealed as the stranger he's been for so long. He rustles and settles, snoring. She almost feels tenderly towards him, out of a habit of trying to keep loving him; then understands that the person she feels tenderly towards, the object of all her compassion, is herself.

*

Tim knows Tamar and Albert don't keep the back door locked, just as he knows that Oszkar keeps a spare key under the door mat and Mrs. Cooper has an alarm system sign that's just for show. He used to go through all the houses in the neighborhood when he was in high school, an anthropologist of the ordinary. Creepy gamer kid is a cliché to which he strenuously objects, but sometimes he just got so bored. His sister Tanya came with him once, in between expeditions to smoke cigarettes in underpasses with her Goth friends, but all she wanted to do was look for booze and drugs and sex toys. He told her that her mind lacked subtlety and she rolled her eyes at him and left, which was how most conversations between them ended.

It's been a while since he visited the houses, but meeting Aziza has sparked his curiosity again. He wants to see her room, her clothes, the whatever-secret-inside she keeps hidden beneath her calm exterior. They've spent hours gaming together but still rarely talk. He needs a clue, some wedge of information he can use to pry her open.

The house smells dead inside; not dirty but too clean, uninhabited, despite the three people living here. In the recycling bin are a surprising number of empty wine bottles and couple of pizza boxes. Tamar and Albert's bedroom is the only messy part of the house, with dirty laundry on the floor and dressers littered with crap. He picks up some stray dollar bills, a necklace, a tie, and stuffs them in his pocket. He doesn't want these items for themselves; he wants to have taken, to have rearranged the air around their possessions only enough for Tamar and Albert to sense the disturbance.

In Aziza's room he sniffs the air for the solution to the riddle of her. But he finds nothing. Her clothes lie neatly folded in drawers. She keeps no journal, reads no books. The place is emptier than a hotel room. She has perfected her own absence. He liked her before, but now, seeing this rigor and demarcation, the discipline of a ghost, he swoons.

*

This time it's Tamar's turn. She actually forgot about the Taymors' party, and had a drink or three at home after a long day at work. This guy Ruben, one of her regulars, was such a dick to her—he always was, grazing her body as she leaned over him; once he'd even stuck out his tongue and licked her hip. All he got was a mouthful of the apron where she stashed her lotion, so what was even the point? Being a dick was the point. She complained to her manager Beth and all Beth said was "business isn't great, Tamar," and that was that. Today Ruben actually pinched her butt and she wheeled around and said, "What in the everlasting godforsaken fuck? I mean what fucking year do you think this is, Ruben?" and stormed out of the spa without finishing her shift. She probably didn't have a job to go back to tomorrow. So she'd downed some gin and chased it with tonic, too upset to even mix them in the same glass, and then, when she saw Oszcar and Tilda parading past her house, their goddamn fruit platter—did they ever bring anything else?—held aloft like an offering to the gods, she remembered. Albert was supposed to meet her there and who knew about Aziza; she kept her own hours these days. Tamar had asked Albert once, in the early morning, just how long the girl was going to stay, but things between them were so frosty that he hadn't even answered the question. She couldn't skip the party because then the Taymors would ask why and if there was one thing she couldn't stand it was Cindy's Wrinkled Brow of Concern. Once, at the grocery store, she'd caught Tamar smiling at a toddler riding in a cart, and she'd placed her palm on Tamar's forearm and said sympathetically, "Albert told Mike about your trouble. It must be so hard," and Tamar, dark with heartbreak, had said, "Actually I'm relieved. Kids horrify me," and Cindy frowned with the greatest look of pity Tamar had ever seen. She can't go through a scene like that again. She must be unassailable. So she puts on a short-sleeved polka dot dress and gels her hair into curls and walks very steadily down the street, carrying a bottle of wine in a silver gift bag.

In the Taymors' yard, plastic sheeting covers the picnic tables, onto which Cindy is throwing down crabs and boiled corn. Albert and Aziza sit together at one end, wearing bibs and expressions of pliant misery. Tamar has never been less hungry, and she escapes to the kitchen, where Oszkar is mixing martinis. When he sees her, he leers, as he usually does; she has never actually seen him with a woman other than Tilda, whom she suspects is more a hired housekeeper than a girlfriend, so she doesn't take it seriously. She deposits her wine and picks up a martini instead. They cheers.

The Taymors' teenage children drift past, glance outside at the party, and refuse it, the girl going upstairs, the boy down. To Tamar's surprise, Aziza wipes her hands, comes inside, and follows the boy downstairs.

"Young love," Oszkar says knowingly. "The hormones do the talking."

"Don't be gross," Tamar says.

"What you call gross, I call beauty. Sex is nature's most beautiful invention."

"That's also gross," Tamar says irritably. "Where's your handmaiden?"

"My what?"

"Tilda."

"She went home to get more fruit."

"Of course she did," Tamar says.

Oszkar is standing very close to her, his spittle bursting against her ear. "You look very nice," he says.

"Are you hitting on me?"

"I've been hitting on you for years."

"Shameless."

"I notice you don't say gross."

Tamar flushes. Oszkar is disgusting, pot-bellied and scruffy-bearded. To this party he has worn shorts that fall below his knees and a yellow T-shirt that reads, "Silence is golden. Duct tape is silver." Looking at him, she thinks about people interviewed on the news after their neighbor commits some terrible crime, saying, "He seemed like a nice guy. You would never suspect." Oszkar is not such a person. You would suspect him of anything.

Outside, Albert is talking to Mike, waving a crab leg around as he makes some point. He has become the kind of man who makes a lot of points, who cares about the winning of unwinnable arguments. Oszkar is kissing her, an attack on her person that she observes more than participates in, though she does not object. *I mean who even cares at this point*. There are arms around her, there are lips moving against her neck, her cheek, her earlobe. The sleeve of her dress slips off her shoulders. Over Oszkar's back some movement catches her eye, and she looks up to see Aziza and Tim watching her, both of their expressions neutral. Without saying anything Tim opens the fridge door, takes out two cans of soda, and leads Aziza back downstairs.

Later, at home, they fight. "This is like some kind of parody," Albert hisses. "Suburban wife misbehaves. Is it a joke to you?"

"Yes, it's a joke," she says grimly. "It is beyond hilarious."

She wants to tell him that this is what adulthood is, to embody a role and not be able to escape it. Self-parody is inevitable. Instead she sits on the edge of the bed with hands folded contritely in her lap, a posture that also feels like self-parody, even though her grief and shame are real.

"Oh for Christ's sake," Albert says, and goes to sleep on the couch. But he can't sleep, and stays up too late watching talk shows. At a certain point Aziza pads into the living room wearing a hooded sweatshirt and yoga pants. He sits up and makes a space for her on the couch. She doesn't look at him or talk to him, just stares at the TV as if spellbound. He is not glad of the company. He has been mortified enough, today.

"I'm sorry," he says finally. "I thought this summer would be better for you."

She shrugs. "It's no worse than at home."

He laughs. "You're a real diplomat."

She tucks her knees up under her chin, and he sees he's hurt her. "I'm sorry," he says again. "I appreciate your honesty."

She doesn't answer. On TV, an actress tells a story about eating too much cheese. The host guffaws. It's not a funny story, but Aziza smiles with what looks like real delight, the blue glow of the screen lighting her face with a spooky fire.

*

Tamar's hangover is extreme. She lies beneath the blanket as if entombed in concrete. Albert came into the room just long enough to dress, and then the front door closed a second time, when Aziza left. Now she stills in silence, her head deep in the pillow like a fossil in the dirt. She is bleached and dry; she is the long ago dead. It's seriously time to stop drinking. Groping blindly she finds her phone and lifts it to her face. A text from Beth says, *Meet me at 10 if you want to keep your job.*

In the bathroom, she makes herself throw up, then swallows four Advil and a Ritalin. She can do this. She armors herself in makeup, then stops by the nightstand for her favorite necklace, the garnet pendant she inherited from her mother and which isn't there.

It is the absence that wakes her up. She stiffens; ransacks her jewelry box; calls Albert, who says he hasn't seen it. "It's probably in a pocket somewhere," he says.

"You know I would never put that necklace in a pocket," she says. Of course he does know; he knows the whole story of the necklace that came with Tamar's grandmother from Germany in 1936 and which her mother pressed into Tamar's palm before she died, requesting that Tamar pass it on to her own children, which her mother died believing Tamar would still one day have. Tamar doesn't need to voice the accusation; it's in the air between them.

"I'm sure you'll find it," is all he says. "I have to go."

In the guest bedroom, she parts the sheets, the pillowcases, opens the drawers, and finds nothing. Most of Aziza's things are still in her backpack; the only items hanging in the closet are the clothes Tamar has bought for her, barely worn and in some cases with the tags still on. Tamar is shaking. It is terrible to be invaded, and even worse to be refused.

Anger dignifies her. Briskly, with little effort, she cows Beth, promising to sue if she gets fired and making Beth promise to ban Ruben from the spa. She treats herself to an almond milk chai latte and then returns to the house and buys Aziza a plane ticket back to Stockholm. That evening, when Aziza and Albert are watching television, Tamar informs them both that it's time for Aziza to go home.

"Wait, what?" Albert says. "This is because of the necklace?"

"No," Tamar says. "It's because of everything."

Aziza doesn't know what necklace they're talking about. She thinks about the apartment in Stockholm which still contains her mother's things, everything waiting to be sorted, sold, given away. The place is too big for Aziza to afford, and she will have to move somewhere. Lately she's been thinking of going to school in London. She's good with computers. She will walk in the rain to high grey buildings, where she will scroll through line after line of code. When she thinks about this distant future, she is calm. Only on the plane, a week later, after stilted farewells, does she burst into tears that disturb her seatmate, a businessman flying through Amsterdam on his way to a sales meeting in Frankfurt.

"Are you all right?" he asks her, and she nods silently. She is embarrassed not because of the crying but because she is in love with Albert, and the thought of never seeing him again is more than she can bear. In her backpack, rolled into a tight tube, is one of his blue striped shirts, stolen from the hamper, dank with his smell. When she hugged him at the house, on her final night, she leaned into him, her cheek wet, and then lifted a hand to his face. She felt him go rigid. Now her grief and humiliation mix together, and she sobs into the tiny oblong window, barely noticing when they leave the ground.

At home, Tamar also cries. She and Albert sit on the couch together in the early evening upon their return from the airport, the windows open, a summer breeze tickling the curtains. They never found the necklace, despite ransacking Aziza's room and bag and asking her about it over and over, unable to make sense of her confusion. She acted as if she had no idea what they were talking about, but didn't defend herself either, seeming to accept their accusations as inevitable. "She must have thrown it away," Tamar says. Passing by outside on his way home, Tim sees Tamar lean her head against Albert's shoulder. He doesn't feel guilty about the necklace; he's forgotten he took it, and couldn't even say where it is. Years from now, his mother will sell it at a garage sale for fifty cents, believing it to be junk. Tim and Aziza will keep in touch for a while, sometimes finding each other in the canyons of that ancient online civilization, sometimes texting or gchatting, until the too-clear longing in his messages makes her uncomfortable and she stops responding. Still he continues to believe that, if only she hadn't left so abruptly, she would have learned to love him back; under very slightly different circumstances, he thinks, they would have stayed together forever.

Wil Weitzel

Geese

We were with the dog out on the road walking toward the grave. There was this heavy fog all over the landscape and frost from the night still clung to the bushes. Crazy draping strands hung on the trees where spider webs covered with dew had turned to slings of ice brought low by this new weight so you could stretch and touch them. We'd barely hit the road when honking came over the forest on the mountain, then the birds themselves arrowed down pastures above the old barn, then the whole phalanx veered off through fog—so bodies were up there, briefly limned and struck with light.

Earlier, two of the horses had ambled down in wet-frozen grass toward the fence by the road and I had called to them. The roan had come. And the dog, nosing among black puddles at the feet of the bushes by the fence where the sky reflected clean despite the fog, and blades of grass stuck through, stiff and shining, didn't notice a thing until I was petting the horse between the eyes. Then she looked up, black muzzle quivering, and leapt back to the road, barking, petrified. "No," I told her with one hand on the horse, and I leaned over and covered her mouth with the other. The horse stood still for another thirty seconds, listening to me speak to him and to the dog, my hands on both of them at once. "It's okay," I was saying to her because she could not believe this animal. "Yes," I was saying to him because he was putting up with it all. Then the big horse moved off and the dog quieted and stood staring with me at the thick mud beside the fence that carried pools of black clarity.

Later, when the two of us were out on the road together with the dog and following the geese toward the grave, there was the same stillness to everything, the fog no higher in the sky, the road yet dark and moist, the strands of spider webs strung unmelted. A spoke from a bush, here or there, kept its tremor, tautly struck in ice. The dog chafed against her leash while you started in about how brutal he'd been, which was true, and just before we reached the small cemetery where two springs back we had buried him, my piling dirt with a shovel as you wandered through graves, there again were the geese, somehow come from behind then suddenly above us now fully enveloped in fog, so that after years under the eyes of my father, all we could make out were the smooth shapes of bodies then the look of their vanishing then the sound of them, permanent and eternal, going bell-like over into silence.

Ellery Akers

Alive With the Others: Steller Sea Lions

I'd never seen a stillborn sea lion pup before. In 1994, I'd been working as a volunteer for a month on the Farallon Islands, 30 miles off the coast of San Francisco, when Peter Pyle, one of the island biologists, brought the body into the lab on a sheaf of newspaper. That morning we'd both noticed the dead Steller pup slumped next to its mother near Sea Lion Cove. The mother cow who had miscarried looked tired and grumpy: she snapped at a gull that swooped down and landed beside her, its pink feet spread out, hoping to get a meal.

I thought the fetus would be a mess, a loose scarf of blood, but when Peter laid her gently down on the table, both of us fell silent in front of her: she was translucent and perfectly formed. The only thing she was missing was fur. It seemed as if she could come back to life any moment, and was waiting patiently for instructions. She was rose-colored, about two feet long, with brown flippers at her side, and her nails and wax-colored whiskers looked chiseled. I'd never seen anything so still in my life: she looked peaceful and obedient, as if she were listening to something I was unable to hear.

"Thought you'd like to see her," he said.

Peter, a wiry, intense biologist with curly black hair, had worked on islands all over the world, and was able to spot a shearwater in the distance just by the way it flew. He was one of the mainstays on the Farallones, a national wildlife refuge that was home to thousands of seabirds and marine mammals. Consumed by his work, he didn't make much small talk, but was happy to show volunteers anything important. I'd been volunteering off and on for years for Point Reyes Bird Observatory, now called Point Blue Conservation Science, which hires a team of biologists to live on the island to study birds and marine mammals for the U.S. Fish and Wildlife Service. I wanted to help out because I felt Point Blue scientists were making a difference: they'd collected information about marine wildlife since 1968, and if anything could persuade lawmakers to protect the ocean, I thought, it was those piles of data.

In my years as a volunteer, I'd seen corpses—elephant seals that looked charred, their pelts covered with flies, their eyes gouged by gulls, the nails on their flippers still gripping the sand—but this was different. An adult sea lion has felt the wind on her fur and sniffed the sea air, has heard the slosh of waves against rocks, has felt the shock of cold as she dropped into the water. But this pup had never experienced anything: she looked pure, like a holy statue. Even Peter felt it. He was reluctant to start the necropsy and take out his surgical saw, and so we both stood there, staring at her moist, closed eyes and delicate eyelashes, surrounded by calipers and strings of bird bands and instruments.

Outside the lab, sea lions were climbing up the rocks, coarsened by life, but in here she would remain as she was, interrupted.

I suddenly became conscious of the holes in my jeans, the stains on my hat. She made everything on the island seem worn: the old light-house keeper's house with its flimsy, guano-covered windows; the cogs of machinery at North Landing, which had lain there, rusting for forty years; even the Boston Whaler, dented from lunging through surf and scraping against rock.

Finally, Peter started to dissect the pup to send tissue samples to a lab on the mainland, along with identifying information: aborted *Eumetopias jubatus*, March 17, 1994. I turned away before the blade sliced into the body, though I could hear the whine of the saw. I knew it was necessary: scientists needed to study those samples to figure out why so many Stellers were miscarrying.

And eventually, they did find some clues: heavy metals and pesticides full of organochlorine pollutants were seeping into the ocean, and it looked as if a virus was also involved. But biologists were becoming more and more concerned about other challenges the sea lions seemed to be facing: overfishing, warming ocean temperatures, climate change, and dwindling fish populations.

That night at dinner, when we started talking about the dead pup, Peter seemed dispirited. I remembered something he'd once said: "By the end of the night, the conversation on the island always turns to one of three things—shit, barf, or death. Maybe because we're surrounded by it."

*

In 1974, when I first went out to the island, long before so many females started miscarrying, the Stellers were everywhere. Every morning I sat by the sea and watched as rafts of Stellers floated past, snorting, sticking their flippers out of the water to cool off, diving and sighing loud whiskery breaths as they rose to the surface again. Steller pups splashed in the tide pools, learning to swim, venturing out into the waves for a few minutes, and then climbing back to the safety of the rocks.

Most people are familiar with California sea lions, *Zalophus californianus*—which are brown, and about half the size of the Stellers, but to my mind, the larger animals are more beautiful: on land, their pelts are golden, and their dark face marks look shocking in their pale faces, which are the color of straw. In the water, their pelts shine, and turn platinum, so that the first time I saw them swimming, I thought the sea was striped with silver.

The Californias are the goofballs of the sea lion world; they bark and play a lot, and for that reason are popular in zoos and circuses. Underwater, they chase their own exhaled bubbles of air.

But the Stellers are heavier—the bulls weigh 1500 pounds—and can't walk as fast, and to me, they're more solemn and stolid: they have gravitas. The Stellers seemed so much calmer than the Californias that one day, when I saw a Steller bull swaying slowly from rock to rock, moving past a pod of noisy, darting Zalophus, I couldn't help thinking he looked like a king, tolerating the antics of his courtiers.

*

One of the happiest afternoons of my life was a summer day in 1974, when the Stellers were still abundant. I watched two Stellers swim after each other in the ocean—a mother and her pup. I was standing on Lighthouse Hill, the highest promontory on the island, and my job that day was to clock the soundings of a gray whale as he dove and surfaced, but as I circled the lighthouse building, I spent most of my time watching those two silvery-blonde sea lions.

Every few minutes, the cow's head broke the surface of the water, her whiskers dripping, and she turned and growled, as if encouraging her pup, who growled back as he swung after her in the water. Every so often, they touched noses. I stood staring at them, trying to hold my spotting scope steady as it shuddered in the wind, and I felt completely alive. I loved the way she encouraged her pup to swim and to follow; I loved the way they glinted in the water as they dove and sank and rose again; I loved the way she seemed to be showing him the rocks and shoals and fishing spots.

It was windy that day, windy enough to blow through the holes in the rusted metal railings along the path so they shook and moaned, windy enough to stop me when I turned a corner. I huddled in a crevice beside the lighthouse, pulled on my hat and pounded my gloves to keep warm. Gull feathers blew around me; gulls squatted so they wouldn't topple over. A gull shuffled off her nest when she saw me and then nervously squatted down again, but not before I could see the fuzzy polka-dotted chicks she was trying to hide; they wobbled a little as they hunched in the wind. Down below, lines of cormorants flew low over the whitecaps. One of the biologists was walking down the path, bent over, his sleeves blowing, waggling his hand over his head to keep gulls from shitting on his baseball cap.

Pigeon guillemots flew into their nests below me in chinks in the rock, whistling as they streamed past, their beaks full of fish. Elephant seals trumpeted in the distance. Then the murres began to call, AGH, AGH, a low moan, a wild gargling sound rising from a thousand bird throats, a sound that told me a marauding gull had just passed over the murre colony, looking for a stray egg or a chick. It was all noise, abundance, sparkle—elephant seals yawning and blowing bubbles in the sea, and on the rocks, California sea lions lying in their hundreds, and the Stellers in their hundreds.

I watched a Steller bull climb slowly out of the water and shake his massive mane, which glistened in the sun. He moved up the rock, stately and imperious, one slow flipper after another. His mane was scarred from fights with other bulls, and he looked regal as he stretched his head toward the sky and surveyed the cows in the colony. Then he stuck his pink tongue out and held it in the air for a few minutes, ruining the whole king-like effect, and I started to laugh, bent over in the wind, I felt so happy.

*

But that had been in the days of abundance, and this was twenty years later. For a few days after I'd seen the dead Steller's pup, I couldn't stop thinking about extinction. I tossed the water sample bucket into the ocean every morning, and hauled it back up and poured a little bit of ocean into a glass bottle, and I thought about it. I took notes on the gulls, and I thought about it. In one El Niño year, many seabirds had stopped nesting in large numbers on the island, leaving the rocks silenced and denuded. In that unsuccessful breeding season, hardly any female cormorants showed up, so that the males, who had built nests out of Farallon weed, got tired of waiting, and abandoned them. The murres arrived late, and only a few birds laid eggs. Though the Bird Observatory biologists cheered on these pairs, calling them by their scientific labels—"You go, X 12! You can make it, G 3!"—the numbers of murre chicks plummeted. And now, along the coast of California, the Stellers were becoming scarce.

I realized that part of my happiness came from knowing there was variety and abundance in the world: bird song pouring from a thousand throats, instead of just one; Steller sea lions and California sea lions and elephant seals diving into the ocean and jumping out of the water and splashing back down again, each in their individual ways. If the Stellers were to leave the world, I had a hunch it would affect me, even unconsciously; perhaps one morning I'd wake up and feel oddly blurred in my life, all because one species of sea lion that swayed slowly over the rocks had vanished. I knew there was something about the depletion of a species—any species—that would make me feel diminished.

*

The last time I went out to the island in 1994, I spent an afternoon in a blind at the edge of the ocean, and the small shack smelled damp—the planks were coated with algae and guano. Clipboards full of data hung on rusted nails and gull feathers drifted across the floor. I lifted the wooden board that served as a window pane and set it down on the floor of the blind with a clonk. Wind poured into the open hole, gulls shrieked, and I leaned out and expected to see what I'd always seen: rafts of Stellers.

But there weren't any Stellers. Instead, dozens of California sea lions—their darker cousins—slid over each other in the water. A few were playing a game of catch—tossing a dead gull back and forth in the water, as its wings floated open in the tide. There were no Stellers on the sand, either. As I was scanning the island with my binoculars, a gull landed on top of the blind and I could hear his feet rasp as he strutted overhead. Finally, I turned and saw a lone Steller on the rocks, one gold animal in a crowd of dark alien bodies.

His snout was blunt and squared off—he looked nothing like the Californias, with their gently sloping faces—and he was growling over and over, stopping and listening for an answer, and growling again. The Steller's call is low and gravelly, unlike the sharp bark of the Californias, and sounds as if someone is trying to start a tractor in a cellar, the roar of its engine muffled by stone.

That Steller called all afternoon. He swung his heavy head around—he had the beginnings of a mane—and looked restlessly out to sea, but there were none of his kind left at Fisherman's Cove. The Californias clambered around him and paid him no attention. They barked and scratched themselves with their flippers, and yawned, and nipped each other, and shuffled down to the water; their wet glistening bellies slapped on the sand. The Steller padded back and forth as he called, raised his head, and sniffed. Then he lumbered down the cliff, settled himself on the rocks, closed his eyes, and went to sleep.

*

*By 2013, the eastern population of Stellers, off the California coast, had recovered to some degree, though the western population, off the Gulf of Alaska, remains endangered. But the Californias (*Zalophus*) have had trouble in recent years. Though the overall numbers of* Zalophus *are still abundant, over 3000 starving pups washed ashore on the California coast in 2015 because of lack of food and higher ocean temperatures.*

Wendy C. Ortiz

Excerpts from Bruja: A Dreamoir

I decided that yes, I would have the baby.

Only one month along, I walked around unfamiliar streets and considered that there were already subtle changes going on in my body. I looked for people to share my news with, and clothes for the baby.

"I'm having a baby," I said to my father. He nodded, patted my shoulder. I took this as a sign of approval. I held open the bag of clothes my mother had saved, the clothes I wore as a baby. My father's face softened, and I saw it–he was impressed, impressed that my mother had saved the clothes, and I would now be putting them to use.

As I took each piece of clothing out of the bag and unfolded it to look at it, I kept coming across smaller and smaller clothes, 70s fashions made for tiny baby bodies. I refolded them and put them back in the bag.

I decided to phone Tara, to tell her the news.

"This is Spencer," the voice on the other end told me. "Can I take a message? She's next door."

I left a message for Tara to call me, not believing she would, but bursting with the news. I wanted her to tell me it was alright, that I was making a good decision.

Later, the little blond boy I was taking care of tried every last drop of my patience. I wasn't sure he was mine, but it was my responsibility to watch him. And so I had to make an issue of the honey box.

"Please don't drink out of that box," I said, and picked him up and moved him far away from the honey.

The phone rang. I picked it up and heard Curt's voice.

Hello, he said.

Hello, I said. My voice was muffled by congestion, as if I had a cold I was unaware of.

We went on talking, a very easy, casual conversation. I hid the excitement I felt deep inside me.

*

My therapist made a house call.

She walked into my childhood bedroom. My single bed was against the south wall of the room, where I like it to be in the summertime. She stood next to the bed while I talked. My obsession, my confusion took over the next hour.

When my time was up I got out of bed and accompanied my therapist to an auditorium. The interior resembled a barnyard. My therapist and I watched animals do tricks. People threw food and other objects at the animals and they caught every scrap in their mouths. We danced with people dressed as various team mascots with great vigor.

I made up my mind to leave. My dancing was just not up to snuff.

*

I was told to choose a knife from the kitchen drawer, and my opponent would enter shortly.

I pulled open a drawer in this unfamiliar kitchen and chose two knives—the serrated one I walked outside with. My mother opened the screen door for me.

Once the knife was concealed in the gutter of a reachable roof next door, I hurried back inside. I held the butcher knife in my right hand the entire time.

My opponent was wheeled in.

He was blindfolded, but I knew this would come off when all the men in the room decided it would come off. His wheelchair had once been mangled then refurbished. I reminded myself I was probably seeing rust on it and not dried blood.

My mother faced me and I caught a scent of helplessness. Every muscle in my body became tense, constricted.

Then it hit me. My body quaked with sobs.

I don't want my mother to see me die, I said, and the blindfold came off the man's face.

I saw nothing.

*

I stood in my apartment.

My boyfriend, looking like Iggy Pop, long and lanky with black hair and blue eyes, stood in the room with me, his black clothes contrasting nicely with my light blue carpet. The south wall of the room was glass, two large windows open like sliding glass doors, with no screens.

A skunk jumped in through one window, crossed the carpet, and jumped out the other window. I barely had time to stand back and freeze, fearful of its spray, the scent of which I normally love, but only when it's carried in on the wind. Before I could recover, a possum tumbled in, and chasing it was a cheetah, right in through the first window, right out the second window.

I was astonished. This was for sure a lucky sighting.

*

Eloise told me of a writer's residency I should attend, but warned me about the snakes on the way.

"If you can get past the snakes, you'll be fine," she said.

I took a forest path that shifted from light to dark. The trees stood tall and skinny with white trunks, their branches blotting out the sky.

The path became a very tight ledge and I held onto the interlocking branches I found at eye level. Some of the branches, mossy and green, were not branches at all, but green snakes. Their heads stuck out in the few open spaces, still and waiting.

I jumped down off the ledge. The sun shone where I landed. I found a residence hall and saw Eloise. I interrupted her conversation to tell her that unfortunately there was no way I could get past those snakes. She seemed bothered by my presence so I turned to leave.

A Green Tortoise bus pulled up. Hippie-looking people tumbled off of it.

I walked past them, back into the forest.

*

The professor of my philosophy class was about thirty-five, very talkative, inquisitive, and moved all around the classroom as he spoke. He had wavy grayish/blondish hair that hit his shoulders. He was dressed very informally.

At one point he directed his lecture at me and to make his point he came up very close to me, touching me in a way that was inappropriate, yet humorous.

Later during his lecture he sidled up to me. I confided in him that it had been years since I was an undergraduate and I had no experience with a traditional classroom setting. I was used to seminars and interdisciplinary programs at liberal arts colleges.

What I didn't tell him was that I hadn't minded when he touched me.

*

I stood inside my fifth floor apartment in the tall brick building. My window was open and it was afternoon. Four young men were running along rooftops towards my apartment. One of the men flung three sticks of dynamite, bound together with one fuse, into my open window.

I panicked, and the other person in the apartment with me grew alarmed and I yelled, *Run!* Off we dashed. I wanted to bang on all the doors of the apartments on our way down but I had little to no energy in my arm. When I tried to pound my fist against one, it came out as a light knock, barely a tap. I yelled at invisible tenants to get out of the building. I ran into no one on the way down.

From a block away I watched the building explode.

The detail of the side of the building that had been my apartment fell into itself, collapsing, crumbling down, a straight line that transformed into a cloud of dust.

I thought of the writing left behind in that apartment, and how I had lost it all.

*

My grandmother walked faster than I had seen her walk in years.

I sat in a station wagon parked at a curb and watched her across the street, walking a small incline, swift. I was amazed. When she walked back to the car, she lit up a cigarette. I was almost as shocked by this as I was by her speed. She hadn't smoked in about 40 years.

I looked down at the business card of the man I was attracted to.

The words on his business card: *Clover Father.*

*

I was in a hotel room when I found out, on the east coast, near the Canadian border.

There was a government man in a blue suit charged with calming large crowds of people. He told us that we could not leave the country and, in fact, we could not go anywhere but the immediate area.

The crowd protested amongst itself. We could not believe this turn of events. I said aloud, *Perhaps we can go underwater and declare water sovereign.* I was half-joking.

At the Canadian border, a woman read a prepared statement telling us why we could not cross. It was clear from the way she held her mouth tensely as she read that she had not written it herself.

A number of us in the crowd protested her outright. In the small swell of panic, I contemplated what I would do—set fires, burn my way out of the country.

*

My grandmother and I, along with three cats, sat in my mother's living room.

A number of adult cats crowded the patio. I started to count them. They were all different colors and relatively the same size. Each time I had a count going, a new cat appeared, and I began the count over.

Finally I settled on 12 cats, 15 in all including the ones rubbing against our calves in the living room.

*

On my way to school in Portland, I saw my professor, Michael Moore, at a bus stop. When I showed up late for the test, he came over to my desk and showed me the many-paged exam with lots of his pen marks on it. He told me I was late and he didn't know if I could finish the test. I looked up at him. "I know I'm late," I said. "They surrounded the bus stop I always leave from with orange cones and the bus was late, making my trip to school two hours long."

He put the exam on my desk.

I carried a large backpack, the one I take traveling, and in it was my light blue uniform from Catholic school. I had to change into it and did, covertly, for Michael Moore's class.

Also in my backpack was a bomb. It looked like a car battery, only instead of a digital readout showing the countdown, it resembled an old fashioned gas station readout: numbers that rolled into the next number.

I had about 4 minutes to place the bomb somewhere it could safely detonate and not hurt anyone.

I wasted 90 seconds trying to figure out where to take it. I jumped into a non-motorized vehicle and drove off under the cloudy sky.

When I found an elementary school set back in the woods, I knew I'd found the right spot. I walked right through the empty classrooms to the backyard, past the playground, where I spotted a deep marsh. It would be best to leave the bomb there. It could create a sinkhole and I might avoid taking any lives.

I left it in the marsh and mud and walked quickly back through the classrooms. The classrooms now had teachers in them, who eyed me as I moved to exit.

I knocked over someone's glass of iced tea. *Sorry*, I said, and left the building.

*

I didn't realize I had a serious cut in the bottom of my foot until I walked down the carpeted stairs of the unfamiliar house. I left a trail of thick blood in my wake.

I sat down in a chair and looked at the bottom of my foot. In the most tender part was a gash, and the blood wouldn't stop flowing.

Sharon Olds helped me clean up the cut. Her manner was gentle, mothering. I grimaced and squealed in her hands with the feel of the liquid she used stinging my open wound.

*

My son was lean, tall, had blonde hair and was clearly popular. His father did not want him listening to music, though it was apparent our son had a proclivity towards music—making it, and listening to it.

I watched my son surrounded by his friends, and yes, he gave off a nice aura, but was he Jesus?

My husband tried to keep music away from our son and I finally confronted him, pleasantly, on Hollywood Blvd. near Highland. I tried to reason with him. *Okay, you think our son is Jesus?* Yes, he replied. *Then that means I'm the mother of Jesus and I'm a virgin? And I can't have sex? No, I cannot accept that.* And left it at that.

*

I held a cooked rabbit with my fingers in an attempt to stuff it. I pulled the skin up, dipped my fingers into the bowls of nuts and stuffing. A bowl of broth stood by.

I lived with Michael in a strange house that we shared with Forbes. I couldn't believe we were in this situation. The house was noisy and dirty. Forbes and his friends had taken over the living room and some of the back bedrooms.

I stood in the kitchen with a washing machine that did not run on electricity. I looked inside its basin at a lot of cold water, bubbly with soap.

*

My mother hired a number of men to work on a garden at her house.

When I arrived, I observed the tools they were all using. The tools looked suspicious.

I understood the men were there to assassinate me.

I walked past, pretending to admire their work. I began to run down the street and the people I was with tried to block the men from reaching me. And they did.

Later, we holed up inside my mother's house. My mother was absent, possibly already dead. The people there to protect me coaxed me away from the windows where I might be seen. Their own fear was palpable even as it was bound up in a somber vigilance.

When I tried to call the police, it was clear the phones had been bugged.

I put the phone back into its receiver. If there was a secret closet or trapdoor in the house I didn't know about, my mother might be hiding out. This thought sustained me even as I could hear my assassins outside.

My mother never arrived.

*

In the house on the vast yellow plain I knew there was something to be scared of.

We stood outside with no cover as thick black storm clouds formed in the sky, moving at an impossible rate. We froze. Once they were positioned overhead, I knew this was something supernatural and, in fact, evil.

The downpour soaked us through. The clouds passed.

The scene repeated: black clouds. Downpour. An engulfing silence when they passed.

In the distance I saw an enormous train headed towards us. It came so fast that I could not tell which way to run—left, or right—and it was so huge there wasn't even enough time to run.

I ducked down on the ground and felt the train move over me. I had somehow placed myself right into the best, safest part of the tracks. The train passed into the distance and left us in the open mouth of silence once again.

The scene repeated. The second time I felt the metal on my back.

On the plain with not a single tree to ground us, we stood together crying and wringing our hands. I recited the 23rd Psalm, as my grandmother had taught me as a child. I recited over and over and over, tripping over some of the words, until she began to recite with me. We shouted it.

Another puncture wound of black clouds formed and began heading towards us.

*

I was over 12 weeks pregnant.

I had become pregnant via saliva or some other liquid. However it happened, it seemed too simple.

My belly protruded and I looked at it in the mirror. My heart sunk. I did not want to be pregnant.

I kept counting and recounting the months until when the baby would arrive. When I thought of the pain involved, a depression folded me up inside its jaws.

I was unprepared for this kind of change, this kind of pain.

*

I gave birth to a baby girl.

I was at my mother's house. I was dressed in a white half-slip and long-sleeved white silk shirt.

A cat asked me if I would nurse her.

I knew it was weird. I looked around. I could find a private place. I said yes.

In my childhood bedroom, I situated the cat on one breast and the little girl on the other. I called the little girl "Lupita."

Claire Vaye Watkins

My Bitch Mama

My bitch mama left me with a stranger, a stranger who insists her name is Miss Moonbeam. A lying stranger baby wearer when what I need is to be free, naked as the day I was born, not so long ago. I like dancing and clapping and being startled. I like the yays at the ends of songs. I hate my lovie. I hate naps. I like putting little rocks into my mouth, and coins and beads, too. I like to find the buffed shiny islands of gum in the carpet at airports. I like to make things go all gone. My bitch mama taught me to say *all done* and *more* and *milk* and *eat* all with my hands but she did not teach me to ask for anything I actually want like *iPad* or *latte* or *make these teeth stop*. Miss Moonbeam says the earth is our mother and I wish she was right that way she'd never leave and always be holding me. My bitch mama hardly holds me, only like 90% of the time I'm awake and 15% of the time I'm asleep. Miss Moonbeam says to share but my bitch mama does selfish things like take a shower and try to finish a meal in peace. My bitch mama says she had a life before me and with my hands I say, *prove it*. Miss Moonbeam says we don't bite and with my hands I say, *oh yes we do*. Miss Moonbeam says we don't hit our friends and I say, Auggie is not my friend; Kayden is not my friend; River is not my friend. My bitch mama signed the barefoot waiver. My bitch mama wants me trilingual. My bitch mama wants me in tumbling class. I want to inchworm under the couch for some alone time. I want to lick lint. I want to jab a stick into the roof of my mouth. I want my body to listen to me, want my fingernails to stop growing, want to hoard my snot. My bitch mama doesn't understand me. She doesn't know what I want. She says this all the time. *I don't know what you want from me*. I want your teeth in my hurting head. I want all the milk you can make and more. I want your slow, whaley heartbeats. I want to rip all your earrings out and your nose ring too, so that there is nothing shining in my way, nothing glinting between your eyes and mine mine mine.

Lisa Chen

Shit Work

On September 30, 1978, the performance artist Tehching Hsieh released a public statement announcing the terms of a work that would become known as "Cage Piece":

> *"I shall seal myself in my studio, in solitary confinement inside a cell-room measuring 11'6" X 9' X 8'.*
>
> *I shall NOT converse, read, write, listen to the radio or watch television, until I unseal myself on September 29, 1979.*
>
> *I shall have food every day.*
>
> *My friend, Cheng Wei Kuong, will facilitate this piece by taking charge of my food, clothing and refuse."*

Who was Cheng Wei Kuong?

If you look closely at the photographs documenting this piece, as well as the photos of the piece that followed a year later ("Time Clock Piece," in which Hsieh punched a time clock, on the hour, every hour), you'll find Kuong's name credited as the photographer. Kuong was a friend of Hsieh's from art school in Taiwan; they had studied with the same painting teacher. At the time of these performances, the late 1970s and early 80s, the two men shared a loft on Hudson Street in Tribeca. Hsieh was working in restaurants, washing dishes, mopping floors, making $1.75 an hour, the going rate for undocumented workers.

It was Kuong who took photos of Hsieh looking pensively in the middle distance; lying with his ankles crossed and hands locked behind his head in the narrow single bed, the only piece of furniture in the cage Hsieh built himself from pine dowels. It was Kuong who must have publicized the periodic events throughout the year, when people were invited to visit the loft and observe the artist at work. And it was Kuong who emptied Hsieh's daily bucket of shit and piss. He is the invisible presence in these otherwise intensely solitary works.

Kuong's internet trail is short. Hsieh makes one spare reference to him in an interview. Every day, Kuong brought him a takeout meal of beef and broccoli over rice. Over time, the repetition of this dish so aggravated him that he threw the contents of the meal on the floor. He felt badly about it afterward, he said. In any case, no other mention of Kuong exists, at least in English-language archives online.

Did Kuong stay or return to Taiwan? Did he continue to paint? Is he living in a brick split-level in Bensonhurst? Was that him I saw, the liver-spotted patriarch in the baseball cap, surrounded by his large brood at the dim sum parlor on 8th Avenue last Sunday?

*

My father's favorite picture of himself is one where he is sitting on the toilet, hunched over the bowl, elbows resting on thighs. His brow is raised; he looks straight at the camera. The shutter clicked so suddenly that he doesn't have time to register shock or surprise. His expression is the look of a man whose contemplations have been interrupted, but whose last thought, the kind that preoccupies a moment of privacy, lingers as a shadow.

Whenever he tells the story of how the picture came to be (an army buddy flung open the door to the can, *click*), he chuckles good-naturedly. It was a good joke. All his life he has not minded being the butt of a good joke. He has enjoyed replaying this particular one so much that he had made multiple copies of the photo and even had it printed on T-shirts to share with family and close friends. The joke is the seriousness of his face.

When they were still married, he mortified my mother for years by wearing a T-shirt emblazoned with an advertisement for Ex-Lax. I didn't find the shirt among his things when we sold his house, which made me wonder if my mother had succeeded in throwing it away.

He had a favorite, if not original gag when we were children. *Pull my finger*, he'd insist. Doing so released a fart.

When he wants to describe an unconditional state of happiness, he favors the colloquialism, *Like a pig in shit.*

At the hospital I remember hoping that his penchant for scatological humor would somehow make having his diaper changed more bearable.

*

Many times when a new doctor or charge nurse entered his room, they would glance in my direction and ask if I was the nurse on duty. No, I would explain. I'm the daughter. This case of mistaken identity was understandable. My father is actually my stepfather and he is white. He grew up in a family of holy rollers in a small town outside Birmingham, Alabama. His father worked for DuPont and built their home with his own hands, using wood beams and other salvaged materials from houses on the other side of town (black?) demolished under eminent domain, where the Interstate now stands. My father's kid brother is a devout Tea Party member who calls Obama the N-word; his sister used to sing for the Psalmsters, a Christian quartet that put out a few albums. My father was the outlier, the one who left.

The other reason for the misidentification, which becomes obvious once you spend more than a few minutes in a hospital, is that the world of the sick and dying is ministered almost entirely by women of color. I blended in with the other health workers. That was okay by me. I was in awe of the nurses.

By the time my father and I entered each other's lives, I was already three years old. As a stepfather, he never had to wipe my ass clean of shit. As his daughter, I make enough money to preclude my ever having to wipe his ass either. It wasn't until I was in college that I saw my father and me as others might see us, sitting across from each other in a restaurant in Oakland, Chinatown or a shopping plaza in El Cerrito, which we often did, sharing a pot of tea. It is the same idly curious look I now give other diners who look like us, an older white man with a much younger Asian woman.

In this country, when the time comes when you are unable to wipe your own ass, chances are someone who looks like me, but not me, will wipe it.

*

In early January my father fell in his house and lay on the floor for two days before my sister, worried that he hadn't returned her calls, had a friend check in on him. He spent the rest of the month at Alta Bates and continued his recovery at a skilled nursing facility in Oakland, where he would stay for nearly another month.

At both places, shit was referred to as "BM," short for bowel movement.

When was the last time you had a BM?

Did you have a BM today?

One can't say *shit*—that's swearing. *Excrement* is a mouthful and even more foul. *Poop* is infantilizing; *Number Two* is too coy. As with so many other matters that people prefer to leave unnamed (and yet that can't remain unspoken), the acronym delivers the truth, slant.

The question of whether my father would be able, at the end of his rehabilitation, to walk to the toilet, take a shit, and wipe himself clean, loomed large in our minds. His facility with performing this task would determine how and where he lived once he got out. My father was a heavy man. Who would help him to the toilet? What would happen if he needed to go in the middle of the night?

In the *lingua franca* of this strange land of the sick and ailing where we had washed ashore, going to the bathroom is considered an Activity of Daily Living, or ADL. In the year leading up to his fall, my father's handle on ADLs had been slipping. He was afraid of falling in his tub, so had stopped bathing with any regularity. He stopped shaving or wearing clothes that involved zippers and buttons; his apraxia, most likely brought on by overdrinking, had confounded these types of small-motor functions.

Some wise-ass with a mordant sense of humor developed a mnemonic to help with the recall of the basic ADLs: Dressing. Eating. Ambulating. Toileting. Hygiene.

Despite his frailty, my father did not lack for energy to wage a month-long campaign to watch Super Bowl 50 at home. He would call a cab himself, if that's what it took. He wanted to be in his favorite chair in front of his big-screen TV with a cold can of beer in his hand. He didn't care if he had to crawl or shoot people to get there. All this thunder and raging for this modest demand cut me to the core. He couldn't see, or didn't want to see, the massive boulders tumbling down on his life.

So of course we used the Super Bowl as a carrot. *If you eat this or do that, you'll be strong enough to go home and watch the Super Bowl!* Yet by the time he transferred to the rehab facility, it was clear to everyone, including my father, that this wasn't going to happen. Once he resigned himself to his fate, he began marshaling his spirits to watching the game on the big-screen TV in the common room that I had been talking up for weeks. When I made the rounds with him in his wheelchair, he rallied the other residents to join him on the day of the big game. By then he had come to be on friendly terms with a few who were well or cared enough to hold a conversation.

I'm going to be there, he said, with his hand pressed over his heart like a pledge, *and my daughter is going to be bringing snacks.* He was as courtly as a lord bestowing gifts on his vassals. They nodded distractedly. Most of them rarely smiled. One got the sense that they were nursing private pains or griefs and had been doing so for so long that it was impossible to shake them from their vigilance.

The day before Super Bowl Sunday, I bought his favorite snacks (Fritos, chili-flavored, and fried pork skins) from the CVS. It was a bright, cloudless day. I took the AC Transit 1 bus, got off on Piedmont Avenue near Fenton's, the ice creamery where my father used to take my sister and me for Black & Tan sundaes when we were kids. From there it was a walk up a slight incline to the nursing facility, which was tucked away from the main commercial drag.

When I arrived he was lying flat on his back in bed, staring at the ceiling. He announced that, because he hadn't taken a shit for some days, the charge nurse had decided to give him a suppository. Now his stomach was upset and he felt that he might "go" at any minute. He refused to move. He said he was afraid that people would laugh at him if he shit his pants. I wanted to tell him that if there was one place where shitting one's pants would be met with forbearance and empathy, this was the place. But I didn't. Instead, I promised that I would wheel him back the second he gave me the signal. He seemed assured by this.

By then a larger group than usual—15 deep—had gathered in the large dining hall. At this hour the room was stifling: the afternoon sun glared from the floor-to-ceiling windows and made the TV hard to see. The activities coordinator, a short blond in a Raiders jersey, had wheeled out two carts of party food: a few liter bottles of root beer, Coke and orange soda; a big bowl of Doritos and catering trays of vegetable sticks and ranch dip. There was even a platter of chicken wings.

I noticed in the back the pretty, older Japanese woman with long, silver hair I had spotted when I first visited the facility. Her seething at the CNAs—*Get the fuck away from me!*—was my indoctrination to mercurial moods of the residents and the bitter sorrows of living in an institution. Another time I saw her squatting, spiderlike in her bed, peering at the contents of her diaper. Now she seemed to be in some kind of daze, her head nearly touching the tabletop.

My father took a few desultory sips of soda out of a straw but refused any food. He looked weak. In the second quarter he leaned over and told me that he wanted to leave, meaning he felt like he was going to shit his pants.

*

I once met a man at a party who lived for a few years on a houseboat docked in the Gowanus Canal. In the course of conversation, it was revealed that the houseboat did not have a bathroom or a shower.

So how, exactly, did he shit?

He explained that he went to a nearby gym where he was a member, and that this arrangement worked because he was fairly "regular." He mused how odd it was that he had now talked to a number of strangers or near-strangers about his bowel movements; indeed it may be one of the few things people remembered about him.

Hsieh seemed to have anticipated and accommodated this natural, human curiosity about this most intimate activity of daily living. For "Outdoor Piece" (1981-1982), the year Hsieh vowed to spend entirely outdoors by not stepping across the threshold of any roof-covered shelter, he kept a daily log of where he slept, where he ate, and where he defecated. Absent a home, downtown Manhattan became his home. Chinatown was his kitchen; the drained swimming pools and public parks of Soho became his bedroom. In winter, the meatpacking district, where blood ran in the gutters and fires blazed in garbage cans at night, became his fireplace. The Hudson River, he said, was his bathroom.

His log, 365 Xeroxed copies of a map of the island, shows that he shat most frequently off the West Side piers. That same wild, abandoned waterfront immortalized by Peter Hujar, David Wojoranowitz, Alvin Baltrop, and other artists who were drawn to the crumbling docks and warehouses and the hustlers, artists, homeless, runaways, the horny and the seekers who took to them. Add to their archive a picture of Hsieh in the act of taking a shit. He is squatting at the lip of a pier, pants pooled around his ankles, ass bared to the wind. It must be late fall or winter; he's wearing a knit cap and boots instead of sneakers. His shit primed to fall directly into the river below.

To get under the skin of Hsieh's towering achievement, you have to go deeper than the material documents—the photographs, the brief 16mm films, the posters and artist statements. The closest you can get to mainlining its metaphysics is to do the time yourself, throw your own body behind the wheel, even for a short turn of 24 hours. Confine yourself, for one day, in a tiny room with no reading material, no radio, no TV or smartphone, no talking. Smell your own shit in a bucket. Spend 24 hours exposed to the elements. Live tied to another human being with eight-foot long rope. Figure out where and how you would defecate in the city if you didn't have a door.

In Alain Resnais's *Night and Fog*, we see a room piled high with a pyramid of abandoned shoes. We see bodies being bulldozed into mass graves. The images of dead people, the possessions of dead people—we can't comprehend the scale of it. But when the camera pans across the latrines—a long concrete slab lined with back-to-back rows of open holes, each cut six inches apart from one another, emptying into a trench—something about the mortifications of the toilet, the *utter lack of privacy* (the mind scrapes against what it knows)—gets to us. Defecation is a preoccupation of the living. When we watch this scene, we are complicit, both shitter and voyeur.

Survivors of the camps say the toilets were one of the few places where they could talk freely. The Germans were more than happy to leave them alone; they couldn't bear the stench. This was where the *scheissekommando*—the squad of intellectuals, rabbis, writers, philosophers and other troublemakers who had been assigned the degrading, literal shit work of removing waste, organized the resistance.

*

My father spent the rest of Super Bowl Sunday in knots of constipation. The nurses coaxed him off his chair and installed him in a bathroom; then they rushed away to handle a more pressing emergency, the soles of their sneakers squeaking as they wheeled by with a mechanized gurney. My father began cussing for help. He was in agony sitting on the toilet. I spoke to him from the other side of the door, assured him the nurses were on their way. I boomeranged between that door and nurse's station. A few times I pretended not to be there, just crept up to the door to monitor the modulation and frequency of his yelling.

Nearly an hour into this ordeal, it was determined that my father was better off back in his wheelchair where he could at least be more comfortable. Meanwhile, the nurses had gathered in a huddle to discuss his case. A decision was made to consult a medical reference book. Well, this was worrisome. I, a lifelong champion of books, became a deep skeptic. How could a pre-digital object made from the skin of trees possibly contain the answers we needed? Were we druids? Warlocks?

We waited. The book was proving difficult to locate. My father looked exhausted. He had withdrawn somewhere deep inside himself, like the swallow my cats once dragged into the house. The bird had sequestered itself into the tightest possible spot under the couch, facing the corner, utterly still, as though willing itself to disappear. We waited some more.

And then, it happened: my father shit himself. As the shit roiled out of him, he cried out in a voice I'd never heard before, *Oh! Oh!*

The locus of his torment wasn't physical pain. He keened because the moment he had been dreading all day—his whole life—had broken open. Relief and shame came spilling out.

*

Annie Ernaux's father operated a small grocery and café in Seine-Maritime, a provincial region in northern France where Flaubert set *Madame Bovary*. In *A Man's Place*, she writes, "He became what was known as a *human man, a simple man* or a *good man*."

But what did she mean, *became*? Wasn't he the same man? It is the daughter who has changed. Years of private schooling and university exams have elevated her to ranks of the bourgeoisie. The father finds himself on the periphery of this metamorphosis. It annoys him, sometimes, to see her studying all day. He blames books for her bad moods, the sullen look on her face. He is "dumbfounded" one day to hear her chattering away to a customer in English. "The fact that I had learnt a foreign language at school, without ever visiting the country, was beyond his comprehension." So he has transformed too, becoming to her how he has always appeared to others, something other than a father. This is when the child stops being a child.

Once, my father said, *You know, I'm uneducated*...as a preface to a point I can't remember. It had not occurred to me that he considered himself uneducated. He enlisted in the army soon after graduating high school. This was in 1965; the draft was four years away. Because he scored high on the armed forces aptitude test, they dispatched him to learn Chinese at the Defense Language Institute in Monterey. He spent the war in a Quonset hut in Phu Bai listening in on intercepted enemy communiqués.

I was the one dumbfounded by my father, a small-town Southern boy who spoke and read Chinese fluently, who had lived through a war and settled among ex-pats in Taipei, living off Sun Li instant noodles and tuna fish salad. When they weren't smoking hash and playing bridge, he and his American friends taught conversational English, which is how he met my mother. My father knew all there was to know about the different types of wood; he could tell in an instant how poorly or well-made a piece of furniture or window was made by looking at the joint work, the finish, the quality of the materials. Furniture made from particle board, like the cheap desk I bought from IKEA, upset him.

Having or not having a college degree didn't account for much in my parents' social universe in Berkeley, where we moved after Taiwan. This was the mid-70s and early 80s, the same time Hsieh was mounting his yearlong performance pieces on the opposite coast. Maybe because our family friends were all social workers, woodworkers, graduate students, Chinese restaurant waitresses, acupuncturists, pottery makers, organic farmers. Maybe because my father and I arrived in each other's lives, strangers to begin with. But I don't ever remember feeling ashamed of my father, or feeling that my education changed us.

Even so. Just as I had hoped with the *coarseness* of his farting and shitting jokes, I found myself wishfully thinking that because he was a *simple man*, that this might mean he would adapt to the conditions at the skilled nursing facility more easily, and to the single room he shared with two other men, one of whom, he confided to us, was a Vietnamese gangster.

But wasn't this exactly how the *classe dominante* thinks, that people from different classes deserve different standards, and to all their rightful place? Of course my father hated it there. Anyone would. But part of him also seemed resigned to his fate. What choice did he have? This passive acceptance of his lot, with no possibility of an upgrade, no angling for more, no questioning of authority—all that was familiar to me because I'd grown up poor, too, meaning I often just took—and take—shit for granted. This was the part of him, of us, I exploited for my own peace of mind.

*

After my father shit, we still had to wait. The shit dripped and puddled to the floor under and around his wheelchair. Again I went to check with the nurses. They asked me to describe the consistency of the shit. Pudding. No, runnier. Like chocolate milk.

I made helpless, beseeching faces at my father's roommate across the room when he waved his hand in front of his nose to register his displeasure. I stuck my head in the activities room across the hall to check on the score. On TV was some kind of tribute to halftime entertainers of years past. Whitney! Michael! The Stones, Springsteen, U2. There was Prince, his hair bound in a bandanna, shredding his guitar at Dolphin Stadium during a fierce downpour, alive then, alive as I watched, but dead as I write this. I reported to my father that the Broncos were winning. He responded with a small smile as though receiving news from a distant planet.

My father was left sitting in shit because it didn't make sense for the nurses to squander what little time they had to change him, only to have to change him again before they identified a solution. Rationally, this made sense. Irrationally, he was still sitting in his own shit. I did not want to touch shit. I wanted the shit to be someone else's responsibility. But no one else was stepping in. Only then did I yank long strips of toilet paper from the bathroom, rolling them around my fist like a boxer wrapping her hands, and wiped the shit beneath him, breathing out of my mouth. The shit was unexpectedly oily, slick; the toilet paper mostly swirled it around on the floor.

At last a nurse appeared with a plan of action: administer an antidiuretic to combat the side effects of the suppository. I stepped away so she could change his diaper in private. The curtain hooks scraped along the rod. When I came back, the nurse emerged from the bathroom with white Costco sneakers in her hands; she had washed the shit off them, even cleaned the grooves in the soles.

We experience kindness as a kind of excess. I wrote down all the nurses and CNAs' names, starting with the round-faced South Asian nurse who made my father giggle with her impression of Road Runner (*beep beep!*) when she was changing his diaper. I wrote them down so I could greet them with respect but also cannily, like a politician's aide, to call in favors. I kept a list of them so I could address a thank you card after my father checked out, but I lost the list and I never sent the card.

*

I was in awe of the nurses. I found an essay online, penned anonymously by a former CNA. She writes about the sadness of her patients. The bright, false cheer of relatives who drop in for the holidays. The inadequate consolations of bingo and checkers. The transition from underwear to pull-ups to diapers. She writes about the rigors of keeping track of each resident's dietary needs, transfer requirements, shower schedule, the oxygen level in their tanks, when they need their blue boots or hand splints changed.

But mostly she writes about time. Management announces they are cutting the number of CNAs on the floor from four to three. Ten minutes is what it takes to thoroughly and gently clean a resident who has soiled her diaper. But under the new regime, ten minutes is considered slacking off. The decision to take the time or not take the time is like slow-drip moral suicide. Cut your own break short to do it right, or rush through the task like a machine. *Caring should not feel like stealing time.*

When we bow down to CNAs what we are really bowing down to is that they do the work that few of us have the temperament for. They do it without registering annoyance, exasperation, hostility, revulsion. We bow down to the smoothness of their foreheads. We bow down to the pitch and tone of their voices, the range of their improvisation—playful, firm, warm, cajoling, scolding. We bow down because they deliver us our loved ones, smelling faintly of soap, properly medicated, nails clipped, buttoned, zippered, groomed. We bow down because when everyone else can walk away, they do not walk away. I bowed down when my father's sun-downing, triggered by the lateness of the day like a werewolf's full moon, became too hard to take; I bowed down when

I stepped outside those glass doors, peeled off my visitor sticker, and breathed in the early evening air, the most intoxicating atmosphere that ever was, as I left that whole shit show behind.

*

Because I did leave. I left over and over again. Then I really had to go—back to Brooklyn. I had been in the East Bay for a month. On one of the last days I visited my father at the nursing facility, I wheeled him out to the parking lot for a smoke. On our way there we crossed paths with another patient, an obese man in an extra-wide wheelchair with eyes that pointed in opposite directions. He wasn't much of a talker, more like a starer, but today he was even more doleful than usual when my father stopped him to chat. *Mmm. Okay, but I gotta go now*, the man mumbled, feet already shuffling his chair forward.

The smoking section was a makeshift roof set atop a few metal poles in the corner of the parking lot, butts scattered everywhere. Two men were puffing away. One of them was possibly the youngest patient there; diabetic, if I had to guess. I'd seen him wheel himself around expertly on his motorized wheelchair. He was never without his sunglasses and fashionable sneakers, which seldom touched the ground.

You might want to steer clear of there, he drawled with a worldly smile, waving his cigarette hand at the general airspace across the way. The noonday sun was beating down on the concrete, glinting off all the parked cars and baking us in its shimmer. My eyes scanned the area and landed on a turd on the ground. It was not a pile of turd. It was a singular excretion, sturdy and buoyant as a walnut.

Ah. So that was why our friend had been so anxious to leave the scene; he had committed the crime of leaving a poo in mixed company. We all four stood there silently, gazing down at it. None of us made a move to clean it up.

Matthew Lansburgh

Memoirs of a Gentleman Caller

His name was Javier, but he called himself Serge. He said he was in New York to make money, and I was lonely, so I went to the bank and hurried home. This was back when most of us still went about our daily activities with a sense of relative calm; no sirens had been installed in my neighborhood, despite the fact that news of Iran banning the U.N. inspectors was on TV all the time.

I lived alone in a small apartment at 159th and Amsterdam. I was 53 years old, and all I had to show for myself was a junior one-bedroom with a stained welcome mat and a shower that leaked. My radiator made a clanking noise that woke me up at night. It sounded like someone was trapped in there, someone with a hammer. I didn't want to be the kind of person I'd become. I wanted to be twenty years old again, to put on shorts and sit outside in the sun—drink lemonade with seltzer and lime.

"Hey, man," Javier said when I opened the door. "I'm Serge." He didn't look like his photo. He was short, with scruff on his cheeks and a partial goatee. His lips were full, his hair the color of obsidian. I could have been his father, maybe his grandfather.

"I'm Aaron," I replied, though that isn't my name.

"Karen?"

"No, Aaron. Like the biblical figure."

"Oh, okay." He shot me a nervous look. I wondered if this was his first time and asked for his age.

"21, bud."

French Boy here for your pleasure, his ad read. *Naughty or nice, Serge delivers.* Nothing about him seemed French. He didn't have an accent or a beret. His eyes were bloodshot. I wondered whether he was on drugs. Once a guy came over who was on Quaaludes or crack or whatever people went for back then. He sat on my couch, shaking. He drank three glasses of water, one after another.

"Really?" I said. Javier's irises were grey, like the sky at dusk when it's beginning to rain.

"What are you, the police?"

"Maybe this isn't such a good idea," I said. "Maybe you should go home." I didn't want to go to prison; I had enough problems.

"No way, man. We made a deal."

It didn't look like he'd showered in days, maybe longer. He had acne. He put his backpack on the couch and took off his shirt. It looked like he could do 30 pull-ups without breaking a sweat. His left shoulder had a tattoo of a crab—a black crustacean with menacing claws. I felt myself growing aroused.

His boxers were baggy, and the waistband had lost its elasticity, and his penis was enormous. His buttocks were firm and perfectly smooth; he told me to get on my knees. Afterwards we lay on the bed, side by side, listening to the traffic. I was surprised he didn't get dressed and take off. I thought he'd just been waiting for me to finish so he could collect his money and leave.

"My name's not really Serge," he confessed. "I'm not French or anything. I kind of made that stuff up."

I told him it was okay, he didn't have to explain. I put my hand on his arm.

"My name's Javier. I was named after my dad."

I asked him where he was from, and suddenly, he was garrulous. He said he grew up in Pittsburgh, but his dad was from Mexico. "He lived near the pyramids where the Aztecs sacrificed people. My dad says Teotihuacán is where the gods were first born. He went there with his brothers to play soccer when he was a kid."

We talked about the pyramids, then I got up to put on my socks. "Do you want some water?" I asked.

"Sure. Do you have anything to eat?"

We went to the kitchen and I opened the fridge. I poured two glasses of water from the pitcher and took out some mustard and ham—Grey Poupon, in case you're curious. I made two sandwiches and we sat at the table across from one another.

"You know, you're a pretty horny bastard," he said.

My body burned. It felt like someone had put me under one of those heat lamps they used to have at Wendy's to keep the fries hot. It was something I struggled with: panic attacks, sweating profusely. For a while I worked as a proofreader for a law firm, but that ended and I got an assignment at an accounting company downtown. My second day, I had to introduce myself at a departmental meeting and I got so nervous I started to hyperventilate. They kept me on for the rest of the week, then, on Friday, a heavyset woman with signs of alopecia and lavender barrettes stopped by my desk. She said she'd enjoyed working with me, but their needs had changed.

"How come you're not at work?" Javier asked, still chewing. We'd finished the ham and were working on the Muenster. We split a can of peaches.

"I'm a writer. I work at home." He looked confused, and I told him I was writing a book.

"Like a horror story?"

"No, I write memoirs." I thought it sounded impressive, though the fact is I've never published a thing.

"No shit."

The conversation went on for a while in this vein, then Javier got up from the table. "Time to bounce, but do you have a copy of the memoir I could see? I'd like to take a gander."

"It's not finished. It's a work in progress."

He said he didn't care if it was done and asked if he could use my bathroom. I told him he knew where it was, then opened the top drawer of my desk and took out the story. It was about a guy in his 40s who lived in Boston and had just gotten fired from his job as a temp. I wondered whether the title I'd chosen—"The Memoirs of M.S. Stevens"—sounded pretentious.

Eventually the kid came back and announced I was out of toilet paper. "Is that the memoir? Did you sign it?"

"Sign it?"

"Yeah, you know put your name on it. Isn't that what you're supposed to do?"

"Sure. If you want me to." I went over to my desk and got out a pen. "To Javier," I wrote at the top. "From Larry."

"Last name too. You have to do both."

I took it back and wrote *Karlov* under *Larry*.

"Satisfied?"

He looked at my signature, as if making sure I'd spelled everything correctly. "Thanks for the story, your honor." He said it like he meant it, then he picked up his backpack and left.

It wasn't until I locked the door that I began to worry, to wonder whether revealing my identity had been a mistake. I imagined men in suits coming to my door and forcing their way in. I pictured them using a crowbar, me cowering in the linen closet. I told myself to calm down. I turned on the TV and sat on the couch, hoping Ramona, my Siamese, would join me.

She'd stayed hidden the whole time the kid was over, which wasn't surprising. She's always been particular about who can pet her, the food she eats, the music I play. Try to put on something contemporary with cymbals or brass and she'll head straight for the bathroom. She'll jump up on the top shelf, refusing to budge. "Come on, lover," I'll say, "You win. I turned it off."

After the kid left, I took out a can of gourmet salmon and scooped it into her bowl. Ramona is smart, knows who butters her bread. She emerged from her hiding spot, trotted over, and rubbed my legs with her slinky body until I set the bowl on the floor. Her salmon cost $3.99 a can. Even then, I considered it an outrageous expenditure, but, afterwards, she sat on my lap the whole night, purring. There was a weekend marathon of *The Love Boat* on TV. Not everyone has the same taste in television, but the episode where Julie McCoy falls in love with a doctor from Acapulco always made me cry. Even when I first watched it, forty years ago, I felt sad. All night, I kept hoping Julie's story would come on.

Ramona cleaned her paws and the length of her legs, followed by the nether regions. Around 11:30, I started feeling anxious again. I imagined Javier coming back with his friends and waking everyone up in the building. I went to the washroom and lathered my face. I wondered whether it was time for a diet. A few minutes later, I took a soda from the fridge and sat down at my computer. I decided I should keep working on the book, so that, come what may, people would have something to remember me by.

This was, as I said, some time ago—before Iran announced it had developed an arsenal of nuclear weapons, before people purchased gas masks *en masse* for their homes and cars. Back when people went to Starbucks on their way to work and got excited when Kelly Clarkson released a new album. The government hadn't started issuing warnings. My living room faced a school, and often in the afternoons I sat at my desk and looked out the window, watching the children skip rope or play hide-and-seek and chase one another.

*

The second time I saw Javier I was coming out of a bodega on Christopher Street. Three months had passed since our initial encounter. I hadn't gone into the store to look at pornography or purchase condoms and lube. Instead, I'd stopped for a packet of peppermint chewing gum. I felt as if my breath had grown rancid, and I was afraid I might run into an acquaintance and be forced into conversation. As it happened, I was right, for I'd just emerged from the store when I practically bumped into Javier. He was with an older individual, a man who I assumed, from his look and demeanor, was a gentleman caller. Javier didn't recognize me, or, if he did, he concealed this fact. He was holding hands with the john as if they were an item.

I had no reason to feel jealous, of course, but the fact is I wished it was I whose hand he was holding as he walked toward the river. I imagined they had just come from the man's apartment, where they'd made love, and were going to a bistro for dinner.

At the time, people were still going out for fettuccine alfredo and organic gelato, despite the fact that the stock market had lost two-thirds of its value and everyone was flocking to platinum and gold. I'd received a flyer from the city asking me to make sure that I had at least six days of water on hand. It said there was no reason to panic but urged vigilance; policemen were checking everyone's bags on the subway.

When I arrived home, I went online and looked at Javier's ad. The light on his profile was red, meaning he was indisposed. I dialed his number, but he didn't pick up. "Javier," I said when the designated moment arrived. "It's Larry. You came over here a few months ago, and I gave you my story. I'd like to see you again, schedule permitting."

*

I should probably state, up front, that these particular events took place around the time the shoplifting started. It's not that I couldn't afford the things I stole; I wasn't *destitute*. I'm not sure why I did it—maybe it gave me a thrill, like those kids in high school who asphyxiate themselves.

The first item I stole was a vase small enough to fit in my hand. I was in a store downtown that sold home furnishings, and everything was overpriced. It was the kind of place frequented by women with too much time on their hands: celebrities and housewives with sunglasses and gold jewelry and large, leather handbags that cost God knows how much. I'd only been there a few times, just to browse.

I was on the second floor, looking at the vintage bottles—bottles that were cloudy and weathered with age. "Where are these from?" I asked a clerk standing nearby.

"They're beautiful, aren't they? Our buyers get them from flea markets all over the country. Those are from Texas."

I looked at the price tag, as if I were the kind of person who would pay $80 for a trinket from the junkyard. The vase was on a shelf across from the bottles. It was emerald green, like something from the ocean, and stout: small, rectangular, made of glass. I picked it up and examined it. It reminded me of something my mother might have owned. My mother, who died when I was just 36, had lived in New Jersey, in a mobile home full of knickknacks. Woodcarvings from Vienna and Salzburg and Munich, glass figurines she ordered online, ceramic dogs and cats made by a woman she met at church.

She and I were never particularly close, but on some level I must have missed her. Why else would I have stood there, holding the little vase in the palm of my hand, enjoying the coolness of its touch, fingering its edges?

Something took hold of me then, a lightness in the stomach like helium. I carried the vase from the second floor to the third, and as I continued to browse, I slipped it into my pocket, nonchalantly.

The store was huge, and none of the salespeople seemed particularly vigilant. They were standing around, playing games on their phones. This was July 5th, and the city was empty, and they were, no doubt, angry they had to work while everyone else was in the Hamptons or at a water park in New Jersey.

Most people seemed unfazed by everything going on abroad. The Sunnis had seized control of Iraq, and Tribeca housewives were still paying $95 for tchotchkes they didn't need; they were taking limos out to Sag Harbor for the weekend. They were in denial. Either that or they were freaking out and moving to Vermont or Montana or a hamlet upstate.

When I returned home, I put the vase on the ledge above my desk, near the window. In the afternoon, when the few slivers of sunlight that graced my apartment found their way to my living room, this light made the vase glow. It changed from deep green to a more ethereal version of itself, and for some reason this metamorphosis brought me immense happiness. As the sun moved across my ledge, I repositioned the vase so that it continued to bask in this light. Each afternoon I waited, almost anxiously, for the sun to arrive. For twenty or thirty minutes I knew that light would transform the object into something alive.

*

The night before Javier was scheduled to come over for our second encounter, I slept badly. I got up at 1:47 to micturate, then again at 3:49. Both times I saw Ramona's luminous eyes staring at me from the foot of the bed. Her tail was erect, flicking from side to side, as if she were expecting a mouse or a rat. "Come here, Ramona. Keep Daddy company," I said, patting the spot next to my pillow. She got up, turned around, and sat back down, her hindquarters directed toward me. I admit that at times, even still, I fantasize about setting her free in the wild. I wonder how long she would last before a mountain lion or a raccoon made off with her.

For breakfast I ate plain oatmeal and three well-formed berries, but my stomach behaved as if I'd devoured a platter of rancid enchiladas from the hole-in-the-wall down the block. Javier wasn't coming until 2:00 so I had time. I gave the toilet a thorough scrubbing, mopped the floors, wiped the stray hairs and particles of dust from the vanity's surface.

I cut my nails and filed them nicely, plucked the errant hairs that have grown for more than a decade on my brow. I brushed my teeth with peroxide toothpaste followed by baking soda. I gargled with organic mouthwash—something with eucalyptus—a product I miss dearly these days.

By 1:20, I'd showered, applied talcum to my buttocks and chest, and trimmed the hair in my ears. I'd thrown out the expired newspapers and magazines next to the toilet. From her perch, Ramona scrutinized my every move.

I fluffed the pillows again, then, in a frenzy, I remade the bed, pulling the sheets taut as a sail in strong wind. I checked my knees and elbows for dryness. I imagined Javier coming out of the subway. Soon he would be turning onto my block, ringing the buzzer. At 1:56, I felt a need to use the bathroom again but resisted the urge. Calm down, I told myself. Javier himself will arrive unbathed, reeking of sweat. His penis will smell like old fish, his mouth of decay.

I sat at my desk and took the vase in my hand. I'd always wanted to learn to blow glass. I'd seen a program about artisans in Milan who made wondrous objects: vases and bowls and plates that sold for $3,000 apiece.

I grasped the vase tightly. Its body felt nice in my hand. It was now 2:04 and my armpits were damp. I imagined Javier walking toward the steps of my building. Above me, the cat flicked her tail, waiting.

"Hey, your honor," he said when I opened the door. He gave me a hug and kiss. "Did you miss me?" He put his tongue in my mouth and squeezed my earlobes with his fingers. We made love on my bed and again on the kitchen floor. He kissed my neck so hard it turned black and blue. It was the first hickey I'd ever received.

I asked him how much it would cost to have him spend the night and he quoted an amount. We ordered Kung Pao Chicken and scallion pancakes, General Tso's Prawns and Shu Mai dumplings; he ate three plates of food. He told me his father was in the hospital. "They had all these tubes connected to him and shit. I couldn't stand seeing what they were doing to him. I wanted to remember him like he was." Between bites, he held my hand.

He stayed with me nearly three days. He said I didn't need to pay more; he just needed a place to crash, and, actually, he sort of liked hanging out. We fell into a rhythm: in the morning, I prepared scrambled eggs and hash browns; in the afternoon, we went for a walk, past the Dominican fruit stands and the vendors that sold soft shell tacos and *churros*, over to Fort Washington Park. It was August, and the air was thick with humidity, and you could hear music everywhere—salsa and merengue and rap laced with profanity. We stopped to watch some kids playing handball in the park and Javier asked whether I'd heard of someone named Juan Rulfo. I shook my head and he said, "That guy is one fucked up dude. He's a genius. He wrote this book about a kid who goes back to this little town in the middle of nowhere, in Mexico, to find his father and everyone turns out to be a ghost."

Javier recounted the plot. He said he'd sat next to a woman on the bus when he was going back to Pennsylvania, and she gave it to him. "I still have it if you want to borrow it. It made me want to learn Spanish. I'm gonna save up so I can fly down to Mexico City and become fluent."

I wished I could impress him by rhapsodizing about *One Hundred Years of Solitude* or *War and Peace* or *The Brothers Karamazov*, but, at the risk of revealing too much about myself, I will say that reading has always been a somewhat problematic endeavor for me. I know this might sound strange, given my literary aspirations, but such is life. In school, despite the fact that I was sometimes grouped together with the gifted students, I never read as quickly as my peers. I accepted the fact that, at recess, the other boys made fun of me, but I was never able to accept the fact that in junior high my teacher expressed concern that I was not reading at what people referred to as "grade level."

On the weekends, I pleaded with my mother to take me to the library, and though I often found books with titles that captured my interest, when I gazed at the pages, I was unable to concentrate on the sentences. I found my mind wandering: I wondered whether my mother would arrive in time to pick me up before the library closed or whether I would have to wait for her out front, in the parking lot. I wondered whether anyone from school would see me alone, in the corner, using my fingers to guide my eyes across the page.

After we ate dinner, Javier and I usually sat on the couch with Ramona, who developed, if not a fondness for, then at least a tolerance of my new friend. I showed Javier the albums I'd inherited from my mother: photos of me as a child, and my parents before their divorce, and my mother in outfits she used to buy at K-Mart—velour warm-up suits she wore for a week, then returned for a refund. "Your mom looks like she was nice," he said, and I nodded, saying that, all in all, she'd probably done her best. I wondered whether it had been a mistake to hold her at bay for so many years.

"My mom's a total bitch," Javier said. "She cheated on my dad. She moved to Arizona to live with a fucking preacher or something. She tried to friend me on Facebook, but I told her to fuck off." I asked him to tell me more about the events that had led to this point in his life, and he told me stories that I am, even now, not at liberty to reveal.

I took him to my favorite Italian restaurant and asked whether he would consider eloping with me. "If I cashed in my 401K and my savings bonds, we could live in Mexico or Guatemala or maybe Argentina. We could get a place on the beach."

He smiled and put his hand on my leg. "What about the puss? You're gonna bring her all the way to Buenos Aires?"

"I don't know. I could give her away."

"Dude, you don't even know me."

I went silent, my thoughts spiraling. When we got home, I busied myself with my bills until around midnight when Javier put his hand on my shoulder and said, "Do you mind if I burn a joint, your honor?" He took a joint out of his backpack and lit it, inhaling deeply. He closed his eyes tight and held his breath. I'd never smoked pot before. I'd never taken any drugs; I'd always thought of them as dangerous. He exhaled, took another puff, then took my face in his hands and pulled me close. He put his lips on mine, blew into my mouth, told me to hold his breath in my lungs.

I held my breath as long as I could, then coughed, which made Javier laugh. My lungs felt as if I'd inhaled asbestos, or silver. He inhaled again and kissed me, filling my lungs. Time seemed to skip forward or perhaps it slowed down. It became elastic and unpredictable. It felt as if I were no longer standing on the floor of my apartment or anything solid at all.

I remember that Javier took off my clothes and made love to me in the living room, as had become his preference. The moon was full and luminous and larger than it had ever been. I remember the metallic taste of my tongue in his ear, like gunpowder or arsenic.

The next morning, I found a note telling me he'd gone to the Bronx to pick up a hard drive from someone he met on Craigslist. I didn't hear from him that afternoon or the next morning or the following day. A week passed, then another.

It caused me pain when I came across things that reminded me of him: the box of half-eaten crackers in my cupboard which he'd wanted me to open when we were high, the smell of him on the shirt I wore that night, which I refused to wash. His scent lingered in the most unexpected places—not just my pillows and clothes, but the dish towel and salt shaker, which smelled of his deodorant, a cloying evergreen I'd come to crave.

I started another story, this time about a family driving from Tallahassee to SeaWorld. They've been on the road for two hours when the woman—the mother—thinks she sees a little dog out in a field. She makes her husband stop the car and back up so she can get out and rescue the creature, and while she's heading through the scrub, a tractor-trailer plows into their sedan, killing the husband and children. The woman is wearing a sundress that she's convinced shows off too much of her legs. This is the thought in her mind when she hears the collision.

*

I let myself go. I went to Whole Foods and stole bars of expensive chocolate from France. I didn't care if I went to jail.

Iran invaded Saudi Arabia; Israel was on high alert; China mobilized its troops. Pundits on TV said another world war was all but inevitable. People in the city bought handguns to protect themselves. Gold was selling for $4,100 an ounce. I went to Bed Bath & Beyond, put a toaster in my shopping bag, and walked out, no questions asked.

My half-hearted efforts to find employment ended completely. I spent my afternoons walking in Central Park, admiring the foliage, and then, when it was colder, staring at the leafless trees, their branches reaching into sky the color of slate. I walked along the Hudson River, wondering how long it would take for my body to hit the water if I jumped from the George Washington Bridge.

On November 22nd, the mayor appeared on TV and said everyone needed to join together. "I know it's hard to be optimistic during this time of tremendous uncertainty. But I want you to know that the city is doing everything possible to make sure our citizens remain safe. We have more officers on the ground than ever before." 72 days after Javier disappeared, after thousands of people had been killed in missile attacks abroad, I received a text from a number I didn't recognize.

Hey, Your Honor. Sup?

Javier?

Yea man. Sorry I've been out of touch. Long story. How RU?

He was at Penn Station; he'd taken the train from Philadelphia. His father had died, and he'd been arrested for trying to steal someone's motorcycle. He'd gone to jail for five weeks and was just now—in his words—getting his shit back together.

Forty-three minutes later, he arrived at my apartment with two large suitcases made of tan leather, each bound with thick straps. They looked like something out of Lawrence of Arabia. "Bud, you look like crap," he said. "I've missed you." He hugged me, and, trite as it may sound, I cried. "This before you is the entirety of my worldly possessions," he said. Or maybe: "My arms are killing me. I had to carry all this shit from the subway." I don't remember exactly.

He wore a T-shirt with a skateboard on the back, and no coat, even though it was 28 degrees outside. I fumbled around, pouring him a glass of juice and helping him get settled. I asked whether he was hungry and, when he said yes, I took out a wedge of Chällerhocker and a generous portion of salami. He told me that on the way up from Philadelphia, he'd seen armored cars on the road.

The previous day, the Navy had deployed aircraft carriers to the Gulf, and that morning ISIL had announced that if they didn't turn back, it would launch warheads at New York and D.C. Already three people in my building had packed up their things and rented a U-Haul. I'd seen them outside and asked where they were going. "We don't know," one of the women said. "We're driving to Ohio and getting a hotel room until we find someplace to live."

Over the next six days, I went to the grocery store every morning and picked up ingredients to make Javier elaborate lunches and dinners—cassoulet and chicken tagine, curried lamb and lasagna with béchamel sauce. We made love and, when he fell asleep, I lay awake, wondering how long it would be before he disappeared again.

I told myself to enjoy the time we had together and not worry about the future. I told myself not to be needy. On the third night, I lit long white candles and we sat at the table as if someone were going to paint our portrait. Ramona, ravenous for a bit of the seafood gumbo I'd prepared, purred loudly, rubbing my legs. We opened a bottle of wine and listened to a Bach sonata, and Javier told me about a game he and his father used to play.

"He got down on the carpet and laid on his stomach and told me to climb on his back like a dinosaur. He'd get up and let out a roar and run through the house with me on his shoulders, pretending to be a T-Rex or something." I pictured Javier as a six-year-old getting ready for school with his lunchbox, his hair combed to the side. "Do you want to see something?" I nodded and he told me to clear everything off the table. "I don't want any food to get on it," he said. He opened one of his suitcases and dug under the clothes. I did as I was told, and when he found what he was looking for, he asked me whether my hands were clean.

"*They're clean.* What is it, the Hope Diamond?"

He put a small object wrapped in grey chamois cloth on the table, and unfastened the string tied securely around its circumference. It was a wooden bird of some kind. The carving was crude and looked like it had been made with a pocketknife. "It's an eagle," he said, holding it up to the light. "My dad gave it to me. It's over 60 years old; his grandfather won it in a bet."

I put my hand out to hold it, and he hesitated. "Okay, but be careful." The eagle's beak came to a fine point and its body looked like it was once painted crimson. Most of the paint had worn off, exposing dark wood. "My dad's descended from the Aztecs. To them eagles are signs of good luck."

I told him the sculpture was beautiful and, as he took it back and rewrapped it, I asked him whether it had brought him good luck.

"Hard to say–I guess."

I didn't tell Javier that the grocery store had begun to run out of basic supplies: bottled water, milk, onions, broccoli. Often, he slept for 12- or 14-hour stretches. Even when I was in the living room, organizing my papers, or in the kitchen chopping vegetables, just knowing he was nearby made me happy. Sometimes I'd crawl back under the covers and feel the warmth of his body. I listened to his deep, even breaths.

On the fifth night, I turned on my computer and began to write.

> *For my 18th birthday, my mother gave me a box wrapped in yellow paper with a green ribbon. Inside was a ceramic figure–a sculpture of an angel playing a lute. At the time I hated my mother; I took the figure outside, placed it lengthwise on a brick, and pulverized it with a hammer while she stood on the porch in her robe, watching me silently. Her hair was red and frizzy, and her houseshoes were pink.*

I wrote about something that happened to me when I was five, about waking up in the middle of the night because my mother was standing next to my bed, crying, in her nightgown, how she put on her coat and her sandals and told me she was going out for a walk, despite the fact that it was snowing. I wrote three more pages, then deleted most of what I'd written. I knew that soon everything would change. I'd seen flyers outside my apartment warning people to be prepared to evacuate at a moment's notice. Sirens had been installed throughout the city to warn us when the time came. Already, several storefronts had been boarded up.

On the seventh day, when I returned from the grocery store with two bell peppers, a can of sardines, and a cucumber, I found Javier in the living room, showered and dressed. "Larry," he said. "I don't know how to say this, but I need to leave. This isn't who I am. This isn't who I want to be."

He said this, and I cried, and then, as he was gathering his things, we heard the warning system go off. I pretended to be confused, but despite my efforts to hide news of the outside world from Javier, he knew what was happening.

"Shit, Larry. Do you hear that? We need to get out of here."

I nodded and went to the closet to get my backpack and my rolling bag and Ramona's little carrier. The night before, I'd packed my photographs and my computer and some clothes, along with the green vase, which I'd wrapped carefully.

I opened the carrier and was down on my knees calling for Ramona to hurry up, but she'd panicked and crawled under the bed. By the time I coaxed her out, Javier was gone. I wasn't surprised exactly—I knew he would end up leaving without me. I'd prepared for this outcome, had kept a part of him with me, tucked away in my pocket.

I had my large suitcase and Ramona's carrier and my backpack, and as I took the elevator down to the lobby and headed onto the street, I wondered whether I would see Javier outside, among the throngs of people who were on the sidewalks, heading toward the subway. It was a silly thought, because of course, he would have moved more quickly than I. He was young; I was old. He had his whole life ahead of him, and I wondered whether I'd made a mistake. I didn't need luck. What good would luck do me now?

I'd had months to prepare for this moment, yet I still didn't know where to go. Perhaps I would head to Penn Station and buy a ticket to the town in which my mother spent the last 20 years of her life. I'd sold her mobile home long ago, but for some reason I thought I might go to the community where she'd lived and see whether anyone had a room they might be willing to rent, if not permanently, then at least on a temporary basis. I wouldn't take up much space.

I stood on the street, watching people hurry past—women with crying children, men carrying enormous bags, an elderly couple pushing a shopping cart full of clothes, and cans of corn and beans, and what looked like a collection of stuffed animals. People were dressed as if a blizzard were about to arrive. Something about the scene felt like a show on TV. Even the sirens seemed unreal.

I fingered the eagle in my pocket and wondered whether perhaps Javier might come back for me, whether he would ask me to accompany him so we could find safety together. I waited and looked at the store across the street that sold wheelchairs and walkers and plastic chairs for use in the shower. I saw a Jamaican couple loading luggage into a large van while their daughters blew bubbles into the air with a plastic wand they dipped repeatedly into a container of soap. The bubbles gleamed in the sunlight and then popped, one by one, leaving iridescent film on the pavement.

I heard Ramona meowing in her bag, long plaintive cries that I didn't recognize, and I gathered my things and headed back to my apartment. I moved against the oncoming crowd. I didn't want to die waiting for the subway underground. If the end had arrived, I wanted to be in my home.

A man asked me where I was going, but I didn't respond. The front door to my building was propped open with an armchair. I walked up the stairs, past my neighbors' apartments. Some of their doors hadn't even been closed. I could have gone into their bedrooms and closets, rifled through their belongings, but I had no interest in stained undergarments or abandoned utensils. I unlocked my front door, unpacked my things, and put on a CD. I sat down at my computer. I thought about the story Javier had told me by Juan Rulfo about the adolescent who went back to his father's hometown. The sentences came slowly:

I'd never seen a ghost before, but there before me was a man with no legs. He was gaunt and wore a thick beard. His skin was wrinkled and dark.

'Father?' I called out to him.

'I am not your father,' he responded. 'My children are dead.' He turned away from me and began to walk down the road.

'Wait,' I said. 'I have something to ask you.'

I got up to look out my window. There were fewer people on the street now, and for some reason the sirens had stopped. I looked up at the sky, but there was no sign of helicopters or bombers or missiles. The sky was devoid of clouds.

I liked the idea of writing a story about a man in search of his father. I wondered whether Javier would be intrigued by what I'd written. It was just a few lines, but, nevertheless, I felt it held promise. When I'd asked Javier what he thought of the story I'd given him previously—"The Memoirs of M.S. Stevens"—he admitted that he found the piece boring. He said he wished something exciting had happened. Perhaps I'd have my new character, the Mexican fellow, try to kill the old man. Perhaps he'd tackle him to the ground and force him to admit that he was indeed the narrator's father. Perhaps I'd have the protagonist arrested by a group of villagers who were also ghosts. I poured myself a glass of water and lay down on the couch. It had been an eventful day, and I needed to quiet my thoughts.

I must have fallen asleep, because when I awoke, it was night, and the city was quiet, and Ramona was purring next to me, licking my cheek. I got up, gave her something to eat, and went back to my desk to continue working. I wrote four pages that evening that I have preserved. In my story, the narrator goes in search of a priest from whom he can seek expiation. He walks from house to house, asking for forgiveness, until, finally, he comes across a decrepit structure that the villagers say is a church. The title of the story is "The Priest" and it is, of course, dedicated to Javier.

*

Did the talisman bring me luck? On some level it must have, for despite the risks I have taken, I write this account in a place of relative safety and comfort. Eighteen months have passed since I last saw Javier, and though I have reason to believe his fate was less fortuitous than my own, I sometimes picture him living in Mexico. I myself ended up in a small town on the Canadian border where I live once again by myself, though my neighbors are friendly and the villagers here have formed close bonds with one another, given the fate of so many of our countrymen.

So the answer is yes, the carving must have brought me some measure of luck, for I do count myself among the fortunate—not only because I found safety where others did not, but also because I have known, albeit briefly, the pleasure of love.

Ron A. Austin

Cauldron

Birds, cats, rats, and dogs had sense enough to fly, burrow, and lope out of the storm's path, but the folks lined up at Teeth's backdoor were senseless and unashamed. Hard rain soaked through their socks and drawers, mud sucked at their sneakers and boots, wind ripped at their coats and hats, blasted their umbrellas crooked, but those fools didn't budge or cry for help. There were about twenty of them, Buddhas in obsidian and bronze, calm and sturdy, heedless of tornado sirens and elements, as if orderliness could stave off a feral sky, keep gusts of wind from flinging them over defunct factories and condemned houses.

I watched from the kitchen window as those folks conducted efficient business, hands snapping from drenched sleeves quick as snakebites. This grossly tall dude named Greenbean guarded the door while my video-gaming-buddy Demetrious served product. Rain slanted and pummeled Demetrious right in his sullen face. He shook the cold and wet out of his dreadlocks and growled all species of *Fuck* and *Motherfucker!*

Once transactions were complete, survival instincts returned. Those folks hustled away with goods in hand only to be absorbed by the dust and furor like wisps of steam and–

WHO THE HELL WERE THEY?

Busted umbrellas, scarves, hats, and hoodies cloaked faces–but I knew these folks. I did. I pictured them as mystery figurines packaged in black plastic. Tearing open a wrapper might reveal the desperate old dude who sold melted candy bars outside the liquor store or that sweet, overbearing lady who once gave me a packet of antibiotic ointment for razor bumps on the back of my neck. These folks running grim errands through the center of a storm could only be my neighbors and no one else. I was already writing eulogies on the ledger of my heart.

I was a punk-ass sixteen-year-old who didn't understand this form of mass suicide at all, but Teeth didn't suffer the same dread and confusion. He cooked a batch of crack on the stove, stroking the chemical broth with a fork, forearms ripping, blue flames hissing and clawing that cast-iron skillet. Harsh

From The Desk of Avery R Colt

Old dude who sells Candy bars: At least I Give a fuck. For real. But I can't give more of a fuck about you than you do. That's crazy talk.

As Always
— A.R.C

vapors polluted the air, filled my lungs with razors. He caught me moping by the window and said, "Don't make no sense, do it?

"Unh-hunh, I know, but let me put it to you like this: fiends make the best waiters, maids, and soldiers." He moved the skillet to a cold grate, lit a cigarette with flame from the burner, and then clicked off the range top. "They'll take shit all day long, don't understand the word no, and would shoot they mama for a solid dollar. I'm dead serious. Throw a pebble on the ground, and I swear these motherfuckers would suck the meat off your big toe."

He took two luxurious drags and peeked through the curtains. His grin revealed a pair of sleek, curved gold fangs.

"Ain't no surprise they out here in this bullshit, finna ride that tornado like whoa." He nodded. "Mm-hmm. Crack will eat holes in your brain, lil' brother. Real talk. Hit that shit, and you might fuck around and put your dick through a brick wall, you be so damned hyped—but you already knew that."

But Teeth was dead wrong. I didn't know anything, even though gossip about crack was so common it could fit into a form letter.

Gossip A: Did you hear? Mister or Miss_______ is on that shit. Gossip B: Na'll! The Hell you say! That ain't (him/her)! Gossip A: Mmm-hmmm. Sho'll is, honey. (He/She) been fucked up since: a) tragic loss of employment b) tragic loss of loved one c) tragic loss of etc. Gossip B: I knew they was doing bad, but not like that. Well, I surely will a) pray for them b) look out for them c) duck that mooching motherfucker like the living plague.

I mean, sure—I heard about crack all the time. It was everywhere, in our bread, in our basements, on our backs, in our sinuses, in our blood, a community health concern, the cocaine flu, yet I had never actually seen the stuff until that day.

I had just wanted to trade Demetrious Final Fantasy 7 for Tekken 3, and then the storm hit, and Teeth said there was work to do, and he told me, *hold up, boy. You don't know me, but I know you. Let me holler at you for a minute*, and so I was caught up in the bullshit too, whether I understood it or not.

*

Teeth took another drag off his cigarette, tapped ashes into a beer can, and told me, "So like I said, I know you don't know me, but I know you. You ain't even gotta tell me your name." He laid a firm hand on my head as if he was a faith healer, and I wasn't about to fight him, find he kept a shank in his belt, a snub-nosed pistol in his sock. He proclaimed, "I was gone for years traveling the world, not for drink and women and all that nonsense—na'll. I traveled all over the world for—uh, what they call it—enlightenment. Mm-hm. *Enlightenment*. I conversated with wise men from throughout history, sho'll did. I chopped it up with Mr. King and Malcom X and the Dalai Lama and Gandhi and Moses, Nebuchadnezzar, even Jesus himself—eyes on fire, wild afro, skin like coal, and everything." Thunder crashed. Teeth tightened his grip. His fingers stank of sweat, nicotine, and bad pennies.

"Them wise men saw my true purpose, laid secrets at my feet, gifted me with powers. And believe me when I say *powers*. Sight beyond seeing, the 6th, 7th, and 8th sense—all that." I was thinking *bullshit* when the kitchen lights flickered out, and lightning flared copper in the window. Ions sizzled through stale air. I tasted ozone, and Teeth spoke my name. "Avery—Avery Colt."

A cold blade carved figure eights in my spine, but I pretended to be unimpressed by his theatrical timing. The lights clicked back on. I brushed his hand away and told him, "Yeah."

"Goddamnme, I knew it! I knew it!" Teeth howled. His enthusiasm would have been charming if it wasn't for those fangs. "After I came back from my travels, I seen you bullshitting with my nephew, and thought to myself," he tapped his chin, "Don't that little yellow bastard look mighty familiar?

"Matter of fact, me and your folks go way, way back, sho'll do. I used to buy Wonder Bread from your grandmama's store every Monday, and your Granddaddy—you know one day I was feeling ornery and stole two cans of beans, and that crazy nigga pulled a machete on me—now what kind of shit is that? Damned if I know, but that ugly, rock-headed motherfucker sho'll was bad. How a girl pretty as your mama ever came out his seed, I'll never know.

"When we was young and hip, she used to kick it with a brotha', sho'll would kick it. That girl would come on through, drink up the last drop of wine then dip when we passed the hat, like she never even touched the stuff, on some sheisty shit. I swear. But after your uncle passed, it was all bad. She turned boosie den' a mug, had her nose up in the air, but I ain't mad at her. Sho'll ain't."

Teeth leveled a blunt glare and asked me, "Now, your mama ever tell you about your uncle?"

No. Not at all. Mom avoided talking about my dead uncle as if his memory could signal demons, would have hooves clopping on our roof, claws tapping on our screen door. A different kid would have been more curious, more demanding. A different kid might have felt cheated, but not me—how much could I feel for a man I'd never know? We shared blood and a name, but nothing else. So I only had one good detail for Teeth. I told him, "I don't know—Mom said he worked in pharmaceuticals."

"She said what? Pharmaceuticals? Boy, she always been mighty clever, your mama, but that's a goddamn shame. Pharmaceuticals? How she gonna give you that man's name, but not the truth? See, if you ask me, secrets will keep you sick."

*

But I couldn't see it: Mom kicking it with a dude who rocked gold fangs and moved crack. Once when I was a little kid, I cliqued up with a shady cabal of local badasses and got caught throwing rocks at cars cruising down Grand. After using one of her slender, fashionable belts to emboss my butt and thighs with zebra-print patterns, Mom gave me a short, bitter speech. A short, bitter speech that she had prepared for a man I'd never be. She told me

Avery, I won't suffer for what you choose to do. If you let foolishness tear a bite out your ass, you're good as dead. That poison is slow and quiet.

I gave you life, but your death is your own.

*

Teeth fussily rattled that skillet of crack like it was fresh Jiffy-Pop, lit another cigarette, then glared at me for a long, hard minute, his rude appraisal radioactive, crisping my skin. "Now, boy, I have plenty to tell you, but I can't go handing Boo-Boo the Fool Keys to the Kingdom." He sat on a stool, crossed his legs, turned his cigarette up, and postured like an intellectual. "Let me ask you this: you ain't one of them folks who washes they feet and ass before washing they face, is you?"

Sometimes, but I told him, "No."

"Good. Question number 2: If a ball rolls in the street, do you chase after it?"

"Hell no. That's stupid."

"Smart man. So let me ask you one more thing." Teeth got up, yanked my wrist, and dragged me over to the stove. He tilted that cold skillet towards me. The crack inside was dingy yellow and looked like fragments from a busted skull, shards of bone and powdery marrow. "Tell me what do you see here?"

My mouth was dry, dead moths under the tongue. I told Teeth the truth. "I don't know."

He pointed at me and said, "You sir, are correct. I'd give you a prize, but I'm fresh outta zoo-zoo's and wham-wham's." He casually scraped a nail along the skillet's burnt rim, collected cocaine residue, and suckled his finger without a hint of shame. "Mm-hmm," he smacked his lips, "don't nobody know what this shit is. Sho'll don't, but use what the good Lord gave you." He rapped the side of my head. "You'll see.

"Some folks might see death and poison. Other folks see the Devil's intentions made flesh. Mm-hmm. But understand, folks like you and me—we have imagination—that's the big difference.

"If you hollered at me, saying 'Yo! Teeth! What you got in that skillet, man?' I wouldn't be shy. I'd say partner, I set that pan on fire, get that shit boiling, and I got me some brand new suits, some thick women, a down payment on a house, and more jewels than you could count all bubbling out that pan—Bloop! Bloop! Bloop!"

Even under the influence of a contact high, I couldn't see pearls popping from the skillet like hot grease, or any other prosperity. I could only see a woman's hand rising from the chemical broth, skin blue as ice, thin wrist laced in fat rubies, fingernails severe as razors.

Teeth smiled and opened his hands in an oratorical pose. "But now I'm about to blow your mind. What's setting in that pan is more than diamonds. I'm talking dynasties. See, your uncle, my partner, he knew something about them wisemen, and he even knew more than that. He knew about blood. He knew about heritage. He knew about legacy. *Legacy*. You hear me? He—"

Teeth was building to a larger point, but he was cut short by shouts and screams. He muttered, scowled, and turned to the window. I followed his gaze, barbed dread coiling in my guts.

*

I turned to the window and watched as Demetrious fought a girl with blue hair. That girl boxed competently, jabbed, set-up hooks to the body, pivoted and pushed, slipped wild punches. She stuck him once, twice, clean busted his nose. Snot and blood bubbled in his nostrils, but the rain washed his face, preserved two cents worth of his dignity. He swung. She slipped, stuck him once, twice, stepped out of his range, sucked in two breaths, and adjusted the chunky rings on her knuckles.

Folks hollered from under their hoods and hats *whoop his ass! That skeet motherfucker! That punk!* They pumped umbrellas like spears and demanded more. Greenbean blocked those folks from jumping in, his height and width good as a brick wall. She ducked a haymaker, tried to pivot, but the mud sucked off her sneaker. She stumbled to one knee, dropped her hands, and Demetrious rushed, suddenly athletic and sure-footed.

He clutched her head, kneed her in the face, once, twice. She scrambled through the muck on all fours as he sneered and kicked her ribs.

Teeth clucked and said, "We ain't playing with you today, partner. No sir. Not today."

*

The only girl I knew with blue hair was Erika Banks, my sister's used-to-be-best friend. At seven Erika and my sister thrashed razor scooters across playgrounds, ran over the feet of old men, crushed toes, and giggled. At ten they challenged curfew and spun orange glow-in-the dark hoola-hoops around skinny hips, starlight on their braids. At twelve they coco-buttered their legs, rubbed and buffed their thighs so shiny you could see your reflection, rode in cars with grown-ass men. At fifteen they lifted King Cobra from the liquor store, smoked weed in abandoned buildings, and one time, stumbled home so jacked up and high they nearly burned down the house with a hot comb. At seventeen they fought over a buster-ass dude, pulled razors on each other while he watched. Erika and my sister had identical scars across their bony chests like matching tattoos. I had heard Erika had been tripping off That Shit since her nephew got shot, but I didn't want to believe it.

*

Demetrious continued to kick Erika's guts in even after she had crumpled on the ground, and I wanted lightning to fall like a blade and cut him in half—but what kind of coward was I?

I just stood there and watched Demetrious beat her without intention of stepping in and getting beaten, stabbed, or shot myself. I closed my eyes and performed crude surgery, snapped open my breastbone, pitched my heart and every organ responsible for sympathy into a fire. I traded decency for survival like everyone else.

Once Demetrious was satisfied, he let Erika get up and collect herself. She staggered off into the dark mist, that blue hair spiteful of humiliation, whipping and blazing in furious winds. At a safe distance, she turned and cried *you punk-bitch!* And I honestly didn't know if that insult was meant for Demetrious or me.

Greenbean shouted and snapped. Those folks bagged up their bloodlust and reorganized the line. There were fewer of them now, but how could the remaining folks be such golems, so single-minded? Craving and desperation had scooped out their brains and filled the cavity with canned peaches.

Demetrious tromped through the muck, kicked open the door, and hollered, "Fuck!"

Teeth turned to Demetrious with the worn patience of an unheeded tutor and said, "Now Demetrious, tell me why you didn't pull your gun? You could have avoided all that wrestling if you had put that thang in her face from the jump, told her shut the fuck up, whoomp, whoomp, wow, she gets her shit, you get her money, and nan one of ya'll look like motherfucking fools."

Demetrious bowed his head and massaged his scalp. "That bitch got sick all over my kicks." There was vomit and muck on the cuffs of his jeans and sneakers. He took off his sneakers and lined them neatly by the wall. He lamented, "they was Jordans, too. Limited editions, can't get 'em in stores."

Teeth jumped to his feet and snatched a small pot off the stove. "Boy, you mean to tell me, you got a gang of money just waiting at your back door, and you worried 'bout some damn shoes?"

Demetrious peeled off his wet socks and snarled. "You can't get them shits in stores, you hear me?"

"Na'll," Teeth said. "I ain't heard shit." He raised that pot overhead as if it was a cudgel. He wasn't threatening so much as he was ridiculous, brooding like an overworked grandmother scorned by dirty carpet and a sink full of dishes. "Go'n before I finish what that bitch started and bust your head wide open."

Demetrious had already been clowned once that day. He had no need for any greater indignation, so he wiped a drip of blood from his nose, put on his sneakers, and resigned himself to the chores of a basement-level crack dealer.

"Boy, don't never forget who feeds you. I will put you out. Have you on the streets, bald-headed, wearing a trash-bag, eating fried baloney sandwiches."

Demetrious shook his dreadlocks and grunted, but he didn't say another word. Resentful yet obedient, he sulked and opened the door. A violent wind barged inside, lashed whips against our backs. I watched Demetrious trudge back into the mud and–fuck na'll–I didn't feel sorry for him. He didn't need to be out there anyway. Not him, not my neighbors. No one I loved.

*

Truth is I was curious about my dead uncle, but mostly I was more terrified he, The Other Avery, would get all salty one day and leave the netherworld, wanting his name and life back. I feared waking in the night to the stench of rotting meat and finding him ransacking my bedroom, his putrefying fingers spreading grease over my comic books, gooey maggots trickling from his suit sleeve, fouling my Playstation, corrupting save files. Hunks of meat would fall off his bones as if he had been slow-roasted in Hell. He'd come close, slap me affectionately on the cheek with an ice-block hand, and rasp, *my turn*. Fuck all that. Teeth could offer me whatever, but I wanted no part of a legacy born from suffering.

*

Now I needed to get the fuck out of that crack house, get away from those crack zombies and those crack dealers. I needed to bury myself in a bunker before that storm ripped all fools in two, but Teeth blocked the door—he wasn't done hollering at me. Sho'll wasn't.

He pointed out the window behind him and retched, "See that? This is what the fuck I'm talking about, lil' brother. Stupid-ass niggas don't know how to wipe they own ass, but they wanna call the shots. Any nigga can act hard and drop a hammer, but it takes a keen mind to survive in this game." He spiked a finger in his temple three times.

"To tell you the truth—a old dummy like me had to learn that the hard way. Oh yeah. Your uncle would tell me, 'T', don't be spending all your money on clothes and jewelry—that's how you get caught up.' So what I do? Spend all my money on clothes and jewelry. I wanted to be shive, goddamnme. Then he'd shake his head and be like 'T', don't be partying, messing with those girls and pillow talking.' And guess what I did? That's right. I'd get paid and get my shit wet. Fuck what he had to say about it."

Teeth casually lit another cigarette, inhaled, and squinted as smoke curled around his weary eyes—but damn, didn't he hear that mean thunder beating like war drums? *Ba-Boom! Ba-Ba-Boom!*

I lunged for the door, but he stepped in front of me and thumped a fist in my chest. "Hold up, lil' brother. Hold up. We ain't done yet. Nothing out there to see no way.

"Like I was saying, boy, a nigga like me only wanted a smooth ride, fly clothes, and some hot pussy, know what I mean? I had all the taste of a simple nigga, and simple is as simple does. But your uncle, he was on some other shit. He'd be like, 'T', stack that bread. Save your money. Invest in a business. Don't play yourself, partner. You make wealth, not money.' Right," Teeth tapped my chest, "But I never understood him, stayed on that dumb shit. But you—you his blood, and I owe this to you.

"You don't know me, Avery, but I know you and your family very well. Peep game, lil' brother." Teeth jaunted over to the refrigerator, swiped a baggie of crack out of the freezer, and tossed That Shit to me.

And when I caught That Shit, my whole arm went numb and fell right off—for real.

Teeth was unfazed and went on. "The flip is easy. I front you, you break 'em off. We'll start you off small. Run that twenty, I'll give you five. That's fair enough and easier than selling a Mr. Goodbar."

I reattached my arm, tossed the baggie back to him, told him, "No."

He thumped that baggie on the stove and then gently pointed a question at me, "Now, Avery. If you see a dollar on the ground, would you pick it up?"

"What does that have to do with anything?"

"All I'm saying is you sho'll would pick up that dollar, spend it too, so why don't you hold something. I'm telling you it's easy."

"No."

"You won't even try? That's all I'm asking. Try."

"I said no."

"Now that's all right. We're not all made for the street hustle. But what I really need is somebody square to keep a little dope in they house. As you can see, this current set up ain't—what they call it—sustainable."

I restated my point in a way he'd understand. "I said fuck na'll."

He stepped back, stunned. "Oh, it's like that?"

"Hell yeah. It's like that." I opened the door and walked out on his punk ass. Rain slapped, and cold sliced. Teeth stood in the doorway and shouted curses after me, called me all kinds of bitches and motherfuckers and pussies, but he could do what he wanted. I owed him nothing.

Those folks concealed in scarves, hats, and hoodies laughed and pointed. Greenbean lurched towards me, but what did I have to fear from him when the storm would kill us all? Demetrious was ankle deep in mud and too defeated to say shit.

I turned to curse Teeth right back, but a battering-ram wind whopped me in the gut, lifted me off the ground, and slammed me into a fence. I blacked out for a good minute, and then those monstrous drums rumbled and roused me—*Ba-Ba-Boom! Ba-Ba-Boom!*

The line of folks had been scattered all over, their scarves, hats, and hoodies ripped from their faces, revealing who they were. Beneath a smoldering tree split by lightning there was Tay Clark who ran a daycare out of her home and Old Bobby who'd fix your car for fifty dollars flat, and by an overturned car there was Get It Steve who had stolen and pawned my bike no less than five times and the sickly Mr. Terrance who won a workman's comp settlement from a chemical company, and there was Miss Denise, a knockout choir soloist and flea market queen, being hurled down the alleyway like tumbleweed, big bones, fat ass, and all. They were all there, and so many other folks I knew, beaten senseless.

I should have snatched Tay and Old Bobby from under that tree, pulled Get It Steve and Mr. Terrance to their feet. I should have leapt, reached out and anchored Miss Denise, kept her from getting smashed against the cobblestone, swallowed by the furor. I should have helped, but it took everything I had just to run and save myself.

Jono Naito

Catch the Snow

Eight, seven, six degrees, and the city became a sea thick with stillness. The homeless who were not camouflaged would huddle around dishes of charcoal at their feet, and the cars flopped over barely plowed cobblestone. Five degrees, the news on the radio didn't get turned off or switched to classical music. Four degrees, even the mailman was late. But not the snow-man. The snow-man always rang the buzzer at seven in the morning and Satoshi, my father, grumbled and smacked his head over and over to banish the hangover, and I counted the smacks echoing up to my room, a small loft space above his living room. In winter, the number of smacks was sometimes the temperature outside.

To keep his current girlfriend, Atsuko, and I from waking up, the exchange was quiet. I snuck down to the door of the studio apartment and took a look at the snow-man. We lived on the second floor, and I could see the tremendous front doors from the stairwell outside Satoshi's studio apartment. Satoshi repeated the same phrases in Japanese over and over again, and the snow-man bowed *un, un,* agreeing in monotone. The snow-man was shivering under three hooded jackets, I could tell by his hands. Money went to the snow-man, and a paper package came to Satoshi, and the snow-man started his goodbye nods.

I stepped back, sock-foot over sock-foot, towards the kitchenette. Atsuko, bundled under two large shirts, was making a cup of coffee for Satoshi's head. She went still; I had never been caught seeing the snow-man before. "Yuu-chan..." Atsuko whispered as I shook. When inside the studio, she always whispered. She put down the coffee and tiptoed to me, pushing against my back. "Go to bed, Yuu-Yuu," she said, pointing up the wooden ladder to my room. "Go on. Get sleep." I was lifted up two steps by her hand in the crook of my back, and so soon in bed that I forgot, for a moment, that I had left. The studio door slammed and no words were exchanged. There was a heavy slurping, the sound of kissing, then nothing, as I pulled down the pillow over my head as tight as possible. It was 1985, and I had been sent by my mother to New York City a year earlier. I wasn't told why then, but she had lost her job. At least Satoshi had money.

*

Two, four, eight inches, and I wondered if the bridges had collapsed into the river, a frigid scar of white. I sat and cried until Atsuko promised me that the fish weren't all dead. Satoshi's previous girlfriends didn't take me anywhere. They left me bundled up in my room, insisted I was stricken with flu. Atsuko wanted to play, and when she squealed over a snowball the first time, my heart stopped.

"Can we reach Maryland from here?" I asked. I was afraid to talk to Satoshi about my mother, but I knew she was in Maryland. There was a place over the river with buildings and trees all in a line. I wondered if that was Maryland.

"With car, Yuu-Yuu," she said. She began to sing under her breath.

"Who comes to the house in the morning?"

"That's the mailman, he gives us the letters."

"The other man."

Atsuko didn't have to squat too low to meet my eyes. "A friend of your dad."

We walked back across the city, Atsuko tossing me over white banks at each crossing. The snow began to fall, a light sugar coating on my puffy sleeves. Atsuko opened her mouth to catch the flakes, leaping about to taste one speck. I opened my mouth and did the same while she chanted *yuki o kyatchi, yuki o kyatchi*—catch the snow, catch the snow. We got the snow on our fingers, palms, the crests of our tongues. Atsuko could catch one in her ear if she tried hard enough. I was not looking and I fell, so Atsuko pulled me up. I began to stumble away, tripping and getting oil-slick snow in my face, then leaping up and running again. Chasing me the few blocks home, she chanted *Yuko o kyatchi, Yuko o kyatchi*. She never *kyatchis* me, until I am against the heavy doors of the apartment building, nestled between the bakery and the metal shop. I pounded my mismatched mittens on the buzzer as Atsuko danced towards me, pinching her fingers like a crab. I felt tickled before she could reach me.

The door opened and Satoshi grabbed me. His head was crowned with a welder's mask. "Why buzz so much?" he said in my face, said with a humid thickness that clogged my ears and throat. "I am working you can't do that, you can't." He sat on the first step of the stairs as I twisted, but didn't strike me; Atsuko pleaded with him instead, their words a flurry of *ka's* and *su's*. He dropped me and grabbed her by the arm, pulling her up the steps. I followed, unsure of what to do, until I heard him tell me to go to my room. The ladder was taller than usual, and I heard, back in his wood-shop, a yelling taking place. The air in the studio felt muddy from smoke and wood dust, and I couldn't hear the words. I crawled under my covers, the pressure of their weight making me smaller again, safer. A creaking came from the ladder, and I hoped it was Atsuko, come to sit with me as she did after a yelling. Instead, it was Satoshi's face, brow trying to furrow.

"You saw something?" I didn't know what he meant, but my instinct was to nod. "What you see?" he said, then again, then a third time. I said I saw someone in the morning, who wasn't the mailman.

"That is a friend. *Yukidaruma*, eh?" he said, chuckling like he made a good joke. "You know what I mean. Snow-man. My friend the snow-man."

His face disappeared, and for a few days, so did Atsuko. I stayed in my room, gathered my oil crayons and waited. They numbered so few since they were given to me in a big set by Satoshi when I first arrived; he got them when he was in Japan for his dad's funeral. He hadn't given me many other things since, and even with new crayons I always took extra care of the rainbow nubs in a small, old chest. I wondered if I could go buy more of the same crayons. I could buy them for Atsuko with the coins I collected in a shoe.

One day, when the buzzer screeched at seven in the morning, I peeked from my little window into the main room, but it wasn't her. It was another delivery from the snow-man, and with it a business card that Satoshi turned over and over in his hand.

*

One, two, three days passed, and Satoshi didn't say anything of Atsuko. When I saw her again, she was sweeping the floor in silence; Satoshi had spilled a box of cereal and charged off to pace in the snowy streets. My face was home pressed against her stomach, hands wrapped around her lower back.

"Oh, my Yuu-Yuu, look at what your father did."

I shook my head against her soft sweater. It smelled like honey and lavender.

"Come out Yuu... you are stepping on them." I looked down, forehead still making an indent in Atsuko. Pieces of cereal crumbled under my toes.

"One way out!" said Atsuko, lifting me straight up and away. There was a sandy mess where I was standing, a smear of brown powder. Atsuko cleaned the rest up and got me juice. Satoshi had other girlfriends before her, and they never realized I was his daughter. I was more of a creature, or a ghost. I haunted them, always watching, and their glances always found me peeking over edges at them. I kept watching until they realized I was a fixture, not a timid thing. Atsuko, though, she could ask me to do anything, and I would have because she didn't forget about me when I left the room.

"Did you have good time while I was gone? Are you still drawing? Show me what you made." Sprinting, I went up to my room and gathered up the drawings. I discarded a few, hiding them under my blankets, just pictures of Atsuko with Maryland behind her. I returned and Atsuko flipped through sketches of windows, trees, animals standing on two paws. None of their mouths were right; we didn't have any pets.

"Look at this Yuu... you are going to be an artist, artist like your father."

I drew because my hands asked me to, but when I sat with my beloved crayons and looked at the off-white walls I called home, I thought: I didn't want to live in that cold box forever, with walls of dirty snow and strange men in the morning. I never let Satoshi see my favorite pictures; if I did, then he would hate them, or worse, I would become him.

There was a rumbling on the stairs, and Satoshi stabbed at the lock with a key. Atsuko opened it, and I was surprised. On a normal day he entered, feet a muddy mess, already half into a bottle or dazed from a party he had attended. This time, he was exuberant. He laid his hand around Atsuko's shoulder, nodding, smiling through the door, and a man in a suit entered. Atsuko was called fiancée, the chairs were brought out. *Suwari nasai, suwari nasai*, please sit down, he said it friendly, like I hadn't heard before. I stared, head barely peeking from the kitchen, and the suited man didn't see me. He was taller than Satoshi, face broader, but still Japanese. His right hand was wrapped in gauze, and he fiddled with a silver pen. When the suited man noticed me, he bowed deeply. When Satoshi saw me, he pointed upstairs, pulling a package from the snow-man out of his pocket.

*

Two, four, six men came, suits not matching, swarming Satoshi each night. One face sometimes exchanged for another, but they arrived and talked and drank late into the night, many nights. I couldn't have friends over anymore. Atsuko wasn't a fairy anymore, flitting from room to room, and was instead a statue sliding between the kitchen and visiting men, picking up, putting down, picking up, putting down, and mopping the melted snow from the edge of the door.

I was not allowed to play on the new table during the day. It was made of glass and looked like a large mirror. It was delicate, Satoshi said, delicate like flower petals. I only ate breakfast on it, but Atsuko insisted on cleaning it many times a day. "Why you, no, no need to. Dirty again," said Satoshi, watching from a distance as she scrubbed.

"Sorry," she said, not stopping.

When the men gathered, they bent backwards when they laughed, and forwards when they looked at themselves in the mirror-table. They snorted, and cackled and wiped their upper lips. I realized one of them was the snow-man. They exchanged cards sometimes, when a new guest came, and Atsuko was called fiancée some more. When they saw me, they crouched and said hello, or tousled my hair forward so it covered my eyes, laughing over and over; they reminded me of pull-string dolls, except with stuffy noses. I watched from my room, or drew in the wood-shop, a new sanctuary made from forbidden territory. Atsuko didn't take me to the river anymore, so I found excuses to be around her.

"Can I have some juice?" I asked, while Atsuko made a phone call; it sounded like pizza again. She kept them on the line as she found a clean glass and hung up with a 'thank you.'

"Yuu-chan loves juice, yeah? Loves the orange juice. Favorite juice." She was shaking as she poured it, and placed it on the counter instead of handing it to me. There was a guttural yell, and she disappeared. I drank my juice, and took some cereal from the box on the counter. Eating and listening, I heard the laughter and the quick lines and the *da me, da me*, no good about this and that and already Atsuko was coming back. I let the corn flakes spill from my hands on the floor. She stepped on the cereal, grabbed three beers, scurried away again. The ground was marred by a spread of sandy brown again, and I cleaned it up. I was angry that the cereal could be cleaned up so easily, that it didn't need a good scrubbing.

*

One, six, nine postcards came for me, and I got them days after I saw Satoshi bring them in. They came from grandmother's house, from beaches, from uptown. I always wrote postcards; even back when I was without words I would draw pictures, and beg mother to send them. One from my teacher came first, then friends, then grandmother. I hoped mother would reply, but she didn't, and I didn't ask if it had disappeared. When Satoshi brought in mail, he threw many things out, like bills and pamphlets and pictures of mayors. Maybe he made a mistake, and mother was wondering where my reply was.

After two days without guests, Atsuko gained some liveliness again, and took me on the subway while Satoshi was out. People squished into train cars like marshmallows, and the advertisements for doctors and schools hovered out of sight. I saw mostly rear ends and clunky bags, stuffed with foods and chocolates; bottles poked at my face as we switched train to train, Atsuko clutching me. I felt as though I was actually going somewhere I wanted to go.

"It surprise," she said, bringing me back up to the surface. On one side of me there were trees, and on the other was the big museum with swinging banners and shallow stairs. We trotted along and I didn't see snow; we were so far from home that there was less snow.

"Where are we? Are we far from home?" I began to wish we had made it to Maryland, even though we didn't take a car.

She shook her head, "No far." She looked around, seeing the clean streets. "They pick snow up here."

I imagined people coming out in a crowd and each making one snowball and throwing it away, over their shoulders into the park. It was a white wilderness across in the park, and where I stood there was city, concrete, a stream of cars and fast walkers. We were among them, in the flurry. I didn't know why Atsuko rushed.

Hyaku, hyaku she said. Faster, faster. I was nearly skipping as we darted across a street as the light changed. She covered my eyes, but I already saw the bakery.

"What's here? What is it?" I asked. We went inside.

Atsuko spoke to someone over the counter, and then came back to me, leading me to a table. We sat quietly, grinning at each other, making strange faces, mouths and eyebrows and tongues parading in warm, indoor air. We were served tall mugs with tiny marshmallows.

"Hot chocolate, Yuu-chan," she said. "Taste it." I almost lapped up the thick, dark liquid, but I saw Atsuko giggling as she blew on hers, and I did the same. It sputtered onto the table a bit, and Atsuko was ready with a napkin. "Okay, now try."

I took a sip and realized it was flavored orange. I couldn't stop grinning and blowing and sipping at the same time, making more of a mess.

"You like?" she asked. She hummed and sipped hers, her eyes not breaking contact with mine.

"Are you and Satoshi getting married?" I asked. She stopped.

"Well Yuu-chan, what do you want? Do you want me be your mommy?" She laughed like it's a joke, like Satoshi.

"I think you should be. You get me hot chocolate. Satoshi doesn't give me hot chocolate."

Atsuko shrugged. "Not everyone gives chocolate," she said. "Priority, I think, yeah, Yuu? Chocolate isn't his priority."

I sipped more carefully, and she asked, her grin gone, "Why do you call him Satoshi?"

I paused. "Priority," I said. I returned to sipping, until a small marshmallow flew into my drink. Atsuko was hurling them at me off a plastic knife.

"Ten point!" she said.

When we returned, Satoshi was there, seated at his table. He looked at Atsuko who began to apologize, too quiet to hear.

"I scared sick! I worried, I was worried," he sputtered, pointing at the door, standing and pacing in a circle, hand on hip. Atsuko kept apologizing, until he held a hand in the air. She ran to the door and closed it behind her. I didn't realize the tears were gathering until I could no longer see. Satoshi shook his head and went to get a beer. I didn't move, hands clenched on the edge of my shirt, teeth still tasting of orange syrup. He sat and stared at the window, then at me.

"What you want? For dinner," he said as he took a large drink. I didn't say anything and he mumbled about food, and in Japanese he made some decision, beckoning me over. When I began breathing again, air going in out in out, I walked to the table.

"Sorry," he said, trying the smile again. The look he gave slid from me to the door and back again. "You and me tonight. No friends."

I wanted to ask about Atsuko, or yelling, or the table, or school, or mother, but I whispered something that could only have led to disappointment: "Why?"

"Fight. They stupid. Lots of stupid. Bad argument." His hands kept shaking, like it was cold. He wasn't angry; he was something else, an emotion I didn't know how to feel.

"You should go to bed."

"No." I wanted answers without asking for them.

"Go up, Yuko." I didn't budge and he sighed. Then he sighed again, deeper, looking at the ceiling. I couldn't hear the argument in his head, but it was thunderous enough to ruin his whole face. "You don't become me, okay?" His finger, pointing at me, nearly grazed my nose. He pulled out a small bag and took a little bit of sugar from it, or not-sugar, or even snow, and put it on the side of his hand. He smelled it so hard it disappeared up his nose, and he threw his whole head back with a grunt.

"You don't do this, okay? You never do this."

"What is it?"

"Snow. Bad snow. Never do this." He rolled his head back, stretching his shoulders. "You know, you should see your mother. You go see your mother soon. I will call her tomorrow."

"Can Atsuko be my mother?"

Satoshi paused and laughed deeply.

"I'm not going to marry Atsuko."

"But, you love her and kiss her. You are getting married right? I want her to be my mom." I felt angry, a spark of him in me.

"I love her, you know what I mean? But no one really gets married." He chuckled and drank beer again.

"What about–"

"No one." He chuckled again. He felt hilarious.

*

Six, nine, thirteen boxes on the calendar, and winter break was almost gone, but the snow-man was not. Even after the fight, he came on schedule. One day, as Satoshi handled a hangover, he crawled into the wood-shop to drink some more, and fell asleep under the table-saw. When the knocking came, I realized Atsuko wasn't home and Satoshi was too far to hear. I hopped down the stairs, unafraid. I wanted to finally meet him, three jackets and all. I wanted to be the host; I wanted to do what Atsuko would do.

"Hello?" said the snow-man, looking down at me. "I–i–is Satoshi here?"

I shrugged. "No, but I'm Yuko. You are the snow-man? You bring Satoshi snow?" He nodded, slow like maple syrup, and I was polite. "Come in *kudasai*."

He came in and I led him to the couch where he sat. I sat across from him on a folding chair. "May I get you something to drink?" He shook his head.

"Where is Satoshi?"

"He is busy," I said. "Tired. Asleep." I hoped to start a pleasant conversation, maybe laugh big like a man in a suit. "So you also like bad snow? You bring it for everyone?"

He looked at me, then at the mirror-table before him. "Satoshi... he tells you about what we do?" I nodded a lying nod. The snow-man's eyes seemed to droop, melting with thought; I thought of drawing him with his forehead wiping the floor. We sat and contemplated each other for some time, with me watching him in the reflection of the table, and him watching nothing.

Before I asked more, Atsuko arrived home, arms full of food supplies, and two shiny, new platters that gleamed like silver.

"You," she said, pointing at the snow-man. He leapt to his feet and moved to the door, bowing again and again. "You," she said again. "Please leave, leave, now." He was out the door as Satoshi entered, eyes still almost closed. He placed his hands high above his waist.

"Who was that?"

"Your friend," she said. She saw me standing there. "Your friend the snow-man."

"Oh."

What came next was in Japanese, and all from Atsuko. I sat and shrunk into the couch as she berated him and he refused to look at her, but she didn't raise her voice much. His face turned red and he yelled back, swinging his hands around like they might strike her, but never came close. It was a very large yelling on his part, all of it, and I listened to the whole thing, but I knew nothing. I didn't understand why bad snow was bad, but Atsuko shoved a pamphlet into his hand and pointed at me. He tore it up; I hated that he did. Then I felt afraid, like Atsuko looked as he stormed into the back, to the wood-shop. I laid down across the couch, and Atsuko sat by my head, hand on my shoulder, just the right amount of comfort for someone who didn't have to take care of me.

*

Ten, twenty, thirty stacks of cash slid into Satoshi's hands. They came by all through the day, and I was just excited about school starting soon. Friends, even sort-of, would return from vacation, a world outside my room, outside the studio. Winter meant no parks, snow meant no warmth, wind meant so many clothes I couldn't move my arms. I was too busy thinking about what school would be like again and rereading my postcards that I didn't see every guest stop by. Everyone but the snow-man.

"Big party," Satoshi yelled over and over, romping about the house in his sweatpants. He kept taking snow off the table in bits and pieces, then grabbed a coat and left. Atsuko stood, arms around herself, watching as he went, and I came down to look at her. She pulled out a small card.

"Your mother sent a card," she said, handing it over. "Satoshi had it."

I didn't even realize she said anything, because I held it in my hands and felt warmth from it. It said greetings from Maryland, but looked nothing like the buildings across the river.

"Maybe that isn't Maryland," I said. Atsuko didn't understand. I felt like I read the card so many times I forgot what it said, and had to read it again.

My Yuko,

The card was so lovely, and I love you too. I promise to come get you when things are better. Listen to Satoshi, and have a happy New Year.

Just use one stamp next time.

your mother

I clutched it and beamed at Atsuko, who was not smiling much.

"Have you talked to your mother on the phone at all?" I shook my head and she got lost in some big thought. I could hear it stirring. Satoshi came back with bags and a briefcase, and he went straight to the kitchen. Atsuko followed him and I heard her yelling at him for the first time, all of it still blurred in the air. She had such a voice in there somewhere.

She stormed out and grabbed me. "You should play upstairs."

"But what about dinner?"

"I bring you dinner."

She took me upstairs, and pinned up a covering on the little window into the main room. She stuffed the crayons in my hand and two of them broke. No notice was taken, and one piece rolled away as she went downstairs, and I heard more noise, more yelling, and Satoshi fighting back.

Peeking out, I watched the big party come together. The most chairs ever were placed, some just blocks of wax or wood or metal. Satoshi polished the table, and food was put out. The whole time I heard Atsuko downstairs. Her hand appeared in my room only to place a plate with a sandwich.

When the guests began to arrive, they came in sets, like matching crayons of only blue and grey all pressed to perfection. Nearly two dozen sat around, each with their own beers, food, and chuckles that jiggled their whole bodies. They couldn't have gone through the flurries outside like they did; the snow did not touch them. They were wizards, old and enchanted, with large wallets they liked to show off.

I crawled down the ladder to Atsuko, who had one of the large silver platters. On it was a great snow-bank, a hill of gleaming special snow. Atsuko shook her head as she prepared it. When she saw me, I expected a yelling, or to be banished again, but instead she looked at me and thought. Thought in a way that brought her back to joy. She pulled out the second plate, identical to the first, and got the jar of sugar, the real sugar that I could eat.

"Yuu-chan," she said. "Help me make a snow, just like that one."

I grinned and helped her push sugar, more sugar, even more sugar into a hill like the first. I sprinkled it on the edge to match the other as close as I could, and Atsuko whispered in my ear, whispered a plan that made me grin. She had lights in her eyes, wild as a storm. I couldn't tell what had her, but it wasn't the bad snow. Maybe it was what fear or anger does when you don't get married. I didn't like it, even if she looked so alive. Instead, I wanted to break something, or cause trouble, and that is what she wanted me to do.

I began my walk into the main room, plate in hand. The guests turned one by one and became still, worrying, with those same floor-ward eyes as the snow-man. Even Satoshi was without words, and I stopped right by the mirror-table. Their faked treasure teetered with weight in my hands, and I felt the eyes in the room belong to me. I wondered if this was what it was like to be famous, or to be a parent, that everything you did, even the slightest breath, was watched and absorbed.

"*Yuki o kyatchi!*" I yelled, tossing the platter up in the air. The sugar became a cloud, raining back down on the thick air of beer smell and smoke. The suited men, enchantments gone, leapt up and grabbed, hand over hand over hand, at the floating powder, rubbing it on their faces, catching particles in every way they could. The whole circus flew about in slow motion. Satoshi, the ringleader, swung an old shirt in the air like a net. Only I seemed to notice the platter crash and roll across the room. Each man wasn't laughing anymore, faces set in the purest of panics, cheeks twitching and eyes wide. I could see the blizzard was the end of days for them, and they tumbled through the air like snowflakes themselves, landing in all ways on chairs and sculptures. One leapt up onto the mirror-table with their polished shoes, and the glass cracked; Satoshi screamed as it shattered like an icy puddle. He stopped to stare at the wreckage before him, but that didn't stop the businessmen, the trick still undiscovered, from wiping the sugar up off their stained suits and the floor, weeping over inches of snowfall.

*

Four, three, two yellings later, fewer than I expected, Atsuko is gone; I would never see her again. It was New Year's Day and a car arrived downstairs, and Satoshi had me pack; clothes, crayons, cereal for the ride. He shook as he did so, no coffee, no beer, nothing in his hands. He had a stack of pamphlets on the chair by the remains of the table.

"You going to Maryland," he said. "I send the rest behind you."

I didn't ask why, and instead gave him a hug. I remember that hug most of all. His whole body shivered, like it lost something to warm it long ago.

NAITO

Beth Uznis Johnson

Behind Me

I went to see my brother because we were headed down to the Keys for a vacation and he lives in Miami. It was just a day thing. One afternoon so what harm could it really do? My husband Hector and me, we had to fly to Miami so it only seemed right we should stop by. It had been seven years after all since the last time I seen my brother Ricky. He had a wife Maria, and a little girl named Shelby. That's not a name my brother would pick. It must have been Maria's choice.

I only met Maria once, at my father's funeral. She was nice enough. She had long thin legs, but her stomach was fat and hung over the edge of her jeans. She had huge tits and it made me uncomfortable to look at them because I knew my brother probably grabbed them like he used to grab mine. Instead I looked at her legs and wished I had legs like that instead of mediocre, average legs like mine. Hers were pretty nice and Maria was pretty nice, too.

When Hector and me got off the airplane in Miami, we had to walk down these metal stairs and across the hot cement so full of heat it burned through the bottoms of my sneakers. I felt pretty sure I shouldn't have worn jeans and sneakers to Florida but it was too late now and here I was wearing the wrong kind of shoes and feeling like some idiot tourist. I tripped on nothing and nearly fell. Hector reached out and grabbed my arm. We don't have to go there, he said to me. I said no, it was okay, it was just on account of the stupid sneakers. Hector didn't let go of my arm and I felt better about things with his hand wrapped around my elbow because Hector knew what hurt me and would never let it hurt me now.

Ricky and Maria lived about ten miles from the airport and Hector drove the rental car while I looked out the window. The Florida grass was waxy and flat, thick spears poking out of sandy ground and pointing in different directions. Nothing at all like the turf up in Hamtramck, where the grass grew in even blankets across the yards in our neighborhood. The trees in Florida were different than I pictured. Seems there are a bunch of different kinds of palm trees. The ones with short leaves and trunks that looked like pineapple rind surprised me a lot. I didn't expect palm trees to look like that. I didn't expect all the flowers growing wild either, bursts of pink along the freeway, and the sides of houses, and the edges of yards.

Hector cut across two lanes of traffic to make the exit, which came up quicker than we expected. I grabbed the side of the door and held it and the sun beat into the window and I felt nauseous. My feet were sweating inside the sneakers so I kicked them off and peeled down my socks. The cool air conditioning on my feet made me feel a little better. I burped up the taste of hamburger and gin from lunch and covered my mouth with my fist as the smell escaped from between my lips. That's nasty, I said, waving the air in front of my face. Hector shouldn't have to smell that shit. I used the power button to roll down my window and was met with hot air. I hung my head out as Hector made a right turn onto the road.

Babe, if this is too much we should just scrap it and keep driving, Hector told me. I said no, it was fine and we should go and what would Maria think if we didn't show up. It would cast suspicion and then I would be accusing my brother of treating me bad in the past, bringing up what was over and done with. And besides, I was an aunt to Shelby and she would think I was unreliable if I suddenly didn't come with the Polly Pocket kit I picked up at Toys R Us because my co-worker Annette said it was what all the nine-year-old girls played with. Shelby should have her Polly Pocket, and I should put the past behind me. It was more than just behind me, it was way back there, like a lost teddy bear dropped onto the dirt road while its owner climbed into the car and it was miles and miles before anyone noticed it was missing. And even the bear knew he was better off. I hoped Maria and Ricky were the type of people who served gin and ice cubes this time of day. I sure could use one. The warm air was a comfortable breeze when the car moved. I was fine as long as the car was moving.

This is it, Hector said as he turned sharp into a gravel driveway right off that main road. It wasn't like what I had pictured, though it did have one of them regular palm trees out front, the kind with the tall smooth trunk and long swaying branches. Coconuts peeked between the fronds, bright green and shiny. Not like the brown kind you see in the supermarket once in a while. The car skidded to a halt as Hector pumped the brake since he hadn't slowed down nearly enough before turning. Ricky and Maria's house was yellow stucco with a roof that looked like red cement Frisbees overlapping one another. Long streaks of rust bled from the bottoms of the windows. Like tearstains. It was a sorry looking house, right off the main road like that, and I wondered if Shelby had trouble falling asleep at night on account of the truck noise.

I didn't want to stuff my feet back into the hot sneakers so I got out of the car without them. The house didn't look like no place you'd need shoes. My toenail polish glittered in the sunlight. They were painted pink for the trip, just about the same color as the flower blossoms. I walked around to the front of the car, connecting with Hector who took my elbow again. I didn't feel the rocks from the driveway much; my heart was pounding beneath my t-shirt and I thought I might faint if Hector hadn't been holding me up. A black hole appeared in the house as the door was pulled open and it seemed like we were being sucked inside by a force we couldn't see. But then Maria was standing there, smiling with a beer in her hand and I was so relieved to see the beer that I almost cried.

Hello, she sang to us. Hello, we said back. She stepped aside and we stepped up into the hole. She pushed the door closed behind us and hugged me. I felt the rolls of her back and noticed her hair was much longer and was bleached blond instead of the brown I remembered. She smelled like smoky perfume.

They here? I heard Ricky's familiar voice call out from somewhere, gruff and nasally. Voices are like that. You remember them like pictures from a book or flashes in your mind from family trips in the station wagon. I saw Ricky and me sitting in the back going God knows where. We were wrestling over the package of Little Debbies and who was going to get the last one in the box. I practically tasted the thing as I fought him for it. Our mom gave us a dirty look from the front seat before turning around and spinning the volume on the radio until it was as loud as we were. Ricky pushed his hand against my forehead and held me from the Little Debbie. He ripped it open with his teeth and squeezed it into his mouth, his other hand against my forehead the whole time. Then he pushed me so hard that I fell backwards and clunked my head on the window, a hot flash of light moving in front of my eyes for a couple seconds. Ha ha, he said in that nasally voice and then opened his mouth big so I could see the chocolate and cream mash inside. It was that same voice now and I don't know if it was the sound of the voice or the rush of air conditioning that suddenly gave me the chills, but I was more than glad I wasn't so hot anymore. Cooling off reminded me that familiar voice was nothing more than something I already knew.

Yeah, it's them, Maria yelled back and then told us to sit, sit as she pointed at the white leather couch in the cramped living room. Drinks, she asked as we sat. Got any gin, Hector asked. He told her, we like gin on the rocks if you've got it. She had it and went through the door where I could see her open a cupboard and pull out two glasses. From the pouring I could hear it was a lot and was glad about it. I always did like Maria. She was a nice kind of woman, sending Christmas and birthday cards to me and Hector. She brought back two glasses filled with gin and ice cubes that were popping and cracking.

Right as she handed them to us, Ricky appeared from the hallway. We stood again. He had grown fat and I looked between the plump cheeks to find the eyes and nose and mouth I recognized. Most of his hair was gone on top and the hair on the sides was mostly brown but peppered with some gray too. It was shocking to see him like this. We were getting old, I guess, but he looked more like 50 than 40. Maybe it was on account of all that sun.

Hey Deirdre, he said, and walked up and put his fat hand on my shoulder. It was heavy like someone was resting a sandbag there. No one had called me Deirdre in so long that I looked at Hector for help and we both laughed. It's Dede, I told my brother. Oh right, he said, Dede. I know, I know that. And then he laughed, real loud, and it didn't seem like a real laugh. I stood there wondering if we should sit back down, but Ricky said we should go outside by the pool.

He led us through the kitchen and opened an old screen door that squeaked something awful, but sure enough there was a pool outside. It was a small pool built right into the ground and had cement around it and a couple of lounge chairs. There was even a table under a big umbrella with rust on the crank so it didn't stand straight. Ricky pointed to the chairs around the table. Hector and me sat down and I asked about Shelby. Ricky said she was in her room doing homework and wasn't allowed to come outside until it was all done. How mean of him, it was Saturday. The way he said it made me wonder if Shelby was afraid in there or worried she'd get in trouble if she came out too soon.

I said I had a present for her, in the bag Hector had left in the hallway. Maria beamed and said how nice, how nice of us to bring a present for Shelby.

Things had been tight since the plant had cut back on Ricky's overtime and there wasn't much money for toys or other things to keep Shelby occupied. That's why they couldn't even fly up for my wedding to Hector two years ago, she said. Ricky just grunted and sat back in his chair drinking his beer. In between swallows, he stared at the blue water in his pool and breathed like he had just run a mile. Maybe it was on account of getting so fat. Now that I knew my brother was turning into a fat old man, I wondered why I had been so nervous to come. He barely looked like the same person I grew up with and he was being nice enough today. Maria moved to a lounge chair and called out to me: Dede, come here, come over here and sit with me so we can get a tan.

So Maria and I sat in the sunshine and I drank my gin and she drank her beer and we went inside to the kitchen to fill a Styrofoam cooler with ice and more beer, and Maria even brought the gin bottle outside for Hector and me, tucked under her arm while she lugged the cooler. I carried a bag of potato chips and the same kind of French onion dip we used to eat before Thanksgiving dinners and Superbowl games at our house growing up. It gave me a strange feeling, looking at that green tub of dip and remembering how it tasted with a Coke chaser. Ricky and I both used to do that.

When we got back outside I heard Hector telling Ricky about our jobs at the truck plant. Hector was saying that we worked second shift since it paid a higher wage, plus we didn't have no kids to pick up from school. Ricky wanted to know how much money we made so Hector told him that his wage was $21 an hour and then he looked to me. Mine is $17.50, I said. Damn, Ricky said, you must be rolling in the dough, you two. It seemed rude that he asked about our money, but Hector just smiled and said we saved enough for this vacation to the Keys for fishing. Ricky scowled and looked back at the pool and I felt bad about this, but he was the one who asked. Everyone knows the Detroit plants pay better wages and Ricky knows this because he used to work there, too. It wasn't mine and Hector's fault he decided to move to Florida to work at a plant that made crates for citrus fruits.

I didn't like the look on Ricky's face so I turned to Maria, who was smiling despite it all and she poured me a fresh drink. I liked Maria a lot, but that didn't stop me from thinking about Hector having to look at Ricky's ugly, jealous face. Anyway the cold gin was hitting me and Maria and I got to talking about the soaps, something we both watched since I didn't start work until three and she was an at-home mom. It was an exciting time on *Days* with the plane crash and all, and we must have talked about it for a while because the next time I looked up my glass was empty and Hector and Ricky were inspecting some shrubs at the edge of yard. Ricky's pissed, she said, about the next-door neighbor crossing the property line with his plantings. She rolled her eyes when she said this. Ricky's gesturing reminded me of him throwing rocks at our old neighbor's dog because of its constant yapping.

The screech of the screen door behind me gave me a start and I jumped up in fright to look while Maria just laughed. I watched the girl coming toward us, slow like she was shy or something. It was Shelby, I knew, but she had grown so big that I barely recognized her. She was just a toddler at the funeral, wearing that red velvet dress Maria bought special for the occasion. She was nine now and had a thick middle and skinny legs like her mom. Her bathing suit hung lower than her crotch. She kept tugging it up and it made me wonder why they'd put her in a suit that was two sizes too big when she was so self-conscious about it. Her hair fell straight as a stick to the middle of her back, no bangs or nothing. It seemed kind of plain to me, but what do I know about hairdos and bows? Maybe that's why I don't have kids.

Maria called over that Shelby should say hello to her Aunt Dede and Uncle Hector so she did in a small voice. But she smiled when she said it and I felt this surge of emotion that was even warmer than the gin so I went over and gave her a tight hug. I told her she was beautiful and I was glad to see her again. Maria called over, show Aunt Dede your dive! So Shelby went to the edge of the pool and dove in, a very nice dive with her toes pointed behind her. Next time, do it straighter! Ricky shouted this when she came up for air. She called back to him, okay Dad. And it hit me hard that Ricky was her dad and could yell at her to dive better or do her homework or anything he felt like saying.

Maria suggested we go swimming and that she had a suit I could borrow so I didn't even have to dig mine out. I got really excited about the idea of swimming with my niece. We hurried into the house, leaving Shelby splashing around in the pool while Hector and Ricky returned to the table and cracked open fresh beers. Maria grabbed a pile of bathing suits from a drawer in the bureau and tossed them onto the bed, telling me to pick one. She undressed right there in front of me, giggling the whole time, so I undressed too. I wasn't sure which was worse—for her to see me from the front or from the back—so I turned sideways and pulled on a red bathing suit that had a gold stripe across the front. Maria said I had a nice body and could probably fit into anything. I just shrugged. I guess that was true, but I never thought about it much. My body was nothing special and I certainly didn't have legs or tits to write home about. Maria put on a white bikini, which actually looked good even though she had rolls of fat around her middle. She was tanned all over so that made it all right. She asked if I wanted to put my hair up, but I said no, I'd rather keep it down. The scars back there are thanks to Ricky. It was best to hide them. The tile floor in the hallway was cold under my bare feet and I thought I could get used to living in air conditioning all year round. I was happy we'd come, felt like I'd made a friend in Maria.

Hector whistled loudly when we went back outside and I laughed and told him to shut up while Maria pranced to the pool like she was a runway model. I stopped at my glass and poured a little more gin on top of the ice and drank it down. Maria was sitting at the edge of the pool with her feet hanging in the water, but I jumped right in and swam over to Shelby. I asked if she could do a hand stand so she showed me one, legs straight up and toes pointed. I showed her mine, though I was feeling a little wobbly and was pretty sure hers was better. She didn't seem to mind so we continued comparing what we could and couldn't do in the water—hand stands, front flips, back flips and how long we could hold our breath. Shelby seemed to take a real liking to me. She lost some of her shyness and tried to dunk me under the water.

Maria got out and poured herself a gin. She made another one for me and set it on the edge of the pool. She sat back on the lounge chair and lit a cigarette, alternating between sips and drags. I told Shelby to get on so she took hold around my neck and I swam with her on my back to get my drink. Her body was light above mine, her belly resting gently on my back as I swam the breaststroke. I imagined this was the very best part of being someone's mother. Not that I wanted to bring a child into this world. What's this, she asked, just as I had tipped the glass to my lips. I felt her girlish fingers run along the scars, exposed when my hair floated over my shoulder. She stopped briefly on each: one, two, three.

I let the gin fill my mouth so I didn't have to speak. I set the glass down with a scratch against the cement and pulled Shelby's arms from around my neck so she could rest on the edge of the pool next to me. I glanced up at Ricky to see if he'd heard what she said. He met my eyes and I was suddenly terrified because I couldn't tell from his expression what he knew. But then he laughed at something Hector had said so I turned back to Shelby. That's nothing, I told her. Nothing you need to know about. It's from a long time ago.

I thought that would satisfy her, but she swam away to the shallow end of the pool and started doing handstands by herself. I felt bad about breaking the bond between us, but there are some things a child should not know. Especially a child of Ricky's. I reached my hand around my shoulder and felt the marks at the base of my neck, tight and wrinkled, beneath my fingertips. They were still taut and tender, even after over 20 years, and glared red like three eyes staring back at the past.

I watched Hector, my sweet Hector, talking to my fat pig of a brother. The tabletop was losing itself to the empty beer cans that rattled each time Ricky let his arm fall. Hector looked like he was having a fine enough time, but he must have sensed me because he stopped smiling all of a sudden and met my gaze. I slowly moved my fingers off the marks and picked up my drink. Shelby had resigned herself to softly humming with her face pushed into the square box where the pool water lapped into the filter. I put my drink back down and this time it fell to the side with a clink and the liquid pooled out, spreading a dark wet stain on the patio.

Come here, Shelby, I said to her as I swam back across to the other side. My arms and legs were awfully heavy by then. The Florida sky was deeper blue than I had ever seen and the sun was sinking to the horizon. Everything was warm, so warm. But Shelby didn't turn away from the filter box and she was still humming when I finally got there. I pulled her by her middle and turned her to face me in the water. She clung to my neck and wrapped her legs around my waist, just as if she were a baby. I hugged her so tight I heard the breath come out of her. Aunt Dede? She spoke it so softly I barely heard her. What Shelby? She pulled a dripping hand out of the water and turned it over to show me her palm. There, in the very middle, was a red eye.

A fourth scar, yet this one wasn't on me, it was on Shelby. I grabbed her wrist and pulled her hand back under the water, looking up to see if Ricky had noticed. He was rubbing his eyes and nodding at whatever Hector was saying. On the lounge chair, Maria had closed her eyes, the ash of her cigarette dangling like a dusty finger.

Shelby and me, we stared at each other for a long time. We didn't say anything, but it seemed like we had an entire conversation while no one else bothered to remember we were there. I was thankful at that moment because it was the most important thing Shelby and I had ever talked about. Under the water, I rubbed her palm and pressed it with my fingers hoping that might make the scar go away. Tears were on my wet face as I looked into her milky blue eyes. She was practically a baby. How could anyone take a cigarette to the hand of a baby?

It was too much. We shouldn't have stopped by. I asked Shelby in a whisper, do you want to come with Uncle Hector and me? She told me no, she wanted to stay. I thought, of course she wants to stay. These are her parents and this is what she knows.

I pulled myself up the metal ladder and went to Hector. It's time to go, I told him, wiping my face and squeezing water from my hair. I picked up a towel from the chair and wrapped it around my shoulders. Already, Ricky asked, and when I snuffled he said, what the hell's wrong with you? I said it must be the chlorine, but we needed to be on our way to the Keys to check into our hotel. Suit yourself, Dede, he told me. Maria woke up and looked over and said, wah? I told her we were getting ready to go. Hector stood and guided me into the house with a hand on the back of my neck. I'll get dressed, I told him. In Maria's room, I stripped off the red bathing suit and my skin puckered against the cold air. I walked over to the mirror and turned around, straining my neck to see the three burn scars.

The boy who sat on my back had been so bony I felt the balls of his knees against my ribs, the sharp elbow in my shoulder blade. I yanked my hair up and remembered the soft crush of the ember pushing into my flesh. And again. And again. And no matter what it felt like, I hadn't screamed and was still so proud of myself that I hadn't given him the satisfaction of knowing how much it hurt. I had thought that his turning into a fat, balding, middle-aged man was punishment enough, but now I saw he could just punish Shelby in the same way he had punished me. That red circle on her small hand was so hard for me to see, worse than if I had a whole back full of burns.

The door opened and Maria walked in with Shelby. She held the bag we brought. Maria told her to open it and Shelby pulled out the Polly Pocket kit and scared me half to death she screamed so loud in excitement. Until then, I hadn't known she was capable of making that kind of noise. Thank you, thank you, thank you, she kept saying and she jumped up and down the entire time. She ran over and hugged me, still jumping around and I was afraid she might pull off the towel I had grabbed when I heard the doorknob turning.

I knelt down to be eye level. Can we be pen pals, you and me? She seemed to like that idea. I thought maybe I could ask her what had happened, what had made Ricky so mad, and maybe I could help her find a way to not make him so mad again. She and Maria left so I could dress, Shelby jumping across the room and out the door with the Polly Pocket box in her arms.

When I came back to the living room, Maria stood against the doorway to the kitchen, leaning against the frame and smoking a cigarette. Shelby sat on the kitchen floor holding Polly, and Ricky sat on the couch in front of some football game or another. Hey, Maria said, so you're sure you can't stay a little while longer? And she was smiling like she was glad to see me but the smile fell away, probably from the expression on my face. And Shelby, she knew. She stared down at Polly and pretended to make her walk in the high-heeled shoes but it was only so she could ignore me, I could tell.

He burned her. I whispered this into Maria's face and she took a step back and her mouth fell open and she turned to Shelby. No. She didn't tell me, Maria. She didn't need to. You see? I pulled my hair off my neck and pointed. Maria did see. Her face was full of horror but it wasn't surprised.

Well, Ricky, he was oblivious, sitting there on the couch watching the game on TV. He was disgusting, he was, and I was close enough to look between the stubble on his chin to find the triangular scar from where the neighbor's dog had nipped him in the face when we were little. Yes, it was still there, that scar, and I leaned even closer to be sure. There it was.

Behind me I heard Shelby say, thank you for my present, Aunt Dede.

My niece was on her hands and knees on the kitchen floor, closer to the doorway than she'd been before. Polly was tossed aside face down on the linoleum. I saw down the front of the sagging bathing suit where Shelby's little girl pudges were visible because the thing was so damn big.

This is too emotional, I said, and had to leave without saying goodbye to anyone or telling Maria and Shelby I loved them.

I stepped outside onto the gravel driveway. After a few minutes, Hector joined me. He closed the door behind him, just as though we'd been paying a regular visit. He came down the cement stairs—one, two, three—and crossed in front of the car to open the passenger door. I sat heavy in my seat.

He asked if I was all right and I said yes. He pushed the door closed with a click and made his way around to the driver's side. He wasn't in any rush. I couldn't take my eyes off the front door. It never opened, though. Ricky never came out before we pulled away, nice and slow and driving the speed limit even when we got onto the highway. And then we were gone and I tried to imagine the Keys and the gentle waves against a boat and the splash of gin in my glass and the sunshine on my face during our vacation. It was just a day thing and it was over.

I couldn't tell Hector yet what had happened in the pool with Shelby, but soon I would calm down enough to talk. Hector would help me know what to do. Whether to call the cops. Whether we should go back for Shelby on our way home. What to say to Maria.

I told Ricky what's what, Hector said. I told the girls it's hard for you to say goodbyes. You always get out fast.

Hector put his hand on my thigh and squeezed so I could feel through my jeans that I had probably gotten a sunburn. Out my window, the crimson horizon burned shadows through the palm trees. I thought about the way Shelby had been so light in the pool, like air as she floated above my body when we swam.

Winners of StoryQuarterly's 2016 Fiction Prize

Judged by Alexander Chee

Ah-reum Han
THE NINKI-NANKA
Winner

Alex Wilson
CONTENT MODERATOR
First Runner-up

Marléne Zadig
SONG FOR UNBELIEVERS
Second Runner-up

Ah-reum Han

The Ninki-nanka

"You listen to me cheppe—you listen to me faht-faht!—or the Ninki-nanka will come and get you, oh yes he will," said Nanna. Her arm jounced back and forth as she waggled two fingers at Nyima. "Of all the days you chose to be your normal fool self, dear girl, why today?"

Nyima's escape to the river had been short-lived, a brief reprieve from the excitement at home. Now, seeing their family compound, Jarjukunda, so clean and all her sisters hard at work, another wave of nausea hit her. It hadn't helped that Nanna had been bustling around since dawn, reminding Nyima that the most important day of her life had finally arrived.

Nanna was the jokester, and Nyima and all the children of Jarjukunda grew up bending their ears to her stories, her songs. It was their best time, their very favorite, when everyone gathered for feasts such as this, chopping onions, baking mangoes, pounding millet, toasting groundnuts, and Nanna would pull up a stool and say, *Have you heard the tale of Hyena and Rabbit?* Or, *What of Ousman and the Crocodile?* If the young girls nodded, Nanna would feign disappointment, sigh deeply, then slap her forehead with a start: *But surely you haven't heard about that creature of the darkness—the demon's pet!—that terrible beast of the swamps.*

The children's eyes always widened. Nyima watched now as the small girls fought for the seat closest to Nanna, squabbling in hushed voices lest they miss a single word.

"My little ones, these are not safe parts, not for the black-hearted, the stone-headed," Nanna began, chewing a stained bottom lip. "Small children are its tastiest snack"—Nanna chomped her mango, licked her lips with a wet white tongue—"and their flesh gets sweeter the naughtier they are. You want to know what's on the other side of those mangroves?"

"Snakes?"

"Oh yes," Nanna said. "But more."

"Monitor lizards?"

"Ah of course. But think bigger."

"Crocs?"

"Even bigger."

And with that, Nanna crooned the Ninki-nanka's tale.

At twelve, Nyima was the eldest of the Jarju household, far too old to believe in Nanna's stories. Even so, she always did what Nanna asked—cook dinners, wash clothes, bathe her sisters—and she never swam after sunset, never strayed beyond the line of mangroves. Nyima was old enough to know there were many things she'd never understand and things you just didn't do: you didn't sweep the house after dark; you didn't throw out the trash at night; you didn't sit on an abandoned anthill; you didn't tempt the spirits because they were often bored, always fickle. Still, in the afternoons when it was too hot to work in the rice fields, Nyima slipped away to the river. The river's wide brown waters bordered the village, and they made her feel safe, like nothing bad could cross over. Cradled by the water, Nyima sometimes thought she could hear music in the water or see something lurk beneath the surface, shaking the weeds, the glint of sad, yellow eyes peering from the murk. At these times, Nanna's voice would creep back to Nyima: *Mark my words*, Nanna added to every order, *or the Ninki-nanka will come for you.*

"They say its breath is like rotting fruit, teeth as sharp as knives, bigger than this even!" cried Nanna. She paused mid-slice to let the kitchen knife sparkle, bouncing the sun's rays into the children's eyes until they squealed and turned away.

"If you dare to look beyond its rows and rows of sharp teeth, its mouth is red as hot coals." She spat on the coals beneath the groundnuts, and it sizzled and spurted. The children shivered deliciously.

Nanna started scaling the caaloo, gripping the fish by the tail. Milky flakes erupted around her wrists. The children followed the movements of the knife: up and down, up and down. Nanna continued, "Upright, it is bigger than four full-grown men, stronger than any jinn or giant. Its body is covered in scales as big as my hand"—she lifted her palm near Nyima's face, slick with fish entrails—"which cannot be penetrated by axe or dented by hammer! In its belly, it stores fires of evil, which sense the rebellion and pride in people's hearts, uncover all their rotten thoughts. And it is always, always hungry for them."

Nanna's voice was almost a whisper, and the children leaned closer.

"And I haven't even told you about its eyes. They are not pure and white like yours and mine, but dirty, yellow, like disease. They say those eyes will show you the most beautiful thing you could dream, your most secret hopes. But don't be fooled. That's how it traps you—faht faht! How many small children and strong men have strayed and fallen, looking into those gleaming disks! Once it lays those devil eyes on you, you are finished! Their beautiful visions will draw you so you come—one step, two step, three—closer and closer until..."

The girls tensed and Nyima stifled a giggle. When Nanna was feeling young, she would leap up, arms wide, and would chase the children around the compound, bellowing until she grew hoarse. One sister dropped an onion in preparation. Another gathered her skirts. Then Nanna took a deep breath, peered out the corner of her eye and chuckled, then continued:

"Oh yes, in the village over between Tambasanasang and Madina, there lived a young girl, around Nyima's age here—a young woman—who married a wise and kind man who loved her with a pure love."

Nyima's heart beat a little quicker at the sound of her name.

"What was her name?" one girl interrupted.

"Name? Let's say Fatou. The girl's name was Fatou. Satisfied?"

The girls nodded.

"So this good man gave Fatou everything-everything: rice for every meal, a strong roof, her own private room, even nice clothes with the new smell for village parties. Everyone in the village spoke of her beauty, her fortune in coming into this household. Hearing all this praise, the girl allowed her pride to grow large and fast, like weeds in the rainy season. She boasted often, flaunted her perfumes, her new jewelry. She became lazy, too, never wanting to bend her back or dirty her hands. She spent her days wasting time, swimming in the river, never serious."

The children shook their heads gravely and Nyima smiled.

"She thought herself better than her own family, forgetting her own mother who raised her, and she never came to visit, always holding tight to her new money. Even more, the girl started to turn her nose up at her elders—can you believe?—snub her mother-in-law. 'Sweep this house,' said the nanna, and the girl responded, 'Why don't you do it?'; 'Go to the market for flour,' the nanna said, and the girl replied, 'Do you not have two legs?'"

The children gasped.

"The nanna—because you cannot fool a nanna!—she knew something was not correct. Something not good inside this girl's heart, but also inside her belly, you understand?" Nanna moved her clean hand to her stomach, and Nyima blushed.

"Next thing you know, years pass, no children. Meanwhile, the girl chob all her husband's money, asking him for this thing and begging him for that thing, never satisfied, always complaining, complaining." Nanna dusted her hands. "Foolish girl. Even when the nanna begged, the man—her son!—would not take another wife. You see how now even the man is not heeding his elder's commands?"

Nanna tittered and the girls joined in, shaking their little heads to and fro.

"One night, something came knocking on the woman's door. Kohng-kohng," said Nanna, rapping her knuckles against her wooden stool. "Kohng kohng."

The girl pounding millet stopped, leaned on her wooden pestle.

"Kohng-kohng." Louder this time.

The children held their breath, waiting for Nanna to rise. Nyima felt the tension, tight as a fist. Finally, a tremulous voice asked, "Who is it?"

"And do you know who it was?" Nanna stood, stretched her back in slow turns and tucked in the loose ends of her skirt. She tossed Nyima another potato to peel, and their eyes met. Strange to think their lives could change in a few short hours.

"The Ninki-nanka?" ventured one small, wide-eyed child.

The children's faces flushed, the smell of good food lifting all their spirits.

"No," Nanna said nonchalantly, "it was the husband."

The children let out a collective breath. The girl at the mortar and pestle giggled in relief.

"But she refused to let him inside that night," Nanna added, "and the next time she was swimming in the river, *Whoosh!*"—Nanna roared and the children screamed, delighted—"All teeth and scales and fire, the Ninki-nanka dragged the woman down, beyond the pier, past the mangroves, into the deep water, and nobody ever saw her again. All they found was one fancy earring washed ashore, right where the men today tether their pirogues. It was her years of overconfidence and disobedience that made her irresistible to the monster, see? And that, my darlings, is a true story. Go there, ask anybody. The Ninki-nanka does not forget, deh! Never. So you be a good girl, now. Look at these grey hairs. Place your fingers on these lines here on my forehead. Would your nanna lie to you?"

*

"He's a very handsome man," Nanna said. "You are a lucky young woman." The sun was setting, the food fragrant and ready. Nanna poured oil into her palm and smoothed it onto Nyima's bare shoulders. Nyima stroked her new bayoo, tracing the fabric's whirling patterns. It smelled waxy and dank, like a secret, like the things she imagined lay on the other side of the river, or the things that prowled the deep swamps.

"You remember him, don't you?" Nanna repeated.

"Yes," Nyima lied. She took giddy breaths as Nanna finished, holding both arms above her shoulders. Her sisters squatted on the floor, watching Nyima's steady transformation: the gold eyeliner, the rouge, the penciled eyebrows.

Nyima willed herself to stop sweating. After all this time, now how would it look for her to enter the room, wearing the clothes that he'd bought, all reeking and sweaty, like some chaat after playing tag? Although it had not been the first gift she'd received. Just last month he'd surprised her with a slice of cake and a whole green apple, without a mark or a bruise.

Nyima has a boyfriend! her sisters had squealed. *Boyfriend! Boyfriend!*

She blushed with the memory. Today, they would finally meet. She still hadn't dared say his name aloud since Nanna had told her the news, elated: *You see how the gods are pleased with the Jarjus, ah? Tell me if I'm wrong. Tell me!* Nanna was bursting with this secret, one she couldn't tell her friends until the formal arrangements had been made.

Of course, at first, Nyima had cried. Every day of the week leading up to the visit, Nanna had slipped away to the sacred baobabs to make her prayers. Nanna once told her that those trees held power, that even the Ninki-nanka protected them from season to season. But sometimes, their swollen trunks reminded Nyima of the other girls like her, tiny brides with puffy ankles and puffy eyes, their taut round bellies lucky enough to have come the respectable way. Now when those sad girls entered her mind, Nyima found herself saying his name over and over. Each time it grew to fill the gaps of her doubts, the tart crunch of the apple blooming into something more intimate and hers alone, unlike the dolls, the clothes, the shoes she shared with all her siblings.

Her chest expanded with each repetition—*Nuha, Nuha, Nuha*—each time, restoring that single memory of him, an image from when she was a small girl peering up into palm-palm trees where Nuha harvested his wine. *The very best sennga you will ever taste,* Nuha boasted, *billai-wollai-tallai!*

With every recollection, his voice grew clearer, arms stronger, colors brighter, etched into her mind: There he was, high above, securing plastic bottles in thick clusters where the branches converged and knotted. The palm wine collected, the sap dribbling, fermented and sweetened, into the containers. Nyima could see Nuha's trousers mushroomed below a thick fibrous strap around the waist, and him, leaning away from the swaying tree and into the tautness of that line, digging his feet into the trunk as he bounced upwards. All below was warm wind and fine sand.

Nyima had watched her sisters wash the last of the good rice this morning, watched her father bend his greying head over a roof that always needed mending, and she felt herself becoming a woman, finally, able to do what her father and Nanna could not. The gods had blessed Nuha, now a successful businessman in the palm wine industry across the river. The villagers whispered about Nuha's homecoming—*the big man's coming back to his roots!*—and they wondered where the next blessings would fall.

"Tell me again," said Nanna, startling Nyima's reveries.

"Take them dinner and smile."

"Show me."

Nyima bared her teeth into a goofy smile, making her sisters giggle.

"The Ninki-nanka!" Nanna cried, and Nyima dodged a swipe, laughing.

Nyima gathered her hands and gave Nanna a soft full-lipped smile, not too wide to look like a child and not too small to look sad. She recited: "Put the nice fish closest to him, gently place the bowl in the center."

"And you will go where?" Nanna crossed her arms.

"I will stand like a lady, in the corner, while my father talks, and I will—not." Nyima's pause incited Nanna's yelps again. She enjoyed seeing Nanna like this, so alive.

"This big mouth! Oh help me, my Nyima likes to chatter-chatter-chatter. Let me tell you," Nanna whispered to the small girls, warming the rouge in her palms, "the Ninki-nanka will remember this."

Behind Nanna's back, Nyima stalked back and forth making Ninki-nanka impressions. The girls smothered their laughter.

Nanna chased Nyima down to reapply the red to her lips and instructed, "Don't pound your heels when you walk. Bend those knees, so you don't scuff these new shoes. You'll have to wear them again soon, at a wedding, god willing."

"I've never been to a wedding," one girl murmured.

Nanna let out an enormous gasp, lifted an oiled hand to her chest, then lowered it onto the girl's small head. "Ah, my darlings, let me tell you about weddings! We Jarju women are known for more than our strength and beauty,"—she winked at Nyima—"we can dance, deh! In this wedding, there will be dancing. Music all night, all week!"

The girls cheered.

"We will slaughter these cows," added Nanna. "Meat so rich the oil will drip from your mouths and hands. You will eat until you can't move, until the music starts again, and then you'll be dancing. You will never forget that day, I promise you."

At this, the girls leapt up and danced, arms out wide, kicking up dust in a circle. They clapped and whistled, and a warmth grew in Nyima's gut, like maybe this was what it meant to be a woman, like maybe this was why she was here all along.

Nanna heaved Nyima up, dusted her skirt, then sent the small girls to go fetch the new shoes. It left the two of them in silence. She adjusted Nyima's zipper before she stepped back, satisfied.

"Well," she murmured. "How pretty."

Nanna touched Nyima's face, ran her fingers along its surface, taking stock of the youth hidden beneath the powders and pigments. Nyima followed Nanna's fingers from under stiff eyelids, felt them waver on her cheek. Without warning, Nanna pulled her in with both arms, pressing her tight against the wide weight of her breasts.

"You understand, Nyima, why this is so important. You understand, yes?"

Nyima burrowed deeper, gripping the skin around her waist, where once Nanna had carried her father, Ebou, who was already on the other side of the compound with Nuha, their future. Nyima pulled away, and Nanna let her. The old woman allowed a few minutes to pass, stilled her hands to place one large hibiscus behind Nyima's ear. Nyima fingered the soft red petals.

"You don't think this is too much, Nanna?"

"No. Oh, hush, child. Here, hold my hand. No, stop, beloved, my baby, my love. Here, wipe here. Yes. There. Shh. Shhh."

*

Even though it wasn't yet dark and the weather held, the two men sat indoors, arguing by the light of a kerosene lamp. When Nyima entered, they stopped.

"Our Nyima here is a natural," Ebou said, changing the subject. "She takes care of us, don't you?" Nyima's ears prickled, her name an oddly tender sound from her father's mouth.

Her stomach rumbled as she greeted Nuha—light pressure from the fingers with a gentle curtsy, just like she'd practiced. Nuha's hands were soft, like lips.

"We are managing," said Ebou. His grin pinched his cheeks. "You can see for yourself." Ebou spread his hands to the full room around him, where earlier Nanna had displayed their most expensive possessions. Before tonight, Nyima had never seen that large mirror—polished, above their sturdiest table—or those woven baskets. Nyima observed Nuha in secret, sampling in glances: his belly, his bald patch, the white wires of his beard. A slight lisp.

"I must admit, you're not looking so well as I remember. I just thought you'd taken another wife!" Nuha wheezed with laughter. Two shiny spoons lay forgotten by the bowl as he scooped a fistful of rice from the shared dinner. Nyima looked away, embarrassed. Her father had taught them all to use spoons as soon as they were old enough to hold one, declaring, *No child of mine will eat with their hands.* Nuha's hands pawed at the rice.

"No, still just me," Ebou said, watching Nuha eat.

"If you had come with me, you would have seen how changed the world is, how fast. It makes a man hungry again for the old way of things." Nuha squeezed the rice, oil spurting between his fingers, then rolled it onto his tongue. He spat out a few bones onto the spoons, then forced another laugh. The chair buckled against his plump thighs. "I've even missed this cheap bony fish. You never do forget the taste of home."

A tense moment passed, then Ebou followed suit. Nyima had never seen her father eat rice with his bare hands. She watched now as her father sucked the grease from his own fingers, watched as he licked the rice off his own palm before reaching to pinch loose pieces of potato and fish. He dropped the fleshiest bits on Nuha's side, a small offering. In the silence that followed, Nyima heard every wet bite the men ate. She avoided her father's gaze, afraid of what she might find there.

Nuha's one good eye veered and swerved, pausing on the table, the baskets, the mirror, then back to Ebou. She tried to ignore the other eye, the stretched black pupil fixed somewhere below her chin. Nervous, Nyima concentrated instead on memories of her sisters playing hopscotch, on her father humming as he fished, on Nanna's dramatic story from that afternoon. But she couldn't help noticing the quiet, how her father barely touched his food. She couldn't help thinking that Nanna hadn't once mentioned Nuha's eyes. Instead she had said: *mark my words.* Instead: *lucky young woman.*

"At least your daughter is everything you promised," Nuha said, mouth full, his eye sinking on Nyima. He turned to face Nyima fully. "How old are you?" he asked, yanking her from her thoughts.

"She's fifteen," her father lied. His temple pulsed just once, quick.

"How old are you really, girl?"

Nyima cleared her throat. "Fifteen," she echoed. A chill skittered across her skin.

Nuha gestured for the water, and Nyima approached. She poured while Nuha rinsed his hand over the now empty rice bowl. The rice slipped off his skin, sinking to the bottom while the oil floated. Nuha flicked the leftover droplets into the bowl. He wiped a moist hand on Nyima's skirt, and Ebou flinched. The damp seeped into her new clothes.

Nuha said, "I heard about one man who married a girl in Bonto just last year. A Karoninka. But the girl's family—chaaa—they brought the lady in all fancy, right up to the edge of the husband's compound and charged, 'Two thousand!'"

Faint perspiration appeared on her father's upper lip.

Nyima tried not to listen, tried instead to picture the bride, sparkling, jeweled, surrounded by uncles and sisters and cousins, playfully bargaining at the threshold. They danced back and forth, singing, bantering, until the bride price came, the woman crossed the gate, and the celebrations began. *Music all night, all week!* She imagined her sisters dancing in a circle, as they had just that afternoon.

Nuha's lisp thickened. "And those people, the husband's family, they have to beg until they reduce. They plead: 'Let it be a thousand-five-hundred.'

Thousand-five-hundred! The wife then enters, and the man later discovers the family tricked him. In fact, not only is she old, she's barren. Can you believe? Pure robbery."

"Yes," murmured Ebou, "terrible."

But Nuha was not done. "Before I came up river, I heard the woman had twins. Both dead in the womb, of course. Or all three in the end, I suppose."

This time Ebou was silent.

"Why do you look so grave?" Nuha cackled, pounding Ebou's shoulder. "Tonight we celebrate our long friendship, shared promises. I am a man of tradition. You can trust me for that one. The old way of things." Nuha repeated the phrase from earlier that night.

"Older does not mean better," Ebou said finally. It was a phrase Nyima had heard many times, usually when Nanna was spouting her stories. This time, Ebou's words lacked air. Since Nyima's untimely entrance into the room, his voice had thinned, making his words slip from his nose, rather than his belly and chest. She now knew Nuha had only come here to humiliate her father. In the lamplight, Ebou's grey hair turned a harsh orange and thick crescents appeared beneath his eyes. The decorated room suddenly felt haphazard, tacky.

Ebou dragged a sticky palm across his forehead as Nuha's eye ambled over Nyima's body, the crook of her blouse, the flare of her skirt. Once again, Nyima tried to return to the happy image of spilled wedding wine, the dust rising to kiss moving ankles and toes, the loud music seeping late into the night, but they were slipping away, away.

Ebou stood abruptly. Nuha remained seated.

"Nyima, go fetch more water," Ebou said.

Relieved, Nyima hurried out with only a brief glance at her father's slumped shoulders. As soon as the door shut, she tossed her shoes aside. Outside, the Jarju compound was quiet. Two, maybe three hours had passed since she'd entered the room.

*

Nyima reappeared with water to find Nuha alone, picking his teeth. He was shirtless, and the green fabric lay crumpled in his lap.

She averted her eyes, unsure. "Where's my father?"

"Do you see these scars?" Nuha said. "They are from when I fell. My profession used to be very dangerous." The chair creaked as he stood and placed the green shirt on the seat.

A prickle began on Nyima's scalp and cascaded down her back.

"Where's Ebou?" she repeated.

Nuha seemed not to hear. Nyima gripped the cup. Perhaps her father had gone to look for her and would return soon. He may have just stepped out to relieve himself or stretch his legs. Or maybe while she was gone, they'd settled their argument successfully and he was now on his way to tell Nanna and the girls the good news. Oh, they would be so happy. Thinking of her family's happiness didn't hold the same comfort as it had that morning. Still, she expected her father to come through the door at any moment.

The minutes passed and the door remained closed, the only sound Nuha's lisped words.

"Come on, now. Look," said Nuha. He raised his left arm, revealing a line of bubbled flesh stretching from his hairless armpit to the base of his skull.

Nyima raised her eyes, and she tried to smile, just like Nanna had taught. The scars were jagged and pitted.

Nuha nodded with approval. "And here," he continued, "is where I hit my head on a stone." His index finger tapped the small bald patch, where the scar tissue shone like a buffed nail. Nyima wished he would put his shirt back on.

The bowl scraped as Nuha pushed it aside. He stepped once, twice in her direction, an arm's length away. Nyima's head throbbed. Her sisters' simmering excitement, their careful preparations, Nanna's stories, it felt like a dream. Could a day be so long? Try as she might, she couldn't forget the lines on her father's face, the slumped figure she had left moments ago. In that moment, she knew Ebou would not come for her.

Nyima still held the silly cup in her hand, and the water spilled a little.

Nuha removed the flower from Nyima's ear. His smile gleamed yellow.

She looked down and realized she forgot her shoes.

"Touch it," said Nuha, bending so her eyes were level with the glossy scar. A vague fishy scent laced his words. In all her stories, Nanna had never mentioned he would smell like palm oil, that his breath would be warm and sticky. What else had Nanna not told her? Her heartbeat felt precious, buried deep like treasure.

Pale stretchmarks streaked Nuha's waist and hips, and he tugged at his clean white trousers. Nyima scrambled for the door, but Nuha grabbed her easily in the tight space. She threw her weight into yanking away, her feet slipping and sliding for traction which never came. Amused, Nuha laughed and let go. It sent her hurtling into the wall. Dazed, on all fours, she began to plead, though to whom she couldn't be sure: *Please,* maybe to her Nanna, Ebou, anyone. *Please–let this not be how this night ends.* Nuha had placed himself between her and the door. She struggled again, darted for the door.

"This is just the way things were meant to be," he said, shoving her to the floor with one firm hand. Only then did she begin crying, and she hated the tears for falling, for making her look like a child.

By her knees, the evening's bowl lay, raked clean and puddled with dirty water. Tomorrow, Nanna would give thanks at the baobabs' feet, then boast to all her friends. Tomorrow, the party would begin, and as promised, her sisters would dance. But what about tonight? What about her? The blood surged away from her skin. The bowl glinted, dotted and streaked with orange stains. There was nothing left, not for her sisters, father, Nanna, not even for her.

Nyima screamed, hoping Nanna was close enough to hear, strong enough to come to her aid. Just one prayer remained: *Please.* She knew they could hear her but would not come, likely instructed not to. Nuha's hand clamped hard against her mouth, and she kicked, bit, scratched, twisting free. *Nanna.* He staggered back, surprised. Nyima tripped, landed heavily, tore her skirt. The lamp shattered. *Nanna, help me please.* All was black except a silver thread of light beneath the door. She could hear Nuha breathing. Fumbling in the dark, broken glass cutting into her palms, she found cool, smooth metal. *Please,* she prayed, as she hurled the bowl toward the noise. It clanked, clattered, and turned on the floor. Before it could settle, Nyima burst through the door. She ran.

*

Nyima spilled into the night. The wind whipped her skirt, making her stumble, so she hiked it over her knees, legs pushing harder, stretching farther. The air stung her eyes, roared in and out of her lungs. She ran through tall dry grass, leapt over uneven ground, dry shrubs. At the river, she splashed and waded in. The silt tugged her body, pulled her ankles, and she paddled, thinking she must keep breathing, must keep moving.

The island of mangroves loomed ahead, a dark smudge in the clear night sky. Over the years, she had seen it shelter birds—from lumbering brown pelicans to little sunbirds—had collected new, wet feathers from shore. No matter how many birds left, they always returned. It made her believe she might find harbor too. Holding tight to this memory, Nyima swam faster. Her arms and legs grew heavy with each passing stroke. Something brushed her leg, and she stifled a sob. Her neck stretched for air. The river pushed her on. The current lifted her body, propelling her forward.

Up close, the island was a tangle of vegetation, rising from the brackish water. Her toes found mud, but it was too soft to stand and the mangroves too dense to enter. So instead, she drifted with the current, using the long roots for guidance. Blackened oysters crowded the waterline, marking the tides, and they scratched her palms. She tugged firmly at each root, testing its give before letting go and grabbing the next. Every few feet, her arm swept away floating sticks, rotting leaves.

Would Nuha follow, or would he slink back home? Would he stalk into Ebou's quarters, shrieking the deal was off? Would they wait for her return? She imagined Ebou's shock when Nuha appeared, clothes ruined. Ebou wouldn't believe it at first. Would he be ashamed or relieved? Perhaps the two men would look for her together. No doubt, Nanna would know exactly where she was. Oh, Nanna. All those hours practicing and preparing, all her wasted prayers. Nyima cried softly. Her small body shuddered with the weight of what she had lost.

In that moment, she longed to hear the sounds of home—her sisters squabbling, Nanna yelling—but instead there was the odd bird call, the water clapping against roots, and the croaks of swamp frogs. Eyes shut, she comforted herself with Nanna's stories. She thought of Rabbit, Hyena, and Elephant, who turned themselves into men to win the annual tug of war contest at Sanjal; or of Ndiiti, the fastest bird, who overcame his friends' betrayal to win all the treasures of the world; or of the Ninki-nanka, who saved the villagers when they were losing hope, watching bad men cross the river to burn their forests and steal their farms. The monster had devoured the army as it disembarked from this very river. *Just as they placed their first step on dry land, the Ninki-nanka rose from the water*—Nanna would exclaim jumping in the air—*and threw fire from its mouth.*

Nyima worked methodically, pulling herself from root to root. She found comfort in the resistance, the repetition. As her breathing stabilized, her surroundings sharpened. A half-moon hung low, and it drenched the world in grey, casting shadows where she had not noticed them before. Snakes slithered in the branches, shaking the leaves. Lights flickered. Crabs scuttled. She became alert to new dangers: in the mangroves, in the water, in her own body. The cold rattled her bones. A rotten odor filled the air, intensifying with her fear.

Then, the sound she had been waiting for: Nuha's voice in the breeze. Onshore, the man untethered a pirogue. The clatter of wood. The splash of oars.

Brief relief flooded her—the danger now visible, audible—before her nerves recoiled in panic. The pirogue traced the shortest route to shore, blocking any chance of return. A small lamp swung from one end of the boat, spreading a dim glow. Nyima realized her mistake. She had poured all her strength into getting here. Now, she had nothing left, nowhere to go: barred out by the mangroves and barred in by the waters, which yawned wide as the sea. Watching the light approach, it seemed a miracle she had come so far. Her stomach growled. She had to eat, sleep a little. Then she believed she could be brave again. As if in sympathy, the waters around her warmed a little.

Pulled by the same, strange current, the man sliced swiftly through the waters. Within minutes, Nuha was so close she could hear him breathe.

Praying to all the gods Nanna had ever mentioned, Nyima wedged herself as deep between the roots as she could. She sank quietly, submerging her chin and, reluctantly, her mouth. She took shorter breaths through her nose, though the stench made her gag.

The boat crept closer. The lamp swayed from side to side. The glow almost touched her. Nyima braced for discovery.

All at once, a dark shape erupted from the waters, overturning the pirogue. Birds rushed from the mangroves, squawking and flapping. Swells of fish scurried, slapping past her legs. Nyima's mouth gaped wide, stunned. Her scream lodged, petrified, in the back of her throat.

Moments later, the water rippled again and, to Nyima's terror, the monster resurfaced, slowly this time. Powerful shoulders, followed by ridges shaped like anvils along its spine. The hulking form loomed just ten feet from where she hid. Nyima could not tear her eyes away. She was paralyzed with fear, but also an absurd fascination. Nanna had been right after all. At least, in part. There was the pointed snout and two curved horns, just as she'd imagined. There, the long angular face, the terrible smell. She saw differences too, small but somehow meaningful. Its body was dotted in scales, though only the size of thumbnails. Its long neck arched high above her, but not as high as the clouds. And then the neat comb of teeth: they were thin, like hair, not at all like knives. The monster cooed. Smoke spouted from its ears.

She now saw that the birds, which she had earlier assumed fled in fear, had actually raced towards the creature. As the waters settled, she noticed turtles, snakes, and new wild birds—one, pink-plumed; another, a dazzling emerald green—and how they all rested on the creature's back, horns, the ridges on its spine. Schools of silver fish circled its belly, zipping between its fins. She pictured the warm glow of flames inside its chest, felt how the waters warmed her again as they had earlier that night. A familiar warm current pulled her in. The smell dissipated. Nyima suddenly realized the creature had been here all along.

She paddled towards the creature. Birds and fish parted, and it gave her a strange courage, which grew as she neared. Now that she'd made up her mind, she feared if she even blinked, the creature would vanish. Bit by bit, the creature sank until its eyes were level with hers. They were really more the color of ripe mangoes, sweet and orange.

At last, face-to-face with the Ninki-nanka, Nyima examined the two round eyes Nanna had loved recounting. If Nanna's stories were true, she knew what to expect: perhaps a vision of beautiful dresses, jewelry, ripe fields before harvest, or better still, her whole family, healthy and happy and together. She was giddy with anticipation.

Over the years, Nanna had occasionally produced a mirror from her mattress, a warped square which familiarized her with the shape of her head, the arc of her cheeks. She had also caught glimpses on the river's surface at midday or in the basins as they washed and prepared for their next meal. Sometimes on the flat blades of knives, she'd spied dulled fragments—nose, lips, eyes—slices of a face she'd hardly recognized as her own. Now, as she gazed into those eyes, she saw for the first time a perfect reflection of her face. She touched her cheek, restored.

Nyima grabbed the creature's neck and swung herself out of the water. Her heart pumped loud in her ears as she waited nervously for what came next. The creature began to move. Muscles tensed and released as it picked up speed and she clung tighter, laughing out loud. The breeze kissed her cheeks. Behind her, the village lights faded, the houses a bare speck from the shoreline, and finally the mangroves, too, disappeared. She breathed in deep, squinting into the night and into the rushing darkness. And really, truly, what lay dormant beyond, who could say?

Alex Wilson

Content Moderator

The photos come in as jpegs or tiffs, RAW files sometimes, if people have the bandwidth and don't care about someone else reproducing their images in hi-res. The videos are mostly .flvs, .movs, or mpegs. Sometimes those are RAW files too, and editable, but it's rare, and that's when they're in .yuv format. I usually have to flag anything in .yuv, since our interface generally doesn't like to support such a big file. They're also a problem because, anyone who wants to give away the ability to color-correct their footage, to download it and take *ownership* of its quality, is someone who wants *permutations* and *reinterpretation*, *messaging* or *artistic license*. So they're either shooting porn, or it's ISIS.

Actually, ninety-five percent of the time, the ISIS vids are usually pretty tight. They're packaged with clean edits and pans, decent framing, 2004-era graphics (but still, graphics), and good color correction. So it's usually some other terror group with those sloppy and massive files, maybe an Al Qaeda cell in West Africa, or some white supremacist assholes in Kentucky. Or porn, like I said.

My boyfriend wonders why I come home and take a shower and drink, like, a half a bottle of wine before I'll even consider looking at him. I don't have the energy to tell him about the posts scrolling vertically on my screen, how I can see, most times, just from the thumbnails, that I'm going to have to flag certain uploads. That I'm going to have to watch the third vid in my queue in its entirety—a fifteen-year-old with pimples and the hint of a mustache. That I'm going to have to wait to see what he's up to with that noose slung over that tree branch. That at forty-five seconds, it's clear he's not going to hang himself. He's hanging a dog, in Massachusetts, instead.

I can tell where he is because of his accent. He narrates as the Chihuahua thrashes and kicks her legs, the bones under her hide moving in her back. The dog is brindled and surrounded by autumn leaves, because, it's November on the East Coast, and that's what happens to the leaves in November on the East Coast, even in the backyards of teenagers who decide to hang the family pet.

The next file I flag is a single frame. I open it to two hundred percent—*best practices policy* in the manual for content moderators on this platform. It's a double penetration, some fat lady, maybe fifty, and two Marines. I tag the video and the photo and drag them from one of my monitors to the next and junk the files. Then I send an email to the account holder, a form outlining our policy guidelines on this social interface.

I hear, up in the Valley, a lot of this work is outsourced to the Philippines. I hear the cafeterias are insane, up there, and they have shuttles that take you to work, and open-concept offices with walls and shit that are glass on three sides, which you can write on like whiteboards. I hear, even at Qualcomm, which is maybe thirty miles from my desk—my table, actually, which I share with six other moderators, thirty desks in this room, all inland in San Diego—that they have cubicles. A cube would be nice. A window would be better. We'd probably be able to see all twelve lanes of the I-15 from our table. The only window we have, though, is Windows, and I think it's pretty much a cliché, in this day and age, to point out that everybody hates Windows.

I hear in Manila they make two hundred and fifty bucks a week. I make $40k a year, plus benefits. I hear a lot of coders and devs in the Valley clear six figures. Even at Qualcomm they do high five, writing code for Snapdragons. I should have learned to write code instead of majoring in poli-sci, with a minor in Near East history.

"Beheading," John says from the other side of our table.

He's just loud enough that I can hear him through my ear buds and over the white noise they pump in from the ceiling. His name *is* John, I think. (Maybe it's Jake.)

It's funny because the beheadings are, almost always, the only things we discuss in the workplace. The guys would probably cluster around some of the porn, and maybe the girls too, if it was really late, like three a.m., and if it wasn't against *best practices policy* in the manual. But the beheadings have the same tag as *combat*, so we're asked to make a note of them, *verbally*. Anything *newsworthy*, deemed by the manual as *current events*, requires *oversight*. *Current events* suck because you have to tag the content and then wait for a manager. You have to hold a *discussion*, of *classification*, of *user impact*, always with beheadings, occasionally with *combat* or other *news items*, like I mentioned.

News-source stuff gets cleared, usually. Other content, especially if it's homemade, requires *deeper assessment*. You have to decide how to categorize the *context*, the *user's intent*, the *viral potential*, all while your queue keeps backlogging new vids and images.

"Which one," I ask John (or Jake).

"The long one."

"It runs twelve minutes and forty-eight?"

"Yeah, they have trouble with the knife."

"Yeah, I saw it."

"Assassin amateur hour."

"I showed it to Scott already."

"You sure?"

"Yeah, flag it, block the user, and dump it. I had the same vid yesterday."

*

There's this construction site that I pass in Mira Mesa during my commute, Monday through Friday. They're building a condo complex and I always see it skimming beside the road, at 8:15 on my way in, and creeping by, at 5:40, as I head north in traffic. It's about ten minutes south of my exit—duplexes that look like each will have a patio facing the freeway. There's a banner tacked on the temporary fencing around the site that says, *Coming Soon: By The Colman Group, Mira Montaña*. More like *Mira Calle Grande*.

The complex grows a little more complete everyday, almost imperceptibly. On Mondays, I'll think back to what the condos looked like the previous Monday. Then I'll think of the Monday, two months ago, when I told myself I was going to quit before the holidays. There's context in there somewhere for how much it's changing. Sometimes, within the same week, I'll compare mental snapshots, between Monday morning and Friday afternoon, just to fuck with myself. Then I wonder what it must be like for the guys building it, if they even see the macro when they merge onto the 15 in their pickups.

I remember when it was just a foundation. I remember when they were framing the walls with plywood and 2x4s. The scaffolding looked like it was assembled from Popsicle sticks, which made me think of the Popsicle vid I flagged, and dumped, in August. I wondered what would happen to all that wood if it rained, and then it did rain, in January, and the complex sat under the clouds, the planks growing dark as sheets of water crept down the wallboards.

I assumed mold would form on the wood if the storm continued. I imagined that the spores would fan out, in uneven rings, the coloring malignant and dark at the center of each new colony. I decided the contractors would simply tack up their drywall, over the fungus, without telling their foremen.

The sun was out the next day, though, and the wood was bright within a week, bleached in the winter heat, like the bones I saw in a *current events* post. The video of the mass grave went live, approved because it was deemed to originate from a user-account registered by a Sinaloan *news-source*.

The thing about the construction site is I try to use it as a switch. I see it and I know there's no way for me to know what else I might see later. I check my makeup in the rearview mirror and, if I'm south of the site, it can be like seeing the eyes of a stranger. Sometimes, though, looking at the site, I try to remember the videos and photos that are easy approvals.

Ninety-five percent of the uploads on our platform offer the benign mosaic of existence—babies on swings and graduation photos, meals people made for themselves with parsley, or some other garnish, sprinkled over their salmon, the edge of the plate ringed in too much glare from the flash on their iPhone. I try to think about the lives that will evolve in the condos once they're completed. I try not to think about how much time I've spent at my desk, or what two-to-five percent of those people will upload.

*

According to the manual, the following content items violate the user agreement for this social interface. All should be flagged for deletion and/or immediate second-level assessment:

* *Messaging, visual or otherwise, intended to advocate for unlawful activity*
* *Messaging, visual or otherwise, intended to advocate for the destruction and/or damage of public and/or private property*
* *Messaging, visual or otherwise, intended to slander, persecute, and/or harass public and/or private individuals and/or entities, including the employees of and/or Lotus Garden LLC and/or its distributors, partners, and/or developers*

* *Messaging, visual or otherwise, intended to slander, persecute, and/or harass groups defined by race, religion, sexual orientation, and/or other subcategories*
* *Messaging, visual or otherwise, intended to advocate for harmful physical acts against public and/or private individuals, animals, and/or other entities, including the employees of and/or Lotus Garden LLC and/or its distributors, partners, and/or developers*
* *Messaging, visual or otherwise, intended to advocate for harmful physical acts against federal, domestic, state, county, local, and/or foreign governments and/or government servants*
* *Messaging, visual or otherwise, intended to advocate for harmful physical acts against groups defined by race, religion, sexual orientation, and/or other subcategories*
* *Grievous vulgarity*
* *Nudity [For exemptions consult Section 8D on p. 111 marked* Second-level Exemptions: Non-pornographic Artwork*]*
* *Requests, visual or otherwise, intended for sexual solicitation*
* *Consensual sexual acts*
* *Sexual acts involving minors*
* *Sexual acts involving minors and/or adults construed as pornography*
* *Rape and/or nonconsensual sexual acts involving minors and/or adults*
* *Rape and/or nonconsensual sexual acts involving minors and/or adults construed as pornography*
* *Content, visual or otherwise, encouraging and/or expressing suicidal tendencies*
* *Torture, maiming, and/or death of animals and/or death of persons*
* *Graphic depictions of the torture, maiming, and/or death of animals and/or persons as a result of natural and/or manmade disasters, accidents, wartime acts, or other circumstances [For exceptions consult Section 5C on p. 126 marked* Second-level Exemptions: News-Source and Current Events*]*

It goes on like that for a few more pages. The rest of the manual is devoted to policies, job descriptives, assessment, modifying clauses, and H.R. instructions. Lotus Garden must have hired a former content moderator, or a team of current content moderators, to write that first section, though, because they nailed all of the broad strokes. Only the details are missing, and you can't blame them, really. No one could preconceive that psycho who works in the morgue, with his ski mask, and monthly blog, and ventriloquist act—*The Vaginas of the Dead in Dialogue.*

I'd like to say that kind of imagination is singular, but that wouldn't be accurate. Sometimes I wish every upload had an abstract, like an academic paper, so I wouldn't have to actually open the videos and photos. Then I think about how much extra time it would take to assess each one, via paragraph. You always know banned content the moment you see it, even from the thumbnails. There's no reason to intellectualize, summarize, and/or list any of it.

*

I drive down to the coast to meet my sister for breakfast. She lives in Cardiff so I take the Del Dios Highway through the orange groves and mansions in Rancho Santa Fe. The road is two lanes and rolls with the contours of the foothills. It's sunny, and warm, like always.

The fruit has come in on the trees and the inside of my car smells like vegetation and citrus. I thank god, if there is a god, that our sense of smell is something they haven't managed to leverage yet on the internet. The orange groves only remind me of oranges—and Saturday mornings, and dropping down to the ocean, driving west.

The restaurant is near the water off the PCH. My sister is at a table on the patio, which is still in the shade, under a heat lamp. The enclosure is crowded and full of voices and it takes her maybe fifteen minutes to flag down our waitress. I watch the sun move on the face of a wave, just before it breaks, and a valet in the parking lot as he runs back and forth from the key box. We order mimosas and I ask for an omelet with feta and spinach.

"So you want the Greek," the waitress asks.

"No, just spinach and feta."

"That's the Greek."

"That's cool," I say. "I'll have that then."

According to the menu, the Greek includes tomatoes, but it isn't worth arguing, ever, with the wait staff. My sister orders a veggie omelet, without asparagus or mushrooms, the grilled peppers and onions on the side, please, not mixed with the rest. "You look tired," she says after the waitress has left.

We talk about her kids for a while and our parents up in Morro Bay. She tells me about her nanny and how, even with two incomes, it feels like the cost of childcare is breaking their backs. We talk about her husband and my boyfriend and I complain about how Mike doesn't wipe down the sink after he shaves.

"You'll get used to living with him," she says. "You just have to get him trained."

Then the food comes and we eat, and I don't check my plate or her plate. I don't tell her about how, when I think of training Mike, I see that dog collar vid still circulating from Abu Ghraib. I don't tell her that when I think of her kids, at home during the day, I see the nanny cam vid I flagged and marked on Thursday.

We hug in the parking lot and I want to hold onto her but I only squeeze her lightly and then let go. As I drive back through the foothills I close my eyes behind the wheel, somewhere alongside the orange groves.

*

Scott is inaudible over the white noise and my ear buds. I lean back in my chair and it rocks too far because the spring in the column needs to be tightened. I rock forward again and remove the ear buds and set them beside my keyboard. The white noise coming from the ceiling is a track, I think, called *Mountain Fountain*.

"Did a Doctor Simi clip go live from your queue yesterday?" He's annoyed because I've already made him repeat himself.

"What," I say.

"The Tijuana kids dropkicking that mascot for the pharmacy."

Simi is an oversized head-and-torso, like the ducks and razorbacks they have at college basketball games. His look is old-man-in-a-lab-coat, with glasses and a tie, and I guess he's supposed to flag down whoever might be trawling for cheap meds in Mex on their lunch breaks. He's the *brand representative* of a national drugstore chain and his handlers have him outside of every sales location, dancing on the sidewalks.

Lately there's been a meme circulating of local teenagers blindsiding him in T.J. They'll take a running start and level whoever's in the Simi suit, or do the one-guy-kneels-behind-him thing and bounce him off a lamppost. It's always executed around a lot of metal and pavement. The faster the kids are moving when they make contact, and the more violent the aftermath, the faster the clip goes viral. I guess one group of kids even shoved Simi into traffic and his foot was run over by a dump truck.

In the vid I cleared yesterday, the guy in the Simi suit was dressed as Simi, obviously, but Simi was dressed as a fireman. He was shaking his ass when this kid in a Xolos jersey sprayed him with a fire extinguisher, then another kid came from the opposite side, through the cloud, and blew him, like, ten feet backward. I think I was laughing a little when I cleared it and hit replay.

"That should have gone *second-level*," Scott says. He's standing closer to my desk now and my head is at crotch-level and he's chewing a cuticle.

"Come on," I say.

"Check the manual."

"That was way less offensive than the lady with the bucket of lye and the knife."

"That's outside of your purview."

"Did you see what was left of her husband," the new guy adds across the table, a replacement for John (or Jake) after John (or Jake) quit in April.

"Carne," I say.

"And salsa."

"Apparently the husband in the lye vid was abusive," Scott says. "Plus, that clip was *news-source*."

*

It's still before midnight when I open my eyes in the dark. The wine I drank earlier has broken down into sugar and my veins race with sweetened blood. I feel dizzy and exhausted and alert all at once. I can see across the bedroom—the World Market art we've hung beside the door, the pictures on the dresser of our families. My eyes are perfectly adjusted to whatever light comes in through the windows. I can hear the streetlamps humming outside, and the freeway, somewhere to the west. I lie under the sheets with my head flat on the mattress. I've pushed away all the pillows while I've slept.

I listen to my boyfriend and focus on the intake of his breath. He inhales and exhales for longer than I could have imagined. Then he inhales again, and I count, silently moving my lips. I recount as he exhales and the outbreath runs for two seconds longer than the inhalation. There should be peace in this sound, I tell myself, the rhythm of his lungs, a comfort in my knowledge of this small thing he couldn't possibly know even about himself.

I wonder what he might know about me, and roll over, and the room and the blankets suddenly grow hot. I try to imagine the sun and how I would feel at this moment if the sky became light. I see the monitors on my desk and climb out of bed and pull on a sweatshirt. I cup my hands and drink from the faucet in the bathroom. My heart still races with the sugar in my blood, and I shut off the water. I hear Mike shift in the bedroom. Then he settles back into the asymmetrical arrangement of his breath.

In the living room I lay down carefully on the couch. My bones ache like I've suddenly become sick. I should be wearing a bra, I think, for some reason. I feel brittle and exposed and old, and keep telling myself that I'm only twenty-six. "You're only twenty-six," I whisper in the dark.

Mike has forgotten to shut off the ceiling fan. I watch it spin and wonder if he remembered to lock the backdoor. I close my eyes and see a hallway paled by fluorescent light bulbs. The ceiling is a grid of particleboard and, in one section, there are open rafters, which reveal bundles of coaxial cable zip-tied to a truss.

I realize I'm asleep. Then I'm awake again on my couch.

*

I think it's late August when I turn into the complex beside the freeway. The condos have been complete for about a month. The roads are so new that they still smell of tar and asphalt. The last upload I flagged tonight began with a little girl in a playhouse. Now it's nearly eight and almost dark.

I drive up and down the streets for a while and then turn into a cul-de-sac. Old-growth palms and sumac have been transplanted here to dampen the noise from the freeway, which rises above the rooftops. I imagine a car leaving the road and sailing through the sumac. I see a family in their kitchen as the drywall shatters and the framing showers them with splinters. I think of that train-derailment vid that keeps popping up from—maybe Virginia. I turn off my engine and close my eyes and decide we can adjust. We can always adjust to living with whatever we live with.

I open the car door and step out onto the sidewalk. The dying hum of an underinflated tire comes from the road, overlaid with the airbrakes of a truck. It's dark now and in the bushes, I think, I can hear crickets. The air smells like fresh water on grass, and exhaust, and even stronger of asphalt. I look up at the sky but the light from the road and the streetlamps have dimmed the stars.

I find myself walking through another cul-de-sac. Someone has left a pink bicycle on its side in a driveway and, in the street, there's a different arrangement of cars. It's difficult to know how far I've come, or where I might find a landmark. I stop, to retrace my steps, and visualize where I parked. The freeway seems louder for a moment, but only because I'm consciously aware of it to my left.

Across the way a bay window flickers with blue light and I hunch over and step onto the condo's lawn. The motion of my body reminds me of the video I saw last week of a coyote. The animal was in a field of mustard plant, ghosting through the flowers, when a man wearing a trucker hat, silkscreened with the state flag of Texas, shot it from maybe a hundred yards.

I'm breathing quickly now and my blood is running but my veins seem narrow somehow, outside, at night, on my feet, in the physical fear that someone might be watching. I stand close to the wall, which is still warm from the sun, which is now long gone.

When the light inside shifts colors to a deeper blue I look through the window. A news anchor is on a television, and the television is on the near wall of a living room within the condo. The ground floor runs back into an open floor plan and is mostly darkened, aside from the flat screen. A track of lights is burning over the granite in the kitchen. Otherwise I can see no sign of life.

I look back over my shoulder at two more condos in the cul-de-sac glowing with the same blue light. I look into the window next door and then again across the street. A man sits alone in a kitchen, clipping his fingernails. A glass of water stands beside him on the table. It's after ten now and I see no children in these windows because the children must be asleep.

Somewhere on the next block two yuppies load a dishwasher. A woman reads from a tablet in full illumination. Then I do see a family and their children must be older because they're still awake. Their faces are lit blue, like the walls, from the television, and the room is dark otherwise behind them.

The boy is lying on the floor with his head propped on a pillow. One girl, maybe sixteen, texts on her phone in a loveseat. Another is in a sweatshirt, the youngest, maybe only nine, sitting on a beanbag that looks soft, but too small for her.

Their parents sit apart from each other on a couch pushed against the wall, angled so they have to turn their heads to watch the TV. The father is eating, I think, ice cream. They each seem unaware of each other and peaceful. A mirror mounted above them returns part of the screen.

In the reflection, a woman at a counter portions a stick of butter and speaks slowly. She isn't fat, and she isn't beautiful, necessarily, and seems to be making pastries. I reach for my phone and switch on the camera and film them for a while. When I'm finished, I continue to watch the mirror. This clip would never go viral. I keep it just for me.

I start my car and merge onto the 15 and I don't look back at the complex. I check my eyes in the mirror and think about my commute in the morning—a Wednesday. I'll quit sometime in September, I promise myself. I promise myself that I'll quit this year, maybe, before the holidays.

Marléne Zadig

Song for Unbelievers

Mine was an unusually percussive household growing up. The *chck-pffst* of our father's beer cans cracking open every half-hour from the tangerine velour armchair in the living room. The *thunk-chck* of eggs whacked into a bowl or pan in our backwoods country kitchen for nearly every meal my mother made (thanks to the massive chicken coop out back)—scrambled at breakfast, hard-boiled at lunch, and casseroled at dinnertime. The tinny *bam-bam-bam* of any one of my six younger siblings colliding a wooden spoon handle into an upended soup pot throughout their collective fifteen-odd years of toddlerhood. And me, the eldest son, perpetually ramming a tennis ball against the beams of my attic bedroom to quiet my own mind by drowning out the commotion below. If you had nerves when you were born into my family, you'd have to have stripped yourself bare of them—renounced their existence entirely—just to carry on.

In part as a reaction to this lifelong blitzkrieg of sound, I was reluctant to start a family myself, but my wife Aoife was ultimately persuasive. "We'll just be starting with one," she pointed out. "We don't have to go beyond that if it's too much chaos for you."

So it's with some degree of amusement and a greater degree of amazement that my own tiny daughter (sixteen months tomorrow) barely makes a peep. She *hates* to make noise. She hates to hear noise made by others. Even as an infant, she resisted the entropy of crowds and parties. She has flat-out refused to unite spoon handle to pan bottom despite universal toddler imperatives to do just that (xylophones, tambourines, maracas, and jingle bells, all similarly eschewed). I tell her, "You would've been eaten alive had you grown up in my house." She gurgles softly but doesn't listen.

Still, I appreciate her affinity for stillness and quietude; I like to think that her antipathy for turbulence is somehow related to my lifetime of enduring pandemonium. They say that epigenetic changes to our DNA can transmit the effects of trauma down through generations, so why not aversions too? Wouldn't that be something.

I will say this, she has a remarkable attention span for the kinds of things she *is* interested in. When deposited on the floor with legs scissored open to a clumsy V, she twirls her little elfin feet in circles and pants in the presence of dust particles, bits of string, lint. The other day she fixated on a clump of dried mud on the floor, rotating her feet inward and chuffing out, "Duht! Duht!"—over and over again until I acknowledged her discovery. It strikes me that she has a remarkable vocabulary for a sixteen month old who abhors sound.

It's not just noise, though, it's everything. I have a hard time keeping her entertained once she's had her fill of fuzz and yarn, considering she expresses an actual fear response to most new toys, foods, and common objects, and as her increasingly baffled stay-at-home father, I have my concerns. Her insistence on the quiet and familiar verges on bonkers, so we recently had her evaluated by a specialist to see if anything was officially "wrong" (although we knew in our hearts that something was; she once burst into tears when presented with a Koosh ball, which should've been toddler crack, and she shrinks—quaking—at the sight of bubbles). Truly, we just wanted a label, because therein lies a diagnosis, and implicit in a diagnosis is a treatment plan. And we got what we were looking for—at least, part of it, anyway.

"Your daughter seems to have Sensory Processing Disorder," announced the social worker who evaluated her for the county's Infant and Toddler Program. "What you perceive as background noise, she perceives as a microphone wailing feedback. What you perceive as interesting textures, she perceives alternately as spiders on her skin or needles jamming into her body, depending on the situation. What is normal for us stimulates the fight-or-flight response in your daughter." She handed me a sedately illustrated brochure, muted in gentle tones of sepia and lavender, as if I were the one who couldn't handle the sensory overload.

My initial response to the diagnosis was relief, then concern. "Isn't that associated with autism?" I asked, plainly upset at the possibility.

"There's co-morbidity with autism spectrum disorders, yes, but she doesn't have any of the markers for those. They can just as well occur independently of one another. One is not caused by the other."

Again, relief. She offered a list of books on the subject and another list of local occupational therapists who specialized in treating the symptoms. I welcomed the information, said thank you, then added on our way out, "I wouldn't use the word 'morbidity,' though, with parents. It sounds too much like you're talking about death."

I carted our daughter back home for a lunch of pureed spinach dal with a touch of applesauce for sweetness. While most of her peers had graduated to sandwiches by now, Sibby still gagged on and regurgitated solid foods. I marveled at the mutability of these other toddlers, whose parents universally complained of the same exact problem: "The only thing that stays the same is that every three months they completely change on you, and you have to figure them out all over again." Not our Sibby. She was precisely the same creature we'd met on the day she was born, but the trouble was, I didn't have the slightest idea who that was. Her eyes, which ranged from carob to beetle-black depending on the light, possessed an opacity that was vaguely alien. I couldn't decipher her at all.

Around the same time we got the diagnosis, Aoife tried to convince me—begged me, really—to agree to raising chickens in our miniscule, suburban backyard in Redwood City, and to this, I would not relent so easily. If there was anything about my upbringing I hated more than having six younger siblings, it was the incessant squawking, prattling, and pooping of our many resident chickens. Aoife (it's pronounced EE-fuh, by the way—her family has a thing for incomprehensible Irish names) ostensibly wanted them for the fresh eggs, but I knew she believed chickens would protect our little Siobhán against the debilitating allergies Aoife has fought against her entire life. (Again, I feel compelled to explain that Siobhán=Shih-VON. "Why do you want to maintain your family's tradition of forcing their daughters to over-enunciate their unreadable names?" I asked my wife when we were deciding what to call our firstborn. "Because it's a rite of passage," she'd shrugged. "Don't you ever get tired of 'Joe'?")

Anyway, I argued with her about eggs.

"Even if you buy the seven-dollar eggs at the farmer's market, it's still cheaper than keeping chickens. You have to feed them. You have to buy a chicken coop. It is never cheaper or more convenient to buy live chickens unless you're going to eat them and breed them. Plus, you know I hate eggs and lost a taste for chicken a long time ago." I grew up in the mountains southeast of San Diego (in not quite a border town and not quite a mountain town because it wasn't even a town), and aside from canned beans and the occasional hot dog, our main source of protein was our chickens.

"Yes, but eggs aren't the only reason or I wouldn't have asked." She recited research suggesting that kids need to be around farm animal feces—not just dogs and cats—to build their immune systems up against allergies. "And I'm not talking the internet, here; *National Geographic* did a feature on it! You don't want her ending up like me, do you? Asthma, Epi-pens, crazy-expensive air filters from The Sharper Image. Come on, I'm practically a girl in a bubble for how little of the year I am able to comfortably spend outside." This was true. "It's no way to live, and we still have time to prevent that. Please?"

She had a point. And though I loathed chickens, I was warming to my own inspiration that a clutch of baby chicks might actually encourage Siobhán to deal with her newly-identified sensory issues. Our first appointment with an OT had been fairly pointless—apparently the main recognized treatment for sensory problems is to literally brush your child all over their body to desensitize them. Regularly. With an actual hairbrush. (Seriously.) So when that didn't go over too well, I figured, who can resist baby chicks?

But nothing ever goes as planned, does it. What's that awful, trite saying? "Men make plans and God laughs." It should really be, "Wives make plans and laugh at their men." Wives who work all day making sure the Internet doesn't break so that you can stay home and read poetry during nap time and raise your daughter without having to put her in a daycare center before her immune system works where she might get, I don't know—*the plague*, or at the very least Hand, Foot, and Mouth Disease (whose name conveniently omits that it also causes sores on the genitals (!!!)). You, who can't even fix the Wi-Fi without calling your wife for help if it involves anything other than switching it off and then on again.

So no, it didn't go how I thought it would. Sibby hated the chicks. They were "ouchy." Sharp beaks, scratchy claws. They relieved themselves inconveniently often in inconvenient places.

"But they're *chicks!*" I tried to reason with her. "They're adorable!" Nope, no dice.

The other day, though, Sibby finally seemed interested in what I was doing. She pointed to the chicks in their incubator while I was refilling their water and said, "Eat! Eat!" At the time I thought she was being prodigious.

"Yes," I confirmed, rather impressed. "We *do* eat chickens!" But I'd misinterpreted. How could I have thought she was capable of that mental leap from animal to food having never witnessed any of the steps? There's nothing new under the sun when it comes to parenting (it only ever seems that way): we all think our own kids are savants.

She raised her barely-there, peach-fuzz eyebrows and widened the apertures of her eyes, then lowered her lips into a profound pout. Her chin wobbled, she cried, then tottered away.

I regarded the chicks, who pecked among the wood shavings for their spilled feed, gobbling up invisibly small crumbs. She'd meant the *chickens* were eating, not that we'd eat the chickens, and here I'd probably guaranteed she'd be a vegetarian for life.

*

I asked my mother once when I came back to visit from college (cross-country scholarship to Cal-Poly San Luis Obispo—*Go Mustangs!*) why she'd felt compelled to have so many children. We weren't religious. She was educated—San Diego State, class of 1977. She'd had access to birth control. And they only had the one income from my father's job as a rural mailman for the U.S. Postal Service. It wasn't in anybody's best interest for her to have seven kids.

This is what she told me: "After I had you—that first night you were alive, in fact—I woke up in the night certain that you were dead. We'd put you on our bed between us so you wouldn't fall out and so I could nurse you easy enough in the night, and I woke up with a start for no clear reason but then saw that our blankets were covering your face. And you were so little, so new, that I thought surely you had suffocated. I didn't want to find out. I had only ever wanted the one—you, that is—maybe two, but I felt then that perhaps it was hubris to just have one, that it was tempting fate. I decided that if you were alive when I pulled back the covers, I'd have as many children as I could to sort of nudge fate in the opposite direction, hoping that it would keep you all alive and well on a lark as sort of cosmic penance for me having so many kids, because I'd have to find a way to care for all of you, and it wouldn't exactly be fun, would it. Motherhood made me superstitious as heck, I'll freely admit it."

*

There's something people have got all wrong about mothers, by the way, and I'm just going to come out and say it. Mothers aren't obsessed with their children because of any biological predisposition or instinct. They are obsessed because they are bored, and their kids are the only things around with any degree of animation or entertainment value. We—yes, "we"—are obsessed because there is nothing else to do.

I didn't set out to be a stay-at-home dad. Hell, I didn't even set out to be a dad. It's funny how it works out that way. I liked poetry but wasn't inclined to write it, so I taught English instead, and frankly, it sucked. You reach maybe one kid out of a-hundred-and-twenty, and those are terrible stats. Those are the kind of numbers that make people jump off a cliff. And the grading took over my life—weeknights, weekends, didn't matter, I couldn't go out. Math teachers, science teachers—they all have computers or assistants do their grading because the answers are just right/wrong, but English? It was forty papers a week, and you had to actually *read* them to do the kids any good. People who teach English are saints, and I don't include myself in that category because I couldn't hack it.

So here I am doing this thing I never thought I'd do, but you know what? It's fascinating. You get this weird window into human evolution by watching a little being develop from nothing into something, and linguistically, it doesn't get more thrilling than this. For instance, first they might start with the word "blue"—but to them it doesn't mean what it means to you, to them it just means "color." They'll point to a fire truck and say "blue" because it has a bright color, and they're trying to point out to you that it's striking, but they don't have any of those words yet—they don't even have "red." Then within a month or two of you correcting them ("No, the fire truck is *red.*"), they have maybe four more colors, and now "blue" actually *means* "blue"—though sometimes it means "green" because those are close together. But then you'll see them look at something in between, maybe aquamarine, and want to label it but not know how, and you see the little gears churning in their heads processing that, and you don't want to confuse them with an advanced word like aquamarine so you jump in with, "It's sort of a blue-green, isn't it?" And they just look up at you with this flash in their eyes, like, *you can just do that? You can just put two words together and it means something completely different?* And you can see that happening in real time, and it's like you're back in the Pleistocene. You're right there in the cave, and they point at the aquamarine thing and repeat what you said—"boo-gean"—but with cognition this time, and you want to hold them up in the cave-light with both of your shadows flickering on the cave-wall and announce "My offspring is a genius! Behold! The new generation is all *right!*"

So yeah, I'm somewhat obsessed. It's kind of incredible to watch.

But Aoife, she's not that interested. Sure, she loves Sibby to pieces, but she comes home from work seeking affection—tickles, snuggles—that sort of thing. I've tried to tell her about the little observations while we're lying in bed at night going over our day, but her eyes glaze over and I can tell she's just chomping at the bit to tell me how they kept the Russians out of their servers at work that day or broke up a spamming ring in Estonia. She doesn't want to hear about the tenth time I elicited a tantrum by trying to introduce Sibby to string cheese.

So tonight I was letting her tell me all about the patches they put on the servers that day until I started drifting off to sleep, but then suddenly what was initially the soothing report of rain on the roof in the background shifts abruptly to a thunder of hailstones, and I open one eyelid to interrupt with, "Did you happen to close the chicken coop?"

The baby chicks have developed into kid chicks by now, and they graduated last week to the small coop that I ordered online and assembled out back, complete with a heat source for night time. They were getting bored and rambunctious in their indoor enclosure, pecking at one another and whatnot, so it was time to broaden their horizons (plus, the house was beginning to smell like a latrine).

All we have to do is herd the little buggers into the coop at sundown and shut and latch the hatch, but we've managed to forget the last three nights in a row until one of us remembers only as we are falling asleep and has to then drag him/herself out of bed, head downstairs, and stumble outside to corral the little guys into the structure so they don't get eaten alive. One of them already *has* (by cats or owls or raccoons, or whoever preys on chicks at night in the suburbs of Silicon Valley), and we only started off with just the six.

So this hailstorm is about as intense as it gets, a full-on drum circle on the rooftops, but by the time I've made it to the back porch, it's already letting up. The yard is white with ice—inches deep and each as thick as shooter marbles. The patio umbrella is in shreds. I hold my breath before checking the coop but can't imagine they'd have been wandering around in the rain at night.

For whatever reason, though, the coop is empty. Maybe they're under the deck? I grab a rake and scoop gingerly among the ice balls so as not to impale a potential surviving chick.

By the time Aoife has put on a robe and come down to join me, I have mounded piles of ice pellets around the yard beside the bodies. All five of the remaining chicks are scattered limp and inert across the lawn.

"Oh dear," she says, as she covers her mouth with the fuzzy cuff of her robe.

"Yes," I say. "Oh, dear."

Then, from behind Aoife in the open threshold of the sliding glass door, Sibby appears in her footed fleece pajamas, presumably roused by the hailstorm. We'd only recently switched from the crib to a toddler bed, and it alarms me to see her up and about on her own recognizance without any help from me.

"Seep?" she asks us. "Seep?" Sibby points to the chick lying closest to the back door, splayed out at the base of the porch steps.

"Yes, they're sleeping," Aoife tells her and looks at me with this broken-hearted expression that I want to wipe off her face with ice balls because I didn't even want these fucking chickens to begin with, and here she is looking at me like I am somehow responsible for all of this. If you can't handle the world being shitty and indiscriminately terrible—I want to tell her—then you shouldn't have children, because the one thing they are guaranteed to do is feel loads of pain and eventually die on you, and the best scenario possible is that you get to die first.

While Aoife and I are giving one another the evil eye, telepathically blaming each other for all the awfulness in the universe, Sibby comes out in her footie pajamas and ambles down the steps to pick up the fallen chick at the base of the deck. It's much larger than a baby at this point, about the size of a rag-doll.

She holds up the dead chick for us to see and we try to hide our alarm. "Seep!" she declares again, then runs into the house with her find.

Aoife makes a move as if to chase her in order to extract the chick from our daughter's grip, but I stop her. "Wait! She's never gotten this close to them before. I've been trying to get her to touch one for weeks and she's flat-out refused. Let's at least see what the deal is before we pry it out of her hands. This could be progress." I know it's a dead bird, but it's not like some decaying corpse that's been rotting on the streets and infected with parasites; this is a thing that until moments ago was alive and kicking, and it was killed not by disease but by blunt force trauma. Aoife looks at me like I am crazy and probably I am, but still she follows me in after Sibby with a degree of deference.

We get to her bedroom and Sibby has crawled back into bed with her dead chick. She is clutching it gently by the neck and holding it under her chin and cheek, the universal resting place of beloved teddy bears and blankies.

"Seep, nye-nye."

"Night-night, sweetie," I say as I kiss her on the forehead, pull up her duvet, and smooth back her raven hair. I put on her lullaby music so she'll go back to sleep quickly and duck back into the hall where Aoife is fuming by the doorway.

"We are not going to let her sleep with a dead chicken."

"No, of course not. But look how triumphant and happy she was! She took a risk and did something she has generally been unwilling to do, and I don't want to slide backwards by telling her she can't. I'll stay up and wait till she drifts off and remove the dead chicken while she's sleeping." That I would jump through such hoops for our daughter's maddeningly incremental developmental progress either makes me seem nuts or noble in my wife's eyes—I can't really tell which, but her posture softens a little.

"Well, I'm not going back to bed until that dead chicken is out of her room, so I'll put the kettle on for some tea while we wait. Maybe I'll clean up the corpses outside and then take a shower too so there's less to do in the morning." She yawns, then trudges into the kitchen and—*tik-tik-tik*—ignites the burner on the stove, and I return to our daughter's room to glide in the corner.

I get into a groove with the glider, which squeaks out a faint, rhythmic plea for WD-40, and then start to frankly wonder about our future. Will we have a drug addict on our hands someday? a mountain climber? a kid with ADHD? a Nobel-prize winner? a daughter who gets raped at the prom? You go into this thinking you have so much sway, and as long as they don't have a genetic disorder of some kind (and you'd deal with that if they did), you've got it pretty much figured out.

But that's not the world we live in, is it. You might just end up being the guy who's let his kid get into bed while clutching a dead chicken, and now you will never *not* be that guy, but if you had asked me a year, a month, a week ago if that was possible, I'd have said no fucking way. Parenting is seeming to me to be more and more of a spectator sport, now. You think that all your cheering, your fandom, your verve has some tangible effect on the outcome, but mostly you get to just sit there and pay a lot of money to watch it unfold.

I wake up abruptly with a searing pain in my chest and realize that I've rocked myself to sleep in the glider. My bathrobe's flopped open, and it turns out that the pain isn't in my chest, it's *on* my chest. There's a young, spry chicken standing on my bare belly—*the* chicken, the one from Sibby's bed (the formerly dead chicken)—and it's tugging out my little black chest hairs with its beak as if they are grubs. I want to squeeze the little guy out of pure joy but don't want to asphyxiate the damned thing because everyone knows you only get one miracle in a generation, maximum, and I doubt it'll come back to life twice in one night.

I glance over at Sibby, who is sound asleep, and then I smell something distinctly unpleasant. There's a smear of chicken shit on my pajama bottoms, which is easy enough to remedy. I take them off and stand there in my boxers and bathrobe, cradling the hungry chick in the terrycloth crux of my elbow. It must have just been stunned or in shock from all the ice, and the warmth of Sibby's body revived the poor creature. The others, I realize, are probably too far gone now to save.

And just as this sad fact is beginning to sink in, the kettle comes to a piercing boil in the kitchen. I hear the shower running in the adjacent bathroom, the kettle's now shrieking, the smell of chicken shit's fresh on my mind—and just like that I'm back home in my attic bedroom, back in the day.

Little Krissy's got croup.

Mom's in the bathroom with Krissy and the shower's on as hot as it can go. The kettle's on, too, to make a steaming bucket of Vaporub to open up her airways. Dad's finished off his six-pack for the night and is snoring on the couch through all the noise (he's the only one who can—none of the rest of us have slept in days from all the coughing). By some quirk of design (our home is not exactly up to code), the steam and sounds from below always vent into my bedroom. Krissy's cough comes through as more of a howl than a bark and is so unnatural that it conjures the image of torpedoes launching from a submarine way down deep in the sea.

The kettle starts to scream.

"Joey!!" Mom cries up into the vent, knowing I am awake and can't help but hear every little thing. "She's turning blue!!"

I am seventeen and slide down the wooden ladder fireman-style without even taking the rungs, collecting more than a few splinters in the process, one of which will become infected later on.

"I'll run and get the doc!" We are in the hills in the sticks and the woods, closer to Tecate, Mexico by mountain road than any American town with a hospital. "The doc" in this case is in fact a veterinarian, primarily for horses, and lives on a proper ranch a half-mile up the way, but he's always there in a pinch for us human neighbors.

I'm seventeen and pissed at the world and don't believe in anything at that point except getting the fuck out of Dulzura, California (population: not freaking enough)—away from the woods, my folks, and all their little snot-nosed rug-rats. But I also very emphatically don't want my 23-month-old baby sister Krissy—the seventh and final snot-nosed rug-rat—to die. Not tonight, not ever.

Given the driveway gates at both ends, it'll be faster to run than to drive, so I bust out of there in my boxer shorts like my ass is on fire. The only shoes on the porch are either for little kids or my mother's galoshes for wading in all the chicken shit around the henhouse, so I yank those on. I am scrawny for a seventeen-year-old boy, and my mother's boots fit me all too well.

It's just me on a country road at midnight now with the *glub-glub-glub* of galoshes clopping on the pavement. If it weren't so damn awful it'd be hilarious. Soon enough it starts to rain, a rare September storm, and I am relieved because I'm quickly soaked through and you can't tell that I've been crying like a blubbering idiot. I'm thinking what grownups everywhere must be thinking all the goddamned time: *Yes, we're all gonna die, but please don't let it be soon.*

The boots are weighing me down, tripping me up, but I'm in track and can run a five-minute mile unencumbered, so I double-down and summon the fastest song I can think of, "The Kids Aren't Alright" by The Offspring. This song is my anthem, and I wail it often enough when feeling sorry for myself in my bedroom (which is always), convinced that "Jamie" from the song, who dropped out and had a couple of kids, and "Mark" who stays home and smokes pot, are somewhat emblematic of my chronically fecund mother and vaguely alcoholic dad. I frequently belt out the final lines at the top of my lungs—"WHAT THE HELL IS GO-ING ON?! / THE CRUELEST DREEEEAM, REALITYYYY!!" to the beat of a broom handle knocking on the ceiling below intended to shut me up. I am usually triumphant in my expressions of teenage misery and ennui.

But now I deploy this punk-rock ode to fragile lives and shattered dreams out of the irrational fear that if I express even the slightest fragment of hope for my sister, even just in my mind, she'll straight-up die on me. Mothers aren't the only ones prone to superstition.

So I sprint to the breakneck beat of this bleak song pretending our baby is already gone so that we might earn her back from the brink. And hell—who's to say that it didn't work?

Tanjil Rashid

A Portrait of the Artist as a Young Imam

In the beginning was the word. But what about the middle? Or the end? The whole religion just made no sense *as a story*. Tipu lay in bed reading and thinking about the Gospel in preparation for his viva. He was desperate to make a better impression this time round (last time his sandals had caught Canon Gellner's cassock and sent the sod tumbling into a terrace).

He got up (Tipu, that is—from his bed—not the Canon, who lay bruised on the lecture hall floor a while muttering, "My hand, my hand! The Mohammedan's given me the stigmata!"). He stood by the window, staring out of it. The thin planks separating its glass panes intersected in a cross...so venerated in these lands. It framed a strange vista, strange even now. Until he emigrated—as long ago as a decade now—Tipu had been no higher than the bole of a palm tree. He'd climb up in search of coconuts—coconuts!—then gaze into the hills, which rose like billows of green smoke into the sky. There lived the magicians, and the tiger-tamers, and the snake-charmers, old Big Beard used to say. Now atop a towerblock in England, it was a city Tipu beheld, its craggy, concrete skyline the inside of a boar's mouth: tooth entwined in tooth.

On the stairwell outside the flat footsteps verged on his door, but they didn't sound portentous enough to belong to the man Tipu was excitedly awaiting—some primeval part of him wished for an auspicious omen. A crown of pigeons capped the apartment block in his view. That would do.

Tipu's face—a thin beard crawling over it like lichen—reflected slimly in the windowpane. As he waited, it flickered into old Big Beard, the village mullah who taught Little Tipu to read Koran.

"All people are born the colour of clay, out of which God made them," old Big Beard was explaining in the dialect Tipu had almost forgotten. "But the feringhees they scrub all the colour off their newborn babies in a bath of milk, dyeing them until it is as if they have been born again, white as goats!"

Little Tipu had seen these fair feringhees in films. How cruelly wrought was their skin, but how nicely they did wear it. And in what flawless West

Bengali accents they apparently sang and spoke. (Olivia Newton John must live in a biiig memsahib's mansion in Calcutta, Little Tipu reasoned.)

"And this," old Big Beard continued, "this barbaric bath the feringhees call bep-tiz-zum, the first rite of the Christianite religion."

'Bep-tiz-zum': its consonants elided like Arabic, that divine idiom from which all Big Beard's big words were drawn. Tipu actually preferred the feringhees' tongue to God's. This he acquired by rote reading of books the British had left behind, preserving in his diction the echoes of an empire long vanished. 'Baptism': now he heard it in its English cadence. A birth rite. As important as a death rite. And in between—in between was marriage.

Tipu looked at his hands and, though his superior education had stripped away old Big Beard's notions as cleanly as the feringhees of folklore had their babies bleached, he was relieved by their colour, reassuringly brown, like the soil that spawned Adam, peace be up—

Bzzz! He heard the intercom ring like it was Gabriel's Horn. He jolted from his reverie. He was no longer a village boy, but a grown man—in the land of the feringhees!—to which unknown benefactors had sponsored him to come study at a seminary. Soon he'd be ordained a maulana—bzzz-bzzz!—to minister to this country's misguided Muslims. He was told a mosque would likelier employ him had he a wife, but the studious bachelor knew no women, nor had he family to arrange nuptials. It was his ever-attentive neighbour Mrs Pirzada who suggested Tipu try a *ghatak*. So he'd responded to the following notice in that week's *Daily Patrika* (the Bengali weekly was inaccurately entitled, much like *Bangla Quarterly*, published monthly):

> Capt. Al-Hajj Mir Najim, M.M. (Rangoon), ghatak-at-large. Bespoke matchmaking throughout UK. Persons of distinction and dignity only. Let me navigate you to the shores of matrimony 061-551 2056

Tipu picked up the receiver to listen. The voice—a disembodied echo—sounded hallowed.

"Salaam. I am the Captain."

"Hello. Come to the ninth floor."

Mir Najim arrived in a double-breasted navy blue blazer with brass buttons and gold stripes around the cuff. His outfit was incongruously topped by a skullcap—black rather than the well-established white—picked no doubt to be mistaken for a hairy clump. He smelt of fish, specifically of *shutki*, the dried Bombay Duck savoured by Bengalis whose palates clung to the *desh*, the old country.

Inside, in Tipu's digs, Mir Najim looked up at the prospective groom. "Mashallah imam sahib, with height you are blessed!" he said. "*Bangalees* aren't usually tall. Maybe you have Pathan blood? Are you Khan, imam sahib?"

"No, Chowdhury," said Tipu. "And please, I'm not an imam yet."

"Chowdhury? Diligent. Chowdhuries are diligent!"

Without invitation Mir Najim seated himself on a chair that chirred in its joints, the one seat in a room furnished for scholarship, not hospitality: besides the bed only bookcases and a desk.

"*Ek* cup chai, imam sahib?" said Mir Najim.

Tipu left the room to see to the tea.

"This is why you need a wife, *theek na*?" the Captain bellowed after him.

He surveyed the stacks. Many books had a beauty apparent especially to the unlettered, bound in teal-tanned leather and painted with arabesques whose golden tendrils straddled one volume into the next. Arabic, Bengali, Urdu (or was that Persian?), many even in English, which surprised Mir Najim. How very learned today's mullahs are!

From one spine he read the name of an author, out loud but to himself: "Ma-ha-mud. *Atcha*."

"Malamud," said Tipu, returning. "It's an 'l' not an 'h'."

"*Atcha*. My reading-glasses I have lost," said Mir Najim. Then, after a pause: "*Bangalee*?"

"No, not Bengali. Jewish."

"A *yehudi*?"

Mir Najim considered the matter.

"But of course all Allah's messengers *were* Jews," he concluded.

The two Bengalis then exchanged laborious smalltalk over tea. Prevarication of this kind was customary. Tipu kept cursory his views on the ongoing Gulf War, while Mir Najim pontificated on the scandalous stationing of US soldiers in holy Mecca—a canard left uncorrected. The tincture of his tongue was betel-leaf brown.

"Imam sahib—you are naturalised?"

"Excuse me?"

"Passport—British?"

"Oh, yes."

"Then I have some ladies of great distinction for you, great distinction."

Mir Najim clicked open a brown briefcase.

"You have pictures?" Tipu asked.

"Family first. *Bangsho*. Then picture."

Mir Najim shuffled papers.

"Shefali Chowdhury. 21. Father in shipping—very fine fellow, personally arranged my own hajj. It was in '73 I went—during the oil embargo. King Faisal had brought America to her knees. If you only saw Doctor Kissinger—"

"Shefali. You were saying about Shefali."

"Yes, her father's from a village in Sri-Mangal. I don't know how much will be dowry. Would you like me to call him?"

"Wait. Tell me more. About the dowry I don't care. What does she *do*?"

"'Do'? First marry her, then *you* decide what she will do."

"But what's she been doing lately?"

"Probably learning to make biryani for you, *theek na?*"

Through ingratiating jokes Mir Najim hoped to implicate Tipu—laughing—into the habits of thought an arranged marriage must be predicated on.

Tipu didn't laugh.

"Mr Najim, I'm about to get my doctorate. I need a wife with some higher education."

"Certainly: the very model of a modern maulana, *theek na?*"

Mir Najim chuckled.

"What about Rabeya Hoq? Father from village of—"

"Mr Najim, I'm not interested in what village her father—"

"Imam sahib. Please," Mir Najim interrupted. Humour wasn't doing it. "I'm no 'mister.' I'm a Captain. A retired master mariner of the Merchant Navy of Burma. My father was in the navy too, like all men of my village. I advise you care about these details—it is our custom, the *Bangalee* custom. Good and bad we learn from our fathers, they from theirs. Didn't you?"

"I'm an orphan."

"Imam sahib is a *yateem* – no matter, he's a Chowdhury. You see? *Bangsho* is the important. Not like these feringhees, are we? Look the man they put in Number 10—son of a clown! Now whole Commonwealth jolly well laughing at us. John Major? I say: John Minor!"—at this Mir Najim roared, before continuing—"Now look Bangladesh. Look at President Ershad! Major-General Ershad. *That*'s what I call *major*."

Tipu didn't know how to respond to such twisted logic, such a mess of reasoning, such an abdication of—

"Now, imam sahib, Rabeya Hoq is granddaughter of AK Hoq, minister."

"Minister?"

"*Interim* minister. For few months, during the war,"

"In Bangladesh?"

Mir Najim shook his head.

"Pakistan? India?"

"The principality of Cooch Behar—"

Tipu was annoyed at being duped into the Captain's habits of thought.

"Tell me about the *girl*," he asked.

"She is 22 years old student at Chittagong University."

Tipu nodded.

"I think a match, a matrimonial match!" Mir Najim said. "But, before we proceed—and I'm sure you will not deter—the girl...how does one say? *Lengra*."

"Lame?"

"You know, the polio—"

Mir Najim paused on seeing Tipu's frown.

"Imam sahib, if you were not now my dearest and distinguished friend I would think less of you. What is the wrong? Was not Timur-i-leng lame, and did he not conquer Persia? So formidable the English writer William Sheksfeeyaar wrote about him a poem. It is called *Tamburlaine the Great* – *maha*-Tamburlaine!"

Tipu opened his mouth, but then thought better of clarifying that this was hardly exemplary. In what in fact is a play by Marlowe, Timur the Lame sets the Holy Koran aflame.

"Would you give a son of yours to somebody who is...physically impaired?"

Mir Najim conceded. He had now a single sheet in his hands.

"I see imam sahib is learned in the western culture and this is most distinguished. Like Naina Khan. From a cultivated family of Kalibari—in their house it is all the time singing-singing. Dowry will be abundant."

"How much?"

"Many pounds. Believe me, I have seen Khan sahib's car. A shining-shining Rolls Rover. Very distinguished—"

"Naina, tell me about Naina."

"She's an English teacher–"

"English teacher?"

"Yes, and how beautiful she speaks it too. Like a nightingale. Born here, you know."

Tipu was impressed.

"Such a girl," he inquired, "might such a girl not have ideas about... about love? How old did you say she was?"

"Not one day older than thirty."

"What do you mean? Is she thirty? Is today her thirtieth birthday? What fault of hers has meant no man has married her yet?"

"That isn't true, imam sahib. Once before she *was* married–"

"Forget it!"

These were the only prospective brides Mir Najim had to offer. He promised there'd be more in the autumn, as though maidens were fruits out of season. Tipu had expected a prophet, but had got a petty hawker; instead of the revelation of his other half, only rotten apples.

The *ghatak* had one parting request. He insisted on praying the noontide *namaz* behind the auspicious imam sahib. Forward Tipu stepped and recited reluctantly before his congregation, his contemptible congregation of one.

*

A few days later Tipu went to Mrs Pirzada's, where he gave her son and some other boys Koran classes. He tutored all the Muslim children in the neighbourhood, the fees fortifying Tipu's seminary scholarship while he sought a position. He was undercutting the seminary's own madrasa by one pound an hour. The pupils Mrs Pirzada supplied from the block's close-knit contingent of Bangladeshi mothers, taking a finder's fee for each which supplemented her dressmaking income and cheques from a husband in Dubai.

Mrs Pirzada's relation to Tipu was not merely commercial, however. It was the envy of the other mothers, who barely saw their husbands away waiting tables in the Curry Mile till midnight. They straightened their saris whenever the handsome teacher walked by. But Mrs Pirzada knew him best– and always *at* her best, bejewelled and sari-swaddled. She plied him daily with *deshi* sweetmeats. She had him interpret her DSS letters. She sought his opinion on the latest in *The Daily Patrika*. "*Ustaz*, should we back Saddam or the Saudis?"; "*Ustaz*, what are these *Satanic Verses*?"; "*Ustaz*, is it true about 'The Miraculous Mango'? Did it really contain the *Fatiha* written out on its seed?"

Before Tipu entered, Mrs Pirzada always turned over the photos of herself and her son and the commemorative plate of Charles and Diana. Tipu told her each time how silly this old taboo on graven images was, but no heed was paid. Today Mrs Pirzada, who had herself wedded young and approximated Tipu's age, was more interested in inquiring about her neighbour's marital plans. Tipu explained what a terrible waste of time the *ghatak* had been, how one woman had no degree, one was a divorcee, one–

"This whole *ghatak ghatana*–rotten like the fish he smelt of!" laughed Mrs Pirzada. "And even if you manage to get married, it probably won't work out. Look at me..."

She spread out a clean cream sheet on the carpet.

"Try another *ghatak*, but they're all *deshi dadas*, you know. Can't be too choosey. All love marriages now. Love, love, love. Terrible, isn't it?"

"Truly," Tipu said.

"Any news from the university?"

"Soon, inshallah."

Then the class began.

Tipu and the children were seated cross-legged on the sheet, the boys bobbing like clock pendulums as they recited, trailing their fingers along the leaves of the Koran on wooden, latticed lecterns before them. Tipu was the melodious metronome, humming verses over and over and over in a low lilt, conducting this chorus of *qiraat* with the commanding charisma of his voice.

In *qiraat* the children were neither interested nor gifted; short vowels became long vowels, long vowels became yawns. In turns they simulated farts, which in a volte-face of classroom custom they eagerly owned up to, so they could leave class to perform lengthy ablutions renewing the state of ritual purity in which alone the Koran could be handled.

Today Mrs Pirzada's son also decided he'd had enough of reading by rote a text in a language he didn't understand.

"*Ustaz*, what's the point?" Little Bozlu asked.

"Well, it's customary to do a *khatam* of the Koran once in our lifetime," Tipu said. "And your ma's paying me to teach you. You may not understand the point now, but...good and bad we learn from our parents and our teachers, *theek na?*"

Little Bozlu thought his teacher was talking a load of—

"And I know you say you don't understand Arabic," Tipu continued. "But I know Arabic and even *I* don't understand the Koran. The Koran can't be translated. Its meaning is in its music, its melody, its mystery, not in any dictionary, it's...incantatory."

"*Ustaz,* what does that mean?"

Tipu was flummoxed.

He liked teaching and, once the university awarded him his doctorate, he planned to do so at a higher level. Everyone enjoyed the final half hour most, when Tipu told a story. He couldn't but think of himself then as old Big Beard (only without the latter's *lathi,* his cane for walking and chastising). At first he told stories from the Koran: of Nuh and the flood, of Yunus and the whale, of Yusuf and his coloured cloak. But after a day steeped in the facts of his thesis, he'd enjoy making things up. He didn't think it ideal to embellish God's word, so he began garnishing stories from the *Arabian Nights*, and later from his own life, his boyhood in Bangladesh climbing palm trees, catching coconuts. The more his research bored him, the more he invented his own tales, about the magicians in the hills, and the tiger-tamers, and the snake-charmers, composing them in his head on his walk from Darul Uloom College to the John Rylands Library, then rehearsing them over and over and over along the canal leading to the block where his pupils and Mrs Pirzada were waiting for him, waiting to be enchanted by his inventions.

"Enchanted," Tipu said. "That's what it means. Like a spell. The sounds of Arabic cast over us a spell. Now, read some more. Let's be enchanted, *theek na?*"

*

At home that evening Tipu had a visitor in his room.

"Salaam, imam sahib," announced Mir Najim. A neighbour had let him in.

"What are you doing here?"

"Wonderful news! Naina Khan—I was confuse. She never married before, and she's twenty-six!"

Tipu smelt Bombay Duck.

"Her father showed me the birth certificate, believe me. And look how beautiful she is," said Mir Najim, showing him a photo.

Tipu showed him out.

On the doormat he saw addressed to him an envelope postmarked "Victoria University." The epistle had arrived! He rushed to his room to read it:

Dear Mr Chowder,

Thank you for appearing viva voce before the examiners of the Faculty of Divinity to defend your thesis, submitted for the degree of: THEOLOGIAE DOCTOR. This was your second attempt.

I regret to inform you that that the examiners' unanimous verdict was:

FAIL, without possibility of corrections and/or revisions.

Although your thesis presents some interesting stories, it has been deemed beneath the standard of Western scholarship. You demonstrate an inadequate grasp of the modern methodology of the scientific study of religion (indeed, one examiner quite reasonably questioned whether you had even read H. Gellner's seminal *The Mohammedan Mind*). Your experiment in imposing a narrative shape on the Koran is ahistorical. Your definition of religion as a literary tradition is absurd and repudiated by social science, not to mention common sense. On these grounds, in addition to insufficient citation, we have concluded your thesis more properly belongs in the realm of fiction, not fact.

I confirm that our verdict is without prejudice to the pastoral studies we understand you to be completing, independently of your research, at Darul Uloom College. We have notified them, separately.

Good luck in future endeavours.

Sincerely,

Canon Dr Henryk Gellner
Praelector,
Faculty of Divinity

Tipu tore the letter up, then stamped over its remains—the academic career he'd dreamt up lay in tatters like the letter beneath his feet. Some fucking feringhee had trodden all over it.

Through the crucifix at his bedside he caught the dusk waving on the beige blocks of flats around him. English sunlight was an insipid ecru, drained—of light! of life!—by the clouds, always knitted together in a grey gauze. (No such celestial stitchwork impeded the bright Bengali sun!) He felt a lifelessness in these concrete constructions. There was flesh, but flesh to his eyes discoloured, denatured, like an autumn leaf, or like the milk here, pasteurised, skimmed, sickly.

He picked up the photo of Naina Khan of Kalibari. Right then her ruddy face reminded him of the earth, of life. He was transplanted from this queer concrete to the terra cognita of his childhood, where, many yards beneath the hills, he felt his roots wound up with those of some faraway coconut palm...

*

Khan sahib's lounge was ornamented in the Bengali-baroque style, lovingly loaded with Bangladeshi bric-a-brac, maps and murtis of the motherland; people like Khan sahib hadn't gotten over the thrill of having possessions, nor the joy of having a country—Bangladesh still younger than his daughter Naina and the man on his sofa presently being assayed to be her husband: Tipu Chowdhury.

"Captain Najim tells me you're a doctor and an imam," said Khan sahib.

"Actually...I'm neither. I'm looking for a job, however," said Tipu.

"Captain-ji must have meant PhD or such?"

"Yes, although...that didn't work out."

"You have brothers? Sisters?"

"None...My whole family died in a flood."

Eventually Khan sahib summoned Naina, leaving the prospective couple to talk privately. Tipu noticed Naina's red-tinged toenails as she descended the staircase, the one speck of colour she exhibited. She was wearing a black *jilbab* and black headscarf. Tipu had never, until now, considered whether he'd like a veiled wife. It might be expected of an imam. He greeted her warily, she him warmly.

"So you teach English?" Tipu asked.

"Yeah, I did it at uni," said Naina. "You like reading?"

"More than anything. It's the stories I like best about my studies. I wrote a thesis on the Koran—"

"Those aren't *just* stories, though, are they? They're true."

"What's not true about a story? Good stories are always truthful," Tipu said. "You have a favourite writer?"

"I used to really like Rushdie. Made me feel part of something...big. But I feel a bit...betrayed, by the last one."

"He was never one of us, though, really. His books were never true to our experience...I feel closer to the stories of American Jewish writers...about being poor and living in tenements and hustling to get by and striving for an education...Spare me all this overdone stuff about coconuts and palm trees, tigers and snakes—"

"But that's also how we remember the *desh*, our memories are built of clichés...I guess it's also hard to write truthfully. As soon as anyone writes anything, or wants to, they stop being normal, they stop being, you know, 'one of us.'"

"We need a Muslim Malamud—"

"A Bangladeshi Bellow,"

They laughed.

"You're no ordinary imam," Naina said, then after a silence: "You should know that I'm...I've been in relationships. Until last year I was living with my boyfriend for 3 years."

So that's what Mir Najim must have meant by her previous...Tipu found her frankness disarming, even charming.

"But now I pray *namaz* five times a day. I'm looking for a husband who, you know, brings me closer to Allah."

Tipu was soon to be ordained, yet he felt so unqualified.

"What's an ordinary imam like?" he asked.

"You know. Big beard, turban."

"It's true. I *am* more cords than kurta."

"I like the look. It's a fuck-you to the NF. You're saying, 'I can be tweedy and English, but still Muslim!' And an imam, at that."

"I'm not an imam, not yet."

"What made you choose it?"

"I didn't, really...I grew up in the orphanage of a madrasa. I just kept studying until...here I am."

Tipu saw disappointment in Naina's eyes.

"I *am* religious," he insisted, then paused to ponder whether he'd just lied. "*Alhamdulillah*...Only, sometimes, I feel like Yunus, you know. God sent me to a madrasa. I'm meant to be an imam. But...I feel like fleeing. I'm at sea. I'm inside the whale. And maybe...I quite like it. Here, inside."

The gulf between Naina's eyebrows had almost closed. She looked bewildered. Tipu realised she had been sold some vision of a spiritual grandmaster, a pure and pious *pir*, a Muslim mystagogue. He felt anger at Mir Najim for his lies, then anguish at himself for his own. From the kitchen he felt the din and the heat of frying samosas. It rose and rose in his head till it was on fire, it began to gyre—he was now a whirling dervish—round and round and round it spun until his eyes he had to close and his body he felt hurled into the deep, into the maws of a beast, then the raging ceased and there was calm, for Tipu found himself captive and capsized and exiled and inside the blubbery belly of a great fish.

*

When Tipu regained consciousness he apologised to Khan sahib who had nursed him on the sofa for half an hour. He'd had a strange and marvellous dream in which he was a fire-worshipping priest on a whaleboat helmed by Captain Mir Najim, M.M., who'd chucked him overboard in a storm only to be swallowed by a whale. These would be no in-laws of his, he'd somehow concluded in unconsciousness, and briskly he left. The tram back to his block drifted that day like a sailboat. He ran up the stairs to his floor. He heard the rapid, machine-gun clatter of a sewing machine. The dusk was so vivid tonight. He knocked at No. 89.

The clatter stopped.

Mrs Pirzada opened the door. Her head was a dartboard, its bullseye the vermilion fleck on her forehead.

She greeted him. Tipu never called outside lesson hours. He must have come to announce the news of his engagement.

"Went well?" she asked.

"Revelatory," said Tipu.

Bidden by the sound of angels blowing their trumpets in heaven—at last the omens—he told Mrs Pirzada that her bindi shone ever so brightly today in the sun, which, in a way, she was, to him, she brightened his days and gave him all the warmth he had in life, he was enchanted by her, by her music and melody, her mystery and meaning, deepened in every meeting, and he didn't want to have an arranged marriage, he wanted to marry the woman he loved, which was her, surely, and he knew that her husband was refusing to grant a divorce and this wasn't likely to change soon, and under the sharia *she* couldn't divorce, but he was about to be ordained, which would grant *him* the spiritual authority to divorce them, that is if she cared about such things, because he didn't, truly, and he didn't care that she had no degree and would be a divorcée, he didn't give a damn about the scandal, how no mosque would ever employ him, because he wasn't going to be an imam any more, no, not an academic either, he was going to be—he was going to be a writer, he was going to write stories, truthful stories about the experience of people like her, and himself, that no one ever wrote about—

until, a few moments later, he returned to his room, sat down at his typewriter and, timing and rhyming the clamour of its keys with the hammer of the Singer needle next door—she, now, was the metronome—he started writing:

In the beginning was the word. But what about the middle? Or the end?

Darrow Farr

The Devil is a Lie

Deirdre squatted outside Daydreams, waiting for her cousin Phuffy to get out of work. Night was bleaching out. She smoked a Newport in the fuzzy halo of pink light radiating from the club's sign. Deirdre never smoked, but the male nurse at the emergency room had slid one of his own personal menthols behind her ear, his fingers brushing the small hairs on her temple. She held the cigarette between two fingers poking out of her fresh cast. Her knuckles were still crusted rusty with someone else's blood.

Phuffy came from the back alley wheeling the scuffed zebra suitcase where she kept her costumes. She'd changed into stretched out plaid boxers and a button-down Piglet pajama top, but her silvery makeup was immaculate.

"What the fuck is that?" Phuffy glared at the day-glo orange cast.

Deirdre shrugged and flung her cigarette in the street.

"How much is that gonna cost me? Five hundred?" Phuffy pressed her lips together, pulled a wallet out of her Michael Kors tote, and began portioning off twenties with a long square fingernail.

"The hospital's sending a bill to the house. I'll figure it out before it's due," Deirdre said.

Phuffy snorted and tugged either side of her ponytail. "Sure, Dee."

Jimmy, the Friday bouncer, shuffled up the alley. "Chris coming to get you?" he asked Phuffy, avoiding Deirdre's stare. She imagined that after eight hours of watching glimmering girls spin around in bits of gauze, her craggy face was a jarring sight.

"S'posed to," Phuffy said, scrolling through her phone. She refused to speak more than two words to him since the previous October, when he downed a dozen shots of Jaeger with a bachelor party and told Phuffy she was wasting her prime white pussy on broke black dick.

"Well, g'night then," he muttered, ambling off.

As Phuffy placed the phone to her ear, Christopher's dumpy Cavalier turned onto Broad Street. He propped his elbow on the windowsill and pointed at Deirdre's cast.

"What'd you do now, young hoodlum?"

"What do you think? She got in a fight," Phuffy said as she lugged her suitcase to the car. She knocked on the trunk and Christopher popped it open.

"I didn't say that," Deirdre said, crawling into the backseat.

"He probably deserved it," Christopher said. Deirdre toyed with the window crank. It was a girl she'd knocked out, not a guy. The crumpled wad of bills she'd snatched from the girl's dumb mini backpack bulged through the pockets of her shorts.

Phuffy slid into the front seat and the scent of chemical fruit filled the car. She turned towards Deirdre, gripping the headrest with her lavender manicure. "Two fights in one month? Unacceptable. If you're in high school and you wanna bust some snotty bitch's mouth against the St. Therese statue, be my guest, but twenty-one is too old. We raised you better."

"Alright, alright." Deirdre slid down until her seatbelt crossed tightly over her neck.

Phuffy, Deirdre, and Steven—Phuffy's ratty Chinese Crested—lived together in a studio apartment, across from St. Monica's. It was a nice enough neighborhood, despite all the ancient wops that spent their days sweeping the steps of their rowhomes, smiling disingenuously as the cousins walked by. Three years before, the girls had lived with Phuffy's parents in the shrinking Irish section around St. Hugh's. Phuffy had been setting rollers for old biddies at a dreary salon in the Northeast, taking only 20% commission.

"That body ain't gonna last," the owner had told Phuffy as she refilled the bowl of Werther's by the cash register. "When I was 21, I looked even better than you. Higher tits, tighter belly, *natural* blonde. Thirty years later, you get this." She grabbed the ring of fat hanging over her knock-off Gucci belt and waggled it menacingly. Phuffy removed the last curler from her last client and auditioned at Daydreams that night. After working ten shifts, she laid down two months' rent on the studio and she and Deirdre moved in the same day her parents hightailed it to the suburbs.

Christopher pulled up to the apartment and Deirdre got out of the car. Phuffy and Christopher would canoodle in the Cav before he drove home to his mom's place. She entered the night-dark apartment, sat on the bed, and turned out her pockets. By the glow of the street lamp outside the window, she smoothed and stacked $153. The sight of so much cash cooled an anxiety Deirdre hadn't previously noticed smoldering inside her.

She hadn't given Phuffy a cent towards rent, groceries, nothing, in six months. The deli where she'd washed dishes for the last four years closed in January when the owner succumbed to a long-anticipated heart attack, and Deirdre hadn't found another job. Not that she'd tried especially hard; she couldn't fathom working in a new kitchen where Denny wouldn't be there to split a mid-afternoon pretzel with her.

Deirdre was sixteen when Aunt Moira brought her to the deli to meet Denny, a typical griddle man: large, pink, and loud.

"Christ, Moi, where'd you find this one?" he'd said, wiping his balding head with a hankie. "She reminds me of a nun that used to make me stick my tongue between my teeth before she knocked me on the chin."

"She's Mike's sister's kid," Aunt Moira said.

Denny had looked at her more softly and Deirdre could see any story he'd ever heard about her mother—the escape from the culty ashram, affair with the cop, subsequent pinched-faced baby, abandonment of said baby to Mike and Moira—flash like a View-Master reel through his greasy head.

"Truthfully, I don't think I can put you anywhere out front. You seem like a nice kid, but you got an unsettling quality. You too good to wash dishes?"

She wasn't; as it turned out, she had an affinity for it. She enjoyed the solitude of her corner in the kitchen, the water's heat through rubber gloves and the synthetic tang of the commercial dish soap; she liked using her strong hands for something constructive. And Denny was good to her; when Little Flower expelled her, he'd let her work full-time as she studied for her GED. After he passed away, Deirdre took the bus to the burial and hovered next to a mausoleum a ways from the ceremony, cheek pressed against the frosty granite. An old deli regular spotted her and waved her over, but her grief felt too potent, too mysterious to share with anyone, and she'd slinked back to the bus stop.

That was months ago now, and she was sick of having to ask Phuffy to spot her lunch or bus fare. Whenever Deirdre hit her up for money, Phuffy grinned and pranced to her purse.

"I know you said ten, but here's a hundred. I don't like you walking around without any cash," she'd say. Her generosity contained no trace of condescension or reproach, but it wasn't entirely selfless, either; supporting

Deirdre validated a career their family found unsavory. Deirdre was grateful for the countless ways in which Phuffy looked after her, but accepting her kindnesses also meant accepting her mother hen tones and worried expressions. *We raised you better,* she'd said in the car, like she wasn't only three years older.

Deirdre rolled the bills and bound them with a hair elastic. It felt like a rabbit's foot in her hand, a good luck charm for when she'd begin her job search tomorrow. As she sank towards sleep, clutching the bankroll, an image bobbed to the surface: The moment before her fist cracked across the girl's mouth, the girl had squeezed her eyes shut, foreseeing what was coming, accepting it.

*

She woke to the smell of dog shit. Phuffy slept on the pullout couch with Steven, who stretched across the pillow looking like a half-skinned rabbit. The veil of blond hair covering his freckled body was the same color as Phuffy's. Deirdre tore a ribbon of toilet paper and wiped the floor. Her bum arm ached in a way that made her immediately exhausted.

It was warm and glowy outside, but blue-grey clouds ringed the sun and the air already smelled like rain. She walked north towards the cluster of restaurants on Passyunk, tensing as she approached the botánica. The young Puerto Rican guy was sitting behind a card table covered with plastic rosaries, embroidery floss bracelets, bags of incense, and unmarked vials of perfume oils. He reclined in a patio chair so that its top rail leaned against the brick storefront and the front legs reared. He crossed his arms and blew mean little pink gum bubbles, surveying the street, looking for someone to harass. He spotted Deirdre and smiled cruelly.

"What happened to your arm, beautiful?" he asked, rocking in his chair.

"I'm gonna knock your ass off that chair if you start your shit today."

"I bet you'd like to knock around, huh, flaquita. I bet you never felt a man's hands on you." He grinned and clapped. "Except maybe a blind dude."

Deirdre's ears popped with anger. She swatted the flimsy card table into the stoop next door, perfume bottles clinking and rolling around the pavement. He laughed, disoriented, and raised his hands in mock surrender. She kicked the chair out from under him, and as his face tautened in anticipation of the shuddering crack of concrete to bone, she felt a moment of calm. He untangled himself from the chair, cursing and patting his head, checking for blood.

"You're fucking insane," he said. "You got a devil in you, I can sense it. You got mad darkness, mad demons congregating inside you."

"Don't you forget it," she spat, but she felt something stir inside her, as if its name had been called.

By the time she reached restaurant row, fat raindrops spotted the sidewalk and her t-shirt stuck to her body. She had left the house without dressing for an interview, in an oversize Señor Frog's t-shirt, cutoff shorts, and Adidas velcro sandals. It wouldn't make a difference. She opened the door to Marra's, a red-gravy joint that seemed less stuck-up than the new wine bars down the block. The restaurant was empty except for a man doing liquor inventory behind the bar. He looked like a neighborhood guy: conservative haircut, thick neck, the lumpy suggestion of a crucifix underneath his button-down.

"Can I help you?" he asked.

"You need a dishwasher?"

He snorted. "Not with a broken arm."

She turned for the door.

"Hey wait," he said. "You're Phuffy's cousin."

"You a customer of hers?"

"No. Well sure, on occasion. I graduated from Roman a couple years before her." He snapped and pointed his finger. "Is your dad that ex-cop makes the lemonade out of the big trashcan over in Delco?"

Her gut fluttered and she narrowed her eyes. "That's the one."

She'd heard rumors about this, that her dad had gotten even odder after his eardrum exploded, that he had refashioned himself as some kind of fixture of local color via his lemonade, which everyone knew was just Country Time, but somehow tasted more delicious from the trashcan. Deirdre couldn't feel embarrassed; she had never fully grasped the fact that she was in any way connected to him.

"He used to come in here when I was still bussing. Had this routine where he'd harass the waitresses, accuse them of taking sips from his cocktail.

All in good fun. Haven't seen him in a while. You don't think about how much damage a dumb thing like a firecracker can do."

"What do you expect when you set off a Hypersonic X-Celerator in a walled courtyard," Deirdre said.

He shrugged. "Come back once you get that cast off, I'll find something for you to do."

She gave him a spiteful thumbs up on her way out.

Deirdre returned to Phuffy and Christopher watching *NCIS* reruns on the pull-out. Summer showers had tempered the heat, but Phuffy set the groaning window AC unit on full blast. Steven nestled himself under the corner of a fleece blanket draped over the couch.

"Is it still raining? You're not supposed to get your cast wet," Phuffy said.

Deirdre ignored her and sat in the old recliner beside the couch. "I might have found a dishwashing job at Marra's."

"Dee, that's amazing!" Phuffy squealed, prompting Steven to expel a whiny bark.

"The manager knew you," Deirdre said, and a muscle in Christopher's neck tensed. When Phuffy had begun dancing at Daydreams, her relationship with Christopher was new enough that the idea of dating a stripper seemed novel, something his people would tease him about, reverently, when he was middle-aged and wifed up. Three years later, he loved Phuffy and tolerated her job. They spoke about her work in euphemisms, as if saying "the office" instead of "the club," or "uniform" instead of "cat suit" could soften the fact that Phuffy was paid to gyrate her body on men's boners until they came sour and warm on their own doughy bellies.

"Brendan Nally?" Phuffy scoffed, running her nails along Christopher's neck. "He's literally worked there since eighth grade. It's kind of sad." Christopher's shoulders relaxed and he kissed Phuffy behind the ear. Deirdre could never look away when they expressed affection; intimacy was an aspect of humanness she'd never known. She remembered going to the Hair Cuttery as a little girl, sitting in a booster chair, leaning her neck back into the plastic basin so her hair could be washed, anticipating the hairdresser's nails grazing soap over her scalp.

"If you could just rinse her out instead of doing a whole washing," Aunt Moira had instructed the woman. Then, apologetic: "She has this thing about being touched."

Deirdre had not protested, and the hairdresser blasted her head with the hose. However, Aunt Moira's caution had confused her, and still did nearly fifteen years later. True, she had not been a very tender child, but of course she longed for a hand on her shoulder, a kiss hello.

"We need to talk about last night," Phuffy said.

"This bitch was bugging me, we tussled, I broke my wrist," Deirdre mumbled.

"What'd she do to you?" Christopher asked, amused.

"Walked into me. Said some shit."

Phuffy raised an eyebrow.

"A job will be good," he said. "Give you some structure."

"Only you can decide what kind of life you lead," Phuffy said, as if reading a cue card.

Deirdre jumped from her chair and skulked to the bed, only just behind the couch. Still, they knew to leave her alone.

*

Deirdre had gone to buy a hoagie the night she broke her wrist. Phuffy had given her a ten for dinner and she was planning on eating at home while watching a *Shark Tank* marathon. She was passing an old auto body shop when she heard the music: fuzzy electric harp, climbing and tumbling arpeggios, a very round and rosy sound. The door to the garage was open, and she nosed in.

"Excuse me, it's five dollars," the girl whispered. Deirdre hadn't noticed her sitting on a stool by the entry, quilted mini backpack between her knees. She was delicate and unfussy, bare-faced. Her limbs were skinny but looked soft, unlike Deirdre's, which seemed like they were made from bundles of wire. She wanted to graze the girl's milky arm with the back of her hand.

"All I got is change," she said.

"That's okay, I'll find you after the show," the girl replied. She had misheard.

Deirdre entered the garage. Kids lined the walls, swaying, sipping tall boys. Only one person stood on the low plywood stage, washed in lavender light, gliding his hands across a synthesizer. *I just want what they all have, I just want what they all have*, he sang over and over. It was dusky and entrancing and crashed through her like a wave.

Deirdre approached him after his set, as he wound cables around his elbow. He was not objectively handsome. His eyes crowded a rat-like nose and his hair hung in an overgrown bowl cut, but his slim hands were pale and satiny.

"You have a CD or something?"

"Seven dollars for a tape."

She handed him her hoagie money in exchange for a cassette, even though she hadn't owned a tape player since grade school. She wanted to express that his music thumbed a tender spot she'd forgotten was inside her, but she didn't have the words; she could only let her crude emotional energy erupt through her limbs in swats and scratches. She watched people smile at strangers, kiss the hands of their lovers mid-sentence, listen to their neighbors' health complaints with genuine interest; and although she longed to integrate, she feared she never would.

"I was just walking past and heard your music and came in," she said, surprising herself.

"Rad," he said. "Do you live around here?"

"Not far, across from St. Monica's."

"It's weird you say 'St. Monica's,' like I should know where that is. You real religious?"

"I dunno. I went to Catholic school, till they kicked me out."

He laughed loud and open-mouthed. "No way, man. I was disfellowshipped from my parents' church a while back. You want a beer?"

She followed him to a red plastic tub of PBR. He handed her a can and sat cross-legged on the dusty concrete floor. Her stomach flipped as she squatted next to him. She couldn't remember the last time she had a conversation with a guy, alone. She couldn't remember the last time she had an effortless conversation with anyone, or the last time someone talked to her under the assumption she was normal.

"You know those people who knock up at your house with pamphlets that say 'All Suffering Soon to End'? Those are my parents. Miserable growing up. No birthday parties, no Christmas tree, definitely no *worldly* music." He took a long swig from his beer and Deirdre watched his throat pulse as he swallowed. "My mom doesn't talk to me now."

She lowered her beer mid-sip. "I haven't heard from mine in five years," she said. "I got expelled for beating up this girl. She was trying to press charges for aggravated assault and I could have been tried as an adult. Anyway, it was a big deal, and my uncle kept trying to get a hold of my mom to tell her; he left voicemails, emailed her. I don't know why he thought she should know. Maybe he was giving her the chance to like, come be my mother. But she never responded. I was lucky, the charge got knocked down to simple assault and I only had to do community service. Then a couple months later I get this call from my mom congratulating me on my high school graduation."

He looked at her, waiting for her to say how that made her feel, but she had nothing left. She felt as if she had wrenched open a swollen window inside herself and he had crawled through it. She took a quick sip of beer and without thinking, darted her face towards his. Her kiss didn't land. He fell back onto his hands, knocking over his beer, which glugged out onto the floor.

"Hey, sorry," he said, as if he had bumped into her. "I'm really sorry, I just don't know you." She saw herself in his eyes: impossibly ugly, so rotten inside that it seeped out and polluted her skin.

She leapt up and someone touched her arm as she rushed out of the garage.

"Hey," the door girl said. "Did you get change from your friend? If not, I have enough singles now." Deirdre whirled towards her. She was so polite and gentle-skinned and inoffensively pretty, and her hand on Deirdre's arm felt like an itch scratched. Deirdre could have kissed her, too. Instead, her arm reared back and fist snapped forward. The small bones in her wrist pushed into her arm, impacted for a moment, then shattered. The girl stumbled back, clawing the air, mini-backpack swinging around her wrist, then sat hard on the sidewalk. Deirdre grabbed the backpack from the girl's unresisting hands, wanting to take whatever she could from her. She felt like the only living person who couldn't get a piece of what joy the world had to offer; and then there were people like Phuffy, or surely this girl, who could reap happiness like a ripe fruit. Deirdre tore fistfuls of cash from the mini-backpack and stuffed it in the pockets of her shorts. A group of girls taking a smoke break watched, uncertain how to respond. She tossed the empty backpack on the ground and saw the girl on her back, staring stunned into the streetlamp over her head, mouth smeared with blood. Deirdre turned and ran, nauseated, punching her own head, wishing she were in the girl's place.

*

Deirdre ignored Phuffy the rest of the day, drifting in and out of sleep. The light coming through the blinds had turned pink by the time Phuffy left for the club. Deirdre could sense her standing beside the bed, staring at her back.

"Don't be mad," Phuffy said. "I'm on your side."

Deirdre waited to sit up until she heard the front door lock. Phuffy would be preoccupied all night. She hated the idea of apologizing for an argument she'd never wanted to have in the first place, but she rolled out of bed, slipped into her sandals, and stuffed the roll of money in her pocket. $153 made her feel less like a child.

Deirdre sat at the bar between a middle-aged couple and a construction worker who had come to Daydreams straight from the site. The club was small and narrow, the bar running the length of one wall and the stage situated parallel. A disco ball swept rainbows across the fuchsia-lit walls.

The bludgeoning guitars of Alice in Chains' "Man In The Box" grinded through the sound system. Phuffy strode onstage wearing a black mesh shirt over a red bikini top, a plaid pleated skirt hemmed to expose the slight curve of her ass, and fishnet thigh-highs. She'd coated her eyes in black cream shadow and her hair was volumized and brightened by blonde clip-in extensions that curled down her back. A dozen men wandered to the tip rail, entranced not by the promise of her body but by the amiable and approachable energy she exuded. Phuffy beamed at her crowd as they settled into pervert's row. When the moaning vocals came in, she grabbed the pole and spun spiritedly. She was a mediocre dancer, her breasts were small and conical, and her bikini line was perpetually razor burned, but watching her, you got the sense that she'd help your mom with the dishes, participate in your fantasy football league, tell dirty jokes to your bros, gaze at you with devotion in her eyes as she executed tremorous blowjobs.

Aunt Moira and Uncle Mike told neighbors their daughter worked at a bar and left it at that; but as Deirdre watched Phuffy sweep singles from the floor into her arms, she couldn't help feeling proud.

She swallowed the rest of her drink when she saw Phuffy emerge from the dressing room, eyes flashing. She clenched Deirdre's upper arm and pulled her into a lap dance booth. The bass-heavy song playing outside rattled the doorknob.

"I'm going to ask you a question and you will not lie to me," Phuffy said, her voice cold and quivering. "Did you take money from that girl you hit?"

Deirdre's body numbed. She stared into the bare ruby light bulb above them and nodded.

Phuffy pressed the heels of her hands into her eyes, smearing her makeup. "She filed a police report, Deirdre. They're waiting for the DA to press charges."

"She doesn't know me," Deirdre said, confused.

"You punched her out on Passyunk Avenue at ten o'clock on a Friday night in July. Half the neighborhood saw you from their windows."

Deirdre bit the side of her trembling thumb. "Who'd you hear this from?"

"A cop client of mine handled the reports. He recognized our last name."

Deirdre squatted on the thin, mildewy carpet, dizzy. She remembered when she was seventeen: the weeks of anxious waiting, standing in front of a judge whose frigid glances communicated a belief that Deirdre was ignorant, unrepentant white trash. She thought of sentencing and her stomach seized. This was her first offense as an adult, simple assault; she'd only have to deal with a fine and probation. Or could they twist it into aggravated? Was jail time actually a possibility? Another judge looking at her the same way, knowing she was in the exact same spot as four years earlier, made Deirdre nauseated. Then again, the judge would be right to assume she was trash. Her parents were bottom-dwellers, but Aunt Moira and Uncle Mike had raised her as their own. They'd told her they loved her, attended field hockey games, spanked her when she deserved it, celebrated her birthday at Dave & Buster's every year. And yet she'd grown into a hollow, angry creature.

She struggled to her feet and pulled the door open.

"Where are you going? We have to discuss next steps!" Phuffy cried. Her hand shot by Deirdre's nose as she slammed the door. Instinctively, Deirdre's fingers curled around her casted fist and her arm rose. She gasped, in part for the pain surging through her wrist and in part for shame. Phuffy's eyes narrowed.

"You wanna hit me, Dee?"

Deirdre lowered her arm and tried to shove past Phuffy, towering in her Lucite heels. "Let me out!" Deirdre yelled.

"What did I do to make you hate me so much?" Phuffy said, her voice wavering. "All that hate is gonna destroy you."

Deirdre halted. "Stop with the greeting card bullshit!" The pain from her wrist seemed to course through her veins like a poison. "You love telling me how I'm fucking my life up, but what's so great about yours? Flashing your worn out pussy for cash and you wanna tell me how to live."

Phuffy let go of the doorknob and sat on the vinyl banquette, staring at her knees. A smudgy black tear hung from the tip of her nose. The pain in Deirdre's wrist iced over and she rushed out of the club.

She tried to breathe deeply as she half-ran towards the apartment, but the air tasted spoiled. The Puerto Rican kid was still outside the botánica, table reassembled. His eyes widened.

"Hell no, keep walking, crazy bitch. You got that devil inside you, you need a fucking exorcism."

She stopped. Something in her chest quivered, like a magnet before it leaps towards its pole. "You can do that?" she asked, panting.

He narrowed his eyes, assessing her sweaty, desperate face. "My grandma can."

"Go get her."

"Hold up, hold up. You got money?"

She touched the round bulge in her pocket. "How much does this sort of thing usually cost?"

He bit his lip, calculating. "Two hundred."

"I got one fifty."

"That'll do." He opened a wrought iron screen door next to the botánica entrance and shut it behind him. Deirdre stared at her bitten nails, thinking of the tear on Phuffy's nose, the bewilderment in the musician's eyes, the girl's blood on her knuckles; she'd seen so many people's blood on her knuckles. After a few minutes, the screen door opened again.

"Let me see the money," he said. She handed him the bankroll, which he counted aloud before waving her into the botánica.

Fluorescent lights glared over the same white aluminum shelves they had at the dollar store, upon which oils and candles were organized according to the affliction they addressed. The kid led her down a set of stairs to an unfinished basement that was as clean as the main floor, though less clinical. Three standing lamps gently illuminated the room and a wheeled buffet table piled with bowls and half-melted candles leaned against one wall. She eyed a large knife resting atop an industrial sink in the corner.

"Don't be nervous," the kid said. "She'll help you. My aunt, too."

Deirdre glared at him. "You're gonna act all nice now that you got my money?"

He snorted and shook his head. The stairs whined with the weight of slow footsteps and the kid jumped up to help the women, although his grandmother didn't seem particularly old or frail. Her red velvet hair was cut in a smart bob and she wore a DKNY t-shirt with capri pants and Chinese slippers.

"We do *lectura*, okay?" She smiled warmly.

The aunt unrolled a straw mat onto which the grandmother arranged an array of objects: a jug of water, a candle, a bowl of white chalk, a chicken wing bone, a black stone, a doll's head. When Deirdre saw the dollar store Barbie head with her tousled, straw-like hair, she backed away.

"Relax, mamita," the aunt said. "It represents your consciousness. Everything on the mat represents a different part of your life. You understand?"

Deirdre pulled at the neck of her shirt, feeling hot.

"Sit down. We're Christians, we go to church. We believe in Jesus Christ. This is all extra credit. Come on, nothing to worry about." The aunt tugged Deirdre's sleeve and she sat on a cushion. "What's your full name, sweetie?"

"Deirdre Marie Copeley."

"Spell it." The aunt wrote Deirdre's name in block letters across a piece of paper as the kid helped his grandmother to the floor. She waved her hand in dismissal and he smirked at Deirdre before running upstairs. She set a tulle bag of cowrie shells on the floor, scooped a handful of chalk, and rubbed it over her hands and between her fingers. She took a second portion of chalk and motioned for Deirdre's hands. Deirdre hesitantly accepted, rubbing it over her skin. She was reminded of baking cookies as a child. The grandmother dipped her hand in the jug and flicked beads of water while muttering words Deirdre didn't recognize. She felt like she was listening in on a secret, and blood thudded in her neck as she thought that perhaps this was a secret she wasn't supposed to be in on. She turned to the aunt, looking for translation, but she'd closed her eyes and begun speaking in counter rhythm to the grandmother, posing questions. She invoked Deirdre's name, and hearing herself called among the strange words made Deirdre's skin prickle.

The grandmother reached for Deirdre's hands and let the smooth, warm shells spill into her palms.

"Toss them," the aunt said. Deirdre did as she was told, and the shells bounced and scattered across the mat. The grandmother pointed to each shell and explained something to the aunt, who scribbled in her notebook.

"Do it again," the aunt said. They discussed in Spanish. Deirdre sat cross-legged, swirling the chalk on the back of her hand.

Finally, the aunt said, "Baby, you have a very dark spirit haunting you. You're lucky to have come to us when you did. Normally, for this type of cleansing, we charge three hundred. Powerful stuff, hard to do right. But we're giving you a deal. You should make a follow-up appointment, too, but we'll discuss that later."

The women led her out the back of the botánica to a small concrete patio bordered by tall brick walls. The aunt lit two citronella torches, dragged a plastic baby pool to the center of the patio, unraveled a hose, and tossed the nozzle in.

"We need to cleanse you of the spirit plaguing you."

"What about my cast?" Deirdre asked.

"Did you not hear me before? This is an emergency," the aunt said over the whistling spigot. "Take off your clothes. We're all girls."

The grandmother emptied a milk jug of torn herbs and oils into the pool, and their scent rose dusky as they hit the water. Deirdre disrobed, thinking of Phuffy dancing down the street, how they were naked together.

The water was cold and silky from the oils, and she sunk deeper until it passed over her face, through her hair, and into the humid, itchy crevices beneath her cast. Deirdre listened to the muffled bass of her heartbeat underwater. The grandmother gently pulled her to the surface and began to rub the herbed water into her neck while the aunt took Deirdre's arm. They whispered their occult language as they ran their hands over her legs, shoulders, and stomach. Their hands were strong and smooth, like river stones, and thrumming with energy. Deirdre gasped for air. The touch of skin on her skin shocked her. She could feel the women's warmth and holiness absorb into her bones, and the fear that coiled around her muscles was pulled out through her pores. She could feel it unwinding, she could breathe, she could cry. The tears ran hot into her hair and she let the sobs escape from her open, twisted mouth. The women continued to massage her body as she wailed to the square of purple sky overhead.

Deirdre howled until she could only expel a rasp. The women pulled her to her feet and hosed her down. Despite the frigid water, her body throbbed with warmth. She felt so aware of her blood flowing and her cells regenerating that she could barely stand. The aunt dried her with a beach towel as the grandmother dumped the pool down a drain by the hose. She said more prayers as the dirty water rushed away. The two women helped Deirdre into her clothes and combed out her hair.

"It's time for you to go now, baby. It's already a new day," the aunt said. "You get more money, you come back this week, okay?" Deirdre nodded distractedly. She understood she now had the chance to be new. The aunt escorted her through the gleaming white aisles of the botánica and back into the night. "Take care," she said.

The street was empty. Through the sherbet haze of sodium vapor lamps, she could make out the dim light of stars. The air smelled like new grass and steaming asphalt and salt from the fish stands. Deirdre ran her fingers through her hair, pulled a leaf off a tree, and pressed it to her lips.

She knew Phuffy was waiting at home, sheets kicked down around her ankles, unable to sleep, picking through Steven's knots as she decided what kind of look to give Deirdre when she came through the door. Deirdre would accept Phuffy's expression of hurt and disappointment and unshakeable love. She'd meet Phuffy's gaze and let the repercussions sink in her skin; this is how she'd ask forgiveness.

Jac Jemc

Half Dollar

I didn't want Patty to see my reluctance, but my conscience won out. "Patty, are we sure? This feels different. We'll be on someone else's turf."

I'd watched Patty walk out of department stores with sweaters only to return them hours later for store credit. I'd allowed her to swap our ginger ales for pints of beer when the men at the tavern stood to take their turns in the darts game. Wandering into a stranger's yard without a plan though seemed more illicit.

Patty responded by pushing the gate open. She started down the path, covered in leaves and brush several seasons old. As soon as I stepped past the fence, all of the street lamps went out. I looked back, but I could still see the iron constellation high above. The shine stopped at the deep shrubs lining the fence. I had trouble seeing as far as my feet and so I stepped gingerly, and clasped a hand on Patty's shoulder. Like always, I wanted to leach some of her assured energy.

Patty shrugged me away, saying, "Get. You're not afraid, are you?"

I shook my head, relieved she hadn't seen me lie my cowardice away. When we reached the front porch, Patty's foot ripped a large creak from the first step. I jumped within, but inhaled deeply, holding steady without.

Patty tilted down to examine the wood of the step with her fingertips. "Soft, nearly rotted through," she said, turning to me. She straightened, and lifted herself easily up the next two stairs. A dim light shone behind the sheer. Patty stood in front of the door, measured, observant. I was too nervous to think of anything but what would happen next. After several seconds, I saw Patty's hand raise. I looked for a shadow, but the absence of light let her knuckles fall without a mark upon the door. She gave three quick raps, and clasped her hands behind her back, raising her head to look toward the small window at the top of the door.

In moments, the fixture above us, light half clouded by dead bugs and grit, flicked on. We heard a chain lock slide and fall slack and a whoosh of air sucked into the house as the door eased back, like a vacuum opening up. Before us stood a woman, not thin so much as empty of herself. She had been fuller at some point, and in the once-full spaces, a lack called attention to itself. Her face bore an exhausted dearth of surprise when her eyes landed on us. She didn't say a word, only looked behind us, searching for some other element of our arrival.

"Mrs. Pengrine?" Patty said, and I snapped my sight on her, wondering what sort of chance she was taking. The woman raised one eyebrow, and nodded her head as slowly as I've ever seen. "So nice to meet you, Mrs. Pengrine. I was wondering, is Mr. Pengrine home?"

Mrs. Pengrine breathed deeply, like that rush of air through the door, and shook her head. "He's not."

Patty took this well, "All right then, might I leave a message for him? It's very important."

It was then I saw the mailbox beside the door with "Mr. and Mrs. A. Pengrine," embossed in gold on the black matte. Patty was the most ghastly. I would never catch up.

The woman brought a hand to her mouth absently, rubbed her forefinger idly against her lips, stalling, like she didn't much care to speak the answer she had at the ready, but her hand dropped, and she had her say, "I'm afraid you can't. Mr. Pengrine is no longer with us."

Patty gulped air. We had practiced our gasps in front of the mirror, rehearsed their timing and strength, trying to make them as believable as possible. Patty played master and I apprentice, as usual. "That can't be," she said. "That just simply can't be."

Mrs. Pengrine stood stock still, interested in Patty's shock. Her face held skepticism, hope, defensiveness, threat, but she said nothing.

"Certainly you mean that Mr. Pengrine has moved away? Not that he's..." Patty acted as though she couldn't bring herself to say it.

"No, I'm afraid he's passed on. Six months ago now, may he rest."

Patty cast a glance my way, shock asking for confirmation, and I did my best to return it to her.

"But my friend and I, just this afternoon, we passed him at the station. He nearly stepped in front of a streetcar, and I pulled his arm back. He thanked me over and over. Said he was distracted, trying to find a gift for his wife."

Mrs. Pengrine's face remained stern, but her eyes were filling. "You must have the wrong man. It couldn't have been my Arnold."

Patty shook her head, refusing to accept this answer. "It can't be. He said his name was Arnold Pengrine, and he said I should stop by this address anytime for a reward. He said he didn't have any cash on him, but if we stopped by this evening, he'd give us each a quarter and fresh cut roses from the garden."

Mrs. Pengrine gazed past us, to the front of the yard, and I realized Patty had noticed the thorny branches on the bushes as we'd approached. "Two quarters? That's hardly...and the roses aren't blooming this time of year," the woman said, like the fault lay in the flowers and not in the ghostly specter of her husband's promise.

"But how could we have seen him, if he's gone?" Patty asked the woman, like Mrs. Pengrine might have the answer, like Mrs. Pengrine ought to defend herself from this accusation.

I felt sick, like perhaps I'd had enough. "Patty," I whispered.

"Margaret, you saw him, too! How can this be?" Patty snapped.

I shook my head, wishing myself away from this front porch, wishing I had no part in this, wishing Patty wasn't so horrid.

"Would you come in? I'd love to hear more," Mrs. Pengrine said, stepping back to open a space in the doorway.

"I don't think we'd better," Patty said, taking my hand, and turning us to leave. "Come on, Margaret."

"Girls, just a moment or two, we can sit on the porch here. I understand if you don't want–"

Before she could finish, Patty let out the slightest shriek, halting us in our steps. She let go of my hand to point, and there on the bottom stair lay two quarters. I thought back to Patty stooping to touch the wood of the rotten stair, and knew it was then she'd placed the coins.

"I–I'm so sorry we've disturbed you, ma'am. We'll be on our way. Goodnight!" She grabbed my hand again, hopping past the last two stairs. I stumbled behind her, but kept my grip. We slammed the gate behind us and raced for what felt like blocks.

"How," Patty beamed at me, "was *that*?"

"Oh, Patty," I said. "The most ghastly. I don't know...That poor woman."

Patty pushed my shoulder roughly, "Oh, come on! We made her night. She thinks her husband's spirit is alive and well and visiting young girls. No harm done. What a miserable sight she was!" Patty collapsed on a bench, panting and laughing, doubled over.

"But how did you know to place the quarters? You used the rose bushes and the name on the mailbox. How did you know it would work out?" I felt hot and red-faced. I wondered if we'd missed our ride home.

"Of course I had no idea *how* it would work out! I just paid attention and followed the clues! Oh, we must do more! You'll need to take a turn, Margaret!"

I nodded. It was true, I knew. If we were to remain friends, I'd need to try to top her. I'd need to draw out some demons and swirl them around some unsuspecting mark. "It's probably time to meet your mother," I said.

Patty slid her watch below the sleeve of her coat, and called out, "Cripes, you're right!"

We walked back to the corner of Nation and Main since Patty had left our streetcar fare on the stairs, and all the way, Patty pointed to houses dreaming up schemes. When we got to the corner, her mother was upset. "Where have you been? It's nearly half-past!"

"Mother, you wouldn't believe! We saved a man's life! He nearly stepped out in front of the streetcar, and I pulled him back! We're heroes!"

I marveled at Patty's ability to turn her first lie so believably inside out into a second.

"Great, great," Patty's mother said, unimpressed. "Next time you save someone's life, be back on time."

Patty just laughed and hooked her arm in mine as we walked to her mother's car. Her elbow dug lightly into my ribs, and she whispered, "You're next, Margaret."

My heart stopped, thinking she meant I'd be her next mark, but in a moment I realized she meant the next prank was mine to perform. I clutched her arm tighter, and wondered at how my mind had looked first for the threat in what she'd said, and doubt fell over where it was I should have laid my trust.

Richard Burgin

Paper Face

He'd always suspected that his mother cheated on his father, and then, eventually, years after he died when she was in her late fifties she told him that she had. She wasn't drinking much when she told him, nor were they having a fight. There was no discernable reason, he thought, for her to tell him other than some misplaced urge to rid herself of some excess guilt and maybe, through a twisted rationalization, hope for some sympathy from him.

"I don't want to hear this," he said, hands over his ears while she called after him. He was running down the thickly carpeted hallway of her condo that seemed to swallow all sound as if he were running in bare feet. Outside, a ghostly white sailboat passed by on the bay in pursuit of another white sailboat. His mother loved sailboats, especially ones with white sails. They both did.

"Not another word," he yelled before finally locking himself in the bathroom.

He had been running like a child, he thought, as if he'd done something wrong. He waited, silent and furious for her to go, thinking about his father while she stood outside calling his name. It wasn't a total shock because for years, they'd lived in separate rooms. His mother had said it was because his father's snoring had gotten worse and his father had made a joke about it that was typically self-deprecating. He remembered the sad expression on his brother's face (who was an innocent like his father) after the joke, while a zigzagging line of peas fell from his spoon.

He never heard her leave, just looked through the tiny space at the bottom of the door before realizing that she'd shut off the lights and gone to her room. He opened the bathroom door as quietly as he could, taking the handgun from the lockbox in his room, then opened the door and headed for the stairs—no longer having the patience to wait for the elevator.

Outside there were two options: Go to the beach or go to the fenced-in condominium pool where the senior set hung out. "Seniors"—what an absurd word, as if they were about to graduate into anything but death, the only thing they'd really be masters of. They told the same stories from their chaise lounges and laughed over and over, as if hearing them for the first time. Still he chose the pool for its comfortable chairs and because it had a good view of the Gulfport Bay and a pleasant breeze through the palm trees—everything conducive to sleep. But when he closed his eyes, he saw images of his father telling him a story about the record store or about the Red Sox, a few of whom patronized his business. He heard his father's laugh, deep and always unforced. His father went to all his games, baseball and basketball, worked like a dog but usually went by himself, rarely with his mother. His father had the most honest face he'd ever seen—so honest it was as if the rest of him, having seen it, had to be that way too. But his mother seemed to be made of secrets. She dominated the conversation at dinner talking constantly about her childhood, her first husband and subsequent admirers, yet never revealed herself. She had trouble listening to people's troubles as if there was only so much space for such things, and by complaining they threatened her territory. Of course it was also true that she was still beautiful, much younger and probably more intelligent than his father as well, who also never seemed to make enough money.

"Sit down, relax," his father would say to her. "Everything's delicious, especially you." It was one of his oldest compliments but it always made her smile. Possibly she could have loved him still even when she weakened with Victor, Brian thought. But why did she have to sleep with someone he knew, the partner of his father's record store, moreover with someone whose kids he sometimes played with? He'd always wondered why Victor's family and his dad's took a couple of family vacations together to Miami Beach, now he knew. He picked up a few pebbles, and threw them towards the beach as far as he could. Maybe that's why he'd had so much trouble with women himself, he thought. Although he also had trouble with work, drugs—everything really.

"Better tone it down," he said to himself, the senior couples were always watching the young (although he was already twenty-four) for breaches of their rules. (What would they think if they knew he was carrying a piece?) They especially watched the ones who were sitting alone, as if they were looking carefully at a dim painting of their childhood they could see but not quite figure out. How distrustful they are, Brian thought, how innately distrustful and scared. Did they think his pebbles were little chips from a nuclear bomb? He felt his gun deep in his jacket pocket and his anger turned to anxiety of a strange kind he wasn't used to. "Officer, some of the places I go to can get pretty rowdy," he would say to explain his gun.

Why had he come to see his mother with whom there was always so much tension? And now he had the worst of both worlds simultaneously, sitting at the pool, brooding about his mother *and* his own past failures at work, etc.

Someone was actually swimming in the pool—an event less frequent than laughter at a library. If he ever made a documentary about the pool, he'd call it "Silent Water." There was never any action at the pool (you'd find more at a mausoleum), rarely women his age either so no point in even looking. Yet it always made his mother so happy each time he went to the pool with her. She liked showing him off—"And here's my handsome son"—and he had to admit she was still the prettiest woman in the condo, looking at least ten years younger than she was. His father was really asking for trouble marrying someone nineteen years younger than him. And of course trouble came. Did he see it coming, see it at all? Or had he trained himself to be oblivious?

*

He had got up and left the pool without even being aware of his decision to do so, the old people no doubt staring at him and wondering why he'd left so soon. Now they'd have something new to yack about for five more minutes.

Tampa and St. Petersburg were too far away so he headed for the most edgy bar in Gulfport, The Fisherman's Catch, where he hoped to meet a woman or maybe score some weed. The bar was dark, malodorous, and vaguely frightening. He remembered he went there once with his father shortly before his father's pneumonia, and the two of them argued about Amazon.com's effect on independent record stores, like the one his parents owned. Typically his father tried to joke it away by making fun of the term "amazon." "The idea is to make the place sound entertaining, not invite you to go to war," he'd said.

Brian laughed as he laughed at all his father's jokes, funny or not. Come to think of it, his mother did too. They were a good match, his mom and dad, business-wise anyway. She knew more about classical music, he about jazz and rock. They both loved the store as if it were their child. Brian never minded working there part-time for a few summers. Once with his younger brother Cole (named for Cole Porter) before he went away to college in the Midwest. His parents never had many fights and even those were more like short-lived squabbles. Yet there was the age difference (this was before the era of Viagra, too) and perhaps her feeling that his father was her intellectual inferior as well.

He felt his gun through his jacket just before he walked into Fisherman's Catch. Soon a black woman approached him wearing tight dark purple pants with gold spangles and half her top open. "Hey cowboy, got a light? My name's Veronica."

"Don't smoke. Sorry."

"You mean you don't smoke cigs?" the woman said with a laugh. He laughed too to be polite.

"You might be interested in smoking something else though, right?"

"Could be."

"Yeah I bet I could interest you in smoking something else."

A short muscular black man dressed in black leather walked up to him.

"What you getting all up in my woman's business for?"

He was going to say 'she approached me,' but thought better of it. "Sorry bro."

"You're damn right you're sorry."

"Come on Marvin, he didn't do nothin' to me."

"Maybe I should be mad at someone else then."

"I didn't do nothing neither. You talkin' crazy. Come on, let's blow this joint. There's nothing here for you."

"You tell me a place that is for us."

"You in a white man's town, I told you that."

"White man's town? I thought they all was that."

"Come on baby," she said, taking him by the hand. "Momma's gonna take you to the best place you can go to."

"Is it safe?" he said in an odd high pitched voice.

"It's a lot more than just safe," she said, pushing him forward.

He looked at them closely for a moment. When he turned around he saw a white man of indeterminate age also dressed in black. (Was it goth night at the bar perhaps?) The man in front of him, who was also staring at him, had an extraordinarily white face, as if it were made of paper.

"Don't mind them. They come here all the time. They don't do no real trouble, they just try to scare people into buying drugs, or just watching them fight, like it's a play. But you're not scared by them are you?"

He said no. He was thinking of his mother getting out of her car with Victor. He saw Victor smiling when he threw a football in their yard with a better spiral than his father's just because he was younger. Again everyone laughed but not everyone was happy. Could his father have known then? He noticed an odd twitch around his father's eye. It wasn't that obvious, especially if a more charismatic man like Victor was commanding attention. It was as if Victor was the commander and everyone else, especially his father, were his troops.

"You driftin' off man?" the man with a paper face said.

Brian shrugged.

"'Bout what?"

"Nothin' really."

"Is there always somethin' or is there always nothing? That's what I'd like to know—so often the two are mixed. Like with death. Is death the hallucination or is life?"

"Hallucinations are from drugs."

"That's a good one kid. You're going to get rich, boy."

"Really? Why's that?" he said, half angrily. He looked to be around Victor's age, maybe older.

"Well I can't tell you that here."

"Listen, man."

"My name's Fabian."

"OK, Fabian. Just to be clear about something, I don't do men."

"This ain't about that. Far from it. Is that what you thought?"

Brian shrugged. "Sorry dude."

"Kinda makes me laugh cause I think of myself as a corpse. Which is about as asexual as it gets, isn't it? No, that wasn't actually even a thought in my head. But I do have a deal to offer you, if you're willing to step outside for a minute to discuss it."

He looked at Paper Face closely, judging himself to be about thirty years younger and substantially stronger. And besides, he also had his gun.

"OK, I'll go outside," he said.

"Like I said, my name's Fabian," Paper Face said. "Parents named me after a dumb rock and roll singer from the 50's."

Oh really, I thought your name was Paper Face. Are you really made of paper, he wanted to say.

"What's yours?"

Brian hesitated. He had been named after Brian Wilson of The Beach Boys.

"You don't have to tell me. Let's see, is it Norman Bates?"

"Very funny. My name's Brian."

They started towards the door when Veronica approached him as if she'd never seen him before.

"You want something to smoke or maybe some E or something?" He looked at her closely. Her eyes were as glassy as water thrown over ice.

"No thanks," Brian said, touching his gun again through his jacket.

"You sure now?"

He nodded. Meanwhile, Paper Face moved closer to him and half whispered, "Stay away from both of them. They're poison."

"I told you not to come in no washed out white man's place like this," Marvin said. Brian hadn't noticed him at first and now stared at him as if he might be a hallucination.

"Don't be in such a hurry," Veronica said, "we might be changing his mind about buying something."

"He ain't got no mind to change. C'mon, wanna walk beside me now or maybe you ashamed of me."

"I'm not ashamed of you and I'm not scared neither so stop threatening me."

"I don't threaten you. I don't do nothin' to you."

"You kicked me last night."

"Kicked you? What you talking about? I was sleeping so how could I kick you?"

"Maybe it was an accident. I try to think so. You take up so much space it's impossible to not be kicked by you. Not for ordinary mammals anyway."

"Well you're far from ordinary. No one on this planet would think you're ordinary. Other planets, I'm not so sure. You ever heard of a jazz musician named Sun Ra?"

"No."

"He said he was from Saturn. Some crackers believed him."

"Is that right? Well keep talking. I'd say your chances of doing me tonight are less than zero and shrinking."

Brian suddenly noticed how their dialect and use of language had become more "white." Were they doing some kind of satirical performance art?

Meanwhile, a small crowd had formed around them, alternately cheering on either Marvin or Veronica.

Then Paper Face approached Brian and said, "Are we going to leave or just die here from poison?"

A few moments later they left the bar. They began walking down the pier on Gulfport Bay. In the daytime it was often filled with fishermen, but late at night there were only a few lovers sitting on the benches at the end of the pier. When they reached the end, Paper Face said, "There's a bench to your left that's free."

"Fine," Brian said, looking at the silent boats and their lights on the water. His father liked walking on piers too, but not so much his mother who said it hurt her feet. To listen to her, some part of her body was always hurting. He wondered if it happened once or twice or more with Victor while he and his father were walking on this pier. You could never know such things, especially then before cameras and smartphones. His father said smartphones make dumb people, and perhaps cameras would soon become so pervasive that the frequency of affairs shown on TV would one day cause them all to seem too trivial to show. Maybe even murder would one day lose its meaning by being overexposed.

Brian sat down, but Paper Face remained standing five feet from his left, bent and only half visible like a damaged scarecrow.

"You know that people give each other money to do all kinds of things right? Some of which seem crazy but if you listen long enough, after a while, it starts to make some sense. Like with Marvin and Veronica. After a while you can't tell theater from reality with them. Am I getting too heavy for you?"

"No, but I'd appreciate you getting to the point."

"Point is, people no longer just pay to have other people killed, they pay to have themselves killed too. It's like people need killing more than water."

He saw an image of Victor with his mother, and felt the index finger of his left hand begin to tremble.

"Personally," Paper Face said, "I think all crimes are committed by people, not ghosts or devils like I used to think. Even though I was told a devil/vampire sucked all the blood out of my face, it's people who are the real devils. So if you stop living you finally stop at least one chain of killing."

"What are you talking about exactly?"

Paper Face shrugged. For the first time he seemed nervous and started looking around himself.

"Could be that strutting actor we just saw. Ripped me off in a drug deal once. Hates white people too, as you may have noticed, and no one is more white than me. But maybe Veronica that black woman's involved too, or then again, maybe it's really just me that needs to go down."

"So what do you want me to do?" Brian said, thinking that Paper Face was a lunatic or on a very heavy drug, but also realizing that now that he was out of work again and couldn't bear to ask his mother, he very much needed money.

"I think you know what I'm saying."

"So why ask me?"

"We've been watching you, noticing your spending habits too–point is, what if you could do someone a big favor and get paid for it at the same time?"

"What's the favor? You don't seem to want to spell it out."

"You know the words. It's just a question of do you accept the job or not."

"Why not just do it yourself?"

"I never said it was a simple thing to do for me. I don't pretend to be the kind of man who can do that. Never was good at it before."

He thought of Victor's eyes again, wondered if he ever had an attack of conscience or was it just a series of unstoppable erections.

"You have an answer?"

"I can't do it. Sorry. You need to get someone else."

He began walking back down the pier half expecting Paper Face to run after him. Then he thought he might see him flying in the sky like a twisted white kite, but he heard nothing and didn't look back, so saw nothing either.

He was walking down Beach Boulevard towards the condominium complex parking lot (where his father's Buick was still parked, his mother's way of honoring him) trying to figure out if during one of her stated "business trips" she might have actually met Victor and used the condominium to make love in, two times? Five times? Ten times? Twenty? Maybe they did it in his dad's car, too. He'd never find out. He knew she'd never talk about it again (he wouldn't let her anyway). He'd only learned that she betrayed him, not how, why, or how often. That would die with her, like so much else. Useless to ask her about him or anything else, for that matter, like why did she make him go to church and Sunday school? Why did she insist, the few times he wasn't, that he be polite to his father? Was she *polite* to him?

He'd walked through the parking lot toward the elevator. Why did everyone lie so much? People do nothing but lie to themselves and then to each other. God was a lie, at least the one they prayed to was. Heaven was also a lie, of course, as was love and fidelity. It was as if our minds were built with lying skills growing like silent cells in one part while gullibility cells grew in another.

Finally he got on the elevator. Was she in bed in her room having drunk herself to sleep, the little lying former cheerleader who loved music so much? Perhaps she was still in her chair gazing out the window trying to spot another boat.

There was no one there. At first he was immensely relieved, like he'd just emerged from underwater. She was in her room, no doubt, and in all likelihood, sleeping. The condo was as quiet as a tomb, the only sounds being the air conditioner—the God of Florida, he thought, that made a constantly repetitive drone like Indian music.

Then he heard a new sound—not clear what it was—other than a half-human noise. He reached for his gun (glad he hadn't taken his jacket off yet), and quietly went forward. There were four other condos in the complex—all with absurdly British names meant to impress: The Empire, The Buckingham, The Ambassador and the Royal Court. His mother lived in the Empire. All the condos had their own pools—which all looked essentially alike—and all were filled with wealthy widows. The security who were supposed to protect the complex were all under forty it seemed. They were all young and bored, as he was too, before their working lives had barely begun. Lately there'd been a number of break-ins and minor thefts and security had acted shocked and swore they were "right on top of it," while of course doing nothing about it.

He heard the sound again like Paper Face was coughing and he walked another five steps forward. Looking out the picture window, he saw a couple of white boats. Instantly he looked to his mother's reading chair but it was empty, as if a ghost or something even emptier had settled there instead.

"Mama," he yelled (her hearing wasn't good but she was far too vain to consider hearing aids).

"Mama," he yelled again, feeling dizzy and wondering if Paper Face had somehow drugged him. He stopped walking and listened but there was no answer except the impervious air conditioner's unvarying hum.

Then he went into her room, surprised that his gun was out, his fingers grasping at it as if it were a lifesaver or at least something that could steady him. A door opened suddenly. It was the bathroom door that adjoined his mother's room. He heard her scream and then he fell and somehow fired the gun into the dark of the room. Or maybe she screamed after the gun went off.

"Mama, it's me, Brian."

"What happened? Were you trying to kill me?"

"I'm sorry, I thought someone had broken in and hurt you! I called out your name, I yelled it, but you didn't say anything so I went to your room." While he spoke he felt a terrible pain spread through him.

"So you tried to protect me? I didn't think you cared after the horrible thing I told you about. Damn vodka. But that was twenty years ago."

She turned on the lamp on her bedtable.

"My God Brian, you're bleeding! What should we do?"

He looked down at his feet and his shoes were soaked in blood. Instinctively, he got up to run but fell down after two steps.

"Jesus Christ!" his mother screamed. "Stay still, don't try to walk."

"It's alright Ma, I'm only bleeding," he said, quoting the Dylan song to make her laugh, but she didn't. She was on her knees now, the lights were on and she was staring transfixed at the blood on his foot.

"Don't try to get up," she said, as she finally stood up. "I don't know who we can get at this time of night. I guess we can call an ambulance and go to the ER."

Victor would know what to do, don't you wish he was here, he wanted to say. Instead he said, "If we go to the ER you may as well kill me now, it'll be quicker."

He remembered when he was five or six being stung by a bee, later bit by a dog, and both times his mother fixed him up in almost no time. Same thing when he had the flu.

"I have an idea, I'll make a tourniquet," she said, stepping over his body and going into her bathroom. The lights went on like an instant sunrise. He heard the sound of water running and imagined it was a waterfall to try to block out the pain in his foot. He wondered how long he would have to stay with his mother now, though when it came to his injuries, she knew how to take care of him, he had to admit.

"I took a Xanax," she said twenty minutes later.

He nodded. He might have said "good."

*

A few minutes later he heard her snoring while he sat up in her reclining chair in the living room (her door open "in case you need me to help you with something," she had said). He waited for sleep with his eyes closed hearing the air conditioner, seeing the bay in his mind's eye then opening his eyes just in time to see two more boats with white sails sliding towards each other slowly as if it had all been planned that way a long time ago.

Ilana Masad

Sand Running

Sand ran barefoot, the hot asphalt spurring him on. His shoes hung round his neck from tied laces and bounced on his thin chest. The air was heavy with potential rain, humidity refusing to evaporate under the hot sun. Running felt like cutting a swath through a sponge cake.

Houses flashed by, windows shut tight. The A/C units purred, trying to outdo the mosquitoes' buzzing. A few old people sat on porches, fanning their faces with cheap touristy handheld fans that their children brought from big cities when they came to visit. The porch-sitters moved their heads to watch Sand run past, but forgot about him almost as soon as he was out of sight. People often forgot about Sand.

His sister, for instance. She was supposed to have picked him up from school, but she hadn't shown up. Sand had waited for over an hour, after the school's offices had closed. He didn't have a cellphone ever since he'd "lost it" by accidentally dropping it in a toilet while getting beaten up in the bathroom. Sand wasn't an idiot. He knew that if he'd told the truth, his father would have just looked disappointed that his kid didn't know how to fight back and would have offered, yet again, to spar with Sand out in the yard with his old boxing gloves.

But Sand preferred running. It was the only way to get ahead of his thoughts, which, though slow and sluggish in the August heat, were usually fox-quick in burrowing through whatever else he tried to occupy his mind with. He also loved the calluses that grew on his soles and toes, so hard that he could tap his nails against them and hear the same noise he got when tapping on the lids of the overstuffed Tupperware containers in the fridge. He was happy when he wasn't able to distinguish one face from another because he passed them all so quickly. He could pretend they talked about him once he was gone instead of forgetting.

Sand wanted to be talked about. He never told anyone about this wish, because he thought it sounded both childish and somehow vain—he didn't know the word itself, only its meaning. He was ten, and his reading skills weren't quite up to par. His teachers had tried parent-teacher conferences, but when his father explained things to them last year, they stopped bothering. They knew that Sand must have more important things on his mind. Sand assumed they forgot about him. It was just as well. Sand hated it when his father came to school. Everyone always thought he was his grandfather because he had white hair and was old. Older.

As for being talked about, Sand wanted people he didn't know to talk about him, not his father and his teachers. If strangers talked about him, they might have sympathy. In some television shows that Sand watched, there were kindly strangers who gave orphaned boys and girls jobs or favors or rides somewhere. In real life, he knew never to talk to strangers, never to take candy from them, and never ever to get into a car with someone he didn't know. But in the magical world of television, it seemed that breaking the rules led to good things, and the trouble on the way was always forgiven, just another part of the adventure.

Sand wasn't naïve, though. He knew about death. He knew about crime. His father's religion was the newspaper and he would often read bits and pieces of particularly horrible articles out loud to Sand while he was eating his morning Chex or Froot Loops or Cinnamon Toast Crunch. Those were the only cereals that Sand liked, and he wouldn't even eat the grocery store's generic brands because they weren't the same. They didn't have the right kind of crunch, he insisted, and the individual pieces weren't the exact right size. Sand had a careful method of loading up the correct amount of cereal and milk into his spoon for the first bite, and his entire day was thrown off if he got it wrong. His father sometimes called him crazy. His sister understood, sort of, and since she was the one who did the grocery shopping for all of them, she always made sure to get the right stuff.

*

Sand ran. A car whizzed by going the other way. A warm gust of bad exhaust pipe smell blew into him. It knocked him back like a big hand with grimy fingers and dirt under the nails appearing out of nowhere in front of him and then disappearing. He shook his head, trying to clear his nostrils of the smoky smell that reminded him of the hellfire that Mr. Doherty, the school's Catholic janitor, told him about when Sand hung around, waiting to be picked up, after everyone else went home.

Mr. Doherty once told Sand that he had two big dogs at home, two Dobermans. Dobermen. Sand wasn't sure which was the correct word, but he thought it was funny that the breed of dog seemed to be part human.

"Damn straight they're part human," Mr. Doherty had said. "Smartest bastards you'll ever encounter." He leaned close to Sand and smiled. Through his teeth, Sand could smell his breath. It was surprisingly pleasant; there was even a little bit of a chocolate scent that made Sand wonder if he ate the leftover brownies from the cafeteria. Raising his eyes from Mr. Doherty's mouth, he saw that the man's eyes were different colors. He'd never noticed it before, but the right one was a light brown and the left one was grey. "They'll also tear your throat out if I tell them to," Mr. Doherty said. Sand had to remind himself that they'd been talking about his dogs.

Time moved strangely for Sand. Some moments seemed to simultaneously stop and stretch on forever, and he'd get lost in them. When he tried to think about how he'd explain it—no one asked, but just in case—he thought he'd say that it was like a whirlpool or a vortex or a tornado that he was getting sucked into. He'd enter through the big end, and time would slow down and he would have all these big thoughts and then he'd be popped out of the bottom and realize that only a second or two had passed. When he was a little kid he'd thought that everyone was like this, but then his sister began to pick him up from school every day and he had someone to talk to about things, at least for the length of time it took to drive to where their mother was staying and then back home. She asked him where he disappeared to when his eyes went all blank for a second. Actually, that's what Sand had wanted her to ask. What she'd really said was:

"Don't do that. You're freaking me out."

"What am I doing?" Sand had asked.

"You look like Mom when your eyes go fuzzy like that. Stop it."

"Okay," he'd said. And he tried to stop it. He didn't think he was very successful.

*

Sand reached his house. The car was still in the driveway. Standing too long hurt; the sidewalk was just as hot as the street. He jumped from one foot to the other, running in place and feeling like a loony. A little grin spread across his face, silly, giddy. He wiped his hand across it before climbing up the porch of his house, erasing the smile from his lips like chalk from a blackboard.

He tried opening the front door but it was locked. His father always kept it locked now. So he had to knock. He gave the family knock that he'd invented after seeing a family on TV use one. Knock-knock-tap-tap-tap-knock-wait-knock. He could finally stand in the shade cast by the eaves of the house. Nobody came to the door and he knocked again, louder. Still nothing. He went to the window and shaded his eyes, trying to see in, but the blinds were drawn.

"What are you doing here?" It was Mrs. Ford who lived across the street. She was the mother of five little children, three of which were triplets. The triplets fascinated Sand and he sometimes went over to play with them. They were identical, three boys who were only two years old. The older girls liked Sand and he played with them, too, but what he really liked was playing with the little boys' Legos and watching them looking at each other like images in a weird mirror. But it was nice to be liked by the five- and six-year-old girls, too. It was just nice to be liked. Mrs. Ford liked him, too, he thought.

She had a bag of groceries in her arms and her mouth was hanging open.

"Hi, Mrs. Ford." Sand had learned to be polite. He sometimes had the urge to say "please" and "thank you" even when he wasn't asking or receiving anything.

"Sam—your sister and your dad went already, Sammy. I thought you were with them." Mrs. Ford never got Sand's name right. He never corrected her.

Sand looked at the car that was in the driveway. He looked back at Mrs. Ford. He looked back at the car. When she didn't seem to get it, he spoke. "How did they get there? The car's here."

"Oh." Mrs. Ford tried to brush a strand of hair out of her face and almost dropped the brown paper bag of groceries. The neighborhood grocery store apparently didn't realize that paper and plastic bags were big social no-nos. At school, they taught Sand that recycling, composting, and bringing your own carrier bags to the grocery store were all good things that everyone should do. There was one particular teacher who made Sand feel deeply guilty, as if it was he, personally, who was destroying the planet. Sucked out the bottom of the whirlpool, Sand focused again on Mrs. Ford's moving lips. "...boyfriend took them."

This was not good news. Now the big man that Sand didn't like was going to be there too. Sand hadn't really thought about it, but he guessed he should have seen it coming. His sister had been seeing the big man for a while now. Ever since the middle of the last school year. Sand wondered whether the big man had refused to go and pick Sand up from school. It was no secret that he didn't like Sand. He told Sand's sister that she shouldn't be driving "the kid" around all the time, and that "the kid" could walk. It wasn't such a big town, after all.

Sand agreed with him. He'd tried to tell him so—that he liked running more than car drives anyway, and that his sister would save gas if she drove him less and that they would both help the planet. But the big man had shot him a dirty look, wrapped his arm around Sand's sister, and steered her outside so that he could smoke.

The Home wasn't so far away. Sand could run there, too. He wasn't sure if he should, though. His father, his sister, and his sister's boyfriend would remember him eventually, and then maybe they'd call the landline, and if Sand didn't pick up they might worry.

Mrs. Ford was still standing in front of him. She was staring across the street at the way Mr. Cress was mowing his lawn. Sand saw her lips moving and he wondered if she was muttering under her breath about how bad for the environment the lawnmower was.

"Mrs. Ford?"

"Yes, dear?"

"May I have the spare key to the house, please? So that I can get inside?"

"Sure, of course, hon. Just let me get inside and I'll look for it. I know your dad gave me a spare once, but I'm not sure which drawer I put it in..."

Sand held his arms out and offered to take the groceries from her, but she smiled, shook her head vaguely, and waddled to the house. Her wide hips swayed, taut against her bright blue knee-length dress. Sand always thought that she looked like the comfiest person in the world. When he saw her hugging her children, he imagined it must feel like having a pillow hug you, and it made him jealous. Mrs. Ford never hugged him.

The little boys were in the house already. They had a babysitter who picked them up from nursery school when Mrs. Ford had errands to run. The girls had a lot of after-school classes—Sand never understood why they wanted extra time at school, but they apparently did, since they both took gymnastics, ballet and pottery—so they weren't home yet. The boys were watching a car race on TV with the babysitter, a college student who Sand knew was a friend of his sister's boyfriend, but who couldn't have been more different from him. For one thing, the babysitter liked Sand.

"Hey, Samboy. Have I introduced you to the wonders of NASCAR yet?"

Sand shook his head, but he smiled, too. He was worried and tense, but he wanted the babysitter to keep liking him.

"I'll just be a minute!" Mrs. Ford called from the kitchen. Sand followed her there and peered through the door. He saw her rummaging through drawers fast, her hands swiping around like the man at the gas station who wiped Sand's father's car window with a rag. Creeping back to the living room, Sand stood next to where the babysitter was sprawled on the couch, his boots hanging over the edge so they didn't actually get anything dirty. The triplets were all in the same position on the floor, heads leaning on their arms and tilted to the left. They gasped whenever the babysitter gasped, and made "oooh" noises whenever he did. Sand didn't think they knew or cared what was going on.

He watched the race for a few minutes while Mrs. Ford seemed, by the level of noise, to overturn every drawer in the big kitchen. The commentator on TV had a nasally voice, and he kept shouting words that Sand didn't understand. The cars onscreen zoomed by so fast that they could only be seen for a second from each camera. Sand didn't get why the babysitter was so entranced by the race. What was the point of driving in circles? Wasn't the point of going fast to get somewhere?

"Here you go, Sam. Are you sure you wouldn't rather stay here? Won't you be all by yourself at home?" Mrs. Ford asked this in a way that made Sand understand that she didn't want him to stay. She was just offering to be polite.

"No, thank you, Mrs. Ford," he said. He took the spare key from her, waved goodbye to the boys and the babysitter, and took the short way across the garden fence to get home.

The key stuck in the lock. It fit, but it wouldn't turn. Sand tried taking it out and putting it back in, but it still didn't work. He went round to the back door and tried it there. He knew both locks were the same, but he still hoped it would work.

It didn't. Mrs. Ford must have given him the wrong key. He didn't want to go back and tell her so, though. He could already smell the dinner she was cooking through the open kitchen window. It was meatloaf. Sand loved meatloaf, but he'd recently become a vegetarian. His stomach rumbled at the scent, and he decided that he would run to the Home after all. If he went back to Mrs. Ford now, she'd invite him over for dinner and he wasn't sure he'd be able to resist her delicious meatloaf.

He left his backpack on the porch, and put the key next to it, but took his shoes with him. They'd yelled at him once, at the Home, for coming in without shoes. He took a deep breath, tried to convince his stomach that it wasn't hungry, and began to run.

His street ended in a small park, and Sand ran through it, wincing at the gravel underfoot. The swings moved a little as he passed, as if ghost children had just jumped off them. A squirrel zoomed up a tree, frightened, and Sand looked over his shoulder, trying to see how high the critter was clambering. When he faced front, he realized he'd begun to zigzag, forcing a woman on a bicycle to swerve. She said a bad word after she passed and Sand heard it.

He grinned into the wind and closed his eyes. It was a game he played with himself, seeing how many steps he could take without chickening out and looking to make sure he wasn't going to knock into anything. His goal was to run the entire way with his eyes closed someday.

It was feasible. He knew the way well enough. Over the summer vacation, when his sister had been working mornings, he and his father had walked to the Home together every day. When they'd reached the park, his father had always taken his hand, and they'd swing their arms in tandem and match their steps in an unspoken dance that they both knew without needing to learn it. Sand loved his father's big hand and the way it spasmed sometimes, squeezing his own littler one tightly but just for about as long as it took Sand to blink. His father typed all day, and he had to exercise his hands every night. He wrote opinion pieces for the local newspaper and also participated in several online publications for which he wasn't paid very well. On Monday and Wednesday nights he also tended bar, but he never allowed Sand to come with him. "When you're older," he always said. "Maybe."

Opening his eyes, Sand was proud of himself; he'd judged right. He was just leaving the park. He ran down street after street until he reached the highway, which was the only place he had to stop at. Everywhere else was so quiet that he could hear a car approaching from two blocks away. But the highway was different, dangerous. It always seemed unreal to him as he stood on its shoulder and waited for a lull in the traffic. Even though he could feel the passage of the cars in the whooshing wind they made, it didn't seem possible for anything to go so fast that it became a blur before his eyes, like the cars on TV. One day over the summer he'd almost convinced himself that the zooming vehicles were just mirages. He'd wanted to walk onto the highway and watch the images dissipate or go right through him, like the projections of films in science class at school did. He'd held out a long stick into the nearest lane first, though, just to make sure it was really safe. It had broken when the next car, a little yellow one with a smiling grille, drove by with an extended honk. The person sitting next to the driver had leaned out and yelled. Sand had heard her voice echoing in his ears for days afterwards, saying horrible things he didn't understand.

The highway wasn't so busy now, and he barely managed to catch his breath before running across it. Cars that saw him from a distance leaned on their horns, but Sand was already gone, running down the slope on the other side of the highway, a shortcut that led to the back of the Home's grounds. He climbed up and over the brick wall, scraping his hands and straining his short nails, and jumped down onto the grass on the other side. It hadn't been cut in a while. It spread out, appearing velvety-green and lush but actually dry, scratchy and tough. If there were little gnomes living in the grass, Sand thought they'd see the grass like humans saw wheat fields, sticking up proudly and waving just a bit sometimes in a friendly greeting. With a few careful steps, he made a crop circle out of the place where he'd landed. If there really were any gnomes nearby, he hoped it would give them something to get excited about.

There were a few people walking around the lawn, pushing wheelchairs, but none of them really looked at him as he walked towards the Home. Maybe they didn't see him because he was small for his age. Or they saw him and then forgot.

He knelt to put on his socks and shoes when he got to the Home's back, where he couldn't go in because then they'd know he'd climbed over the wall again. The socks felt like towels straight out of the dryer. His feet pulsed in protest. The shoes were too tight; the laces were cruel ropes binding their footy prisoners.

Gingerly, uncomfortably, on mittened feet, Sand walked around the perimeter of the grounds, staying close to the wall, so that he ended up in front. Yes, there was the big man's car, with the big man sitting in it and smoking out the window and nodding his head at the music he was no doubt blasting. Sand waved at him, but his sister's boyfriend didn't wave back.

The double doors of the big building were made of glass and Sand could see himself grow larger as he walked towards them. His walk looked unnatural, and he noticed for the first time that his right shoulder slumped lower than his left, as if he were holding something heavy on it. He looked down at his right hand to make sure there wasn't anything there.

He reached out to open the door but jumped back as it swung toward him and he was faced with the horrific sight of an old man, hairless and toothless with his mouth hanging open. The man's eyes were empty, staring right through everything into something black or maybe something very white. Sand felt the urge to wave a hand in front of that face and see if he'd get a reaction, but the wheelchair the old man was slumped in began to move, pushed by a nurse with breakable little chicken legs whose big stomach and hefty bosom looked like they came from another body. A misplaced breeze swept by and a shiver crept up Sand's spine as he stared after them.

He walked through the still open door and into the overheated Home. The smell was similar to that of the cafeteria at school, except that underneath it was the antiseptic, too-clean scent of dentists' chairs. The staircase he climbed was the only place that seemed to retain any dust, which made sense, Sand thought, because nobody used it. The people who lived there used the big, stainless steel elevators.

He didn't notice it, but he slowed down the nearer he came to room 203. He was distracted by the smallest things: he walked up to the wall to inspect a fly and bent down to examine a patch of dirt on the floor that he thought might be blood. The details of the wallpaper were fascinating and he traced his fingers along a blue thread until it curled in on itself. But there was no avoiding it; he'd run all the way here and now he had to go in.

He stood in the doorway for a moment and watched the tableau in front of him. There was his father, his white hair still covering most of his head, sitting in a big chair that made him look small. He had his legs crossed tightly. There was his sister, her back ramrod straight even though she sat on the empty bed. And there, by the window, was his mother, younger than many of the people who lived in the Home, her red hair faded but still thick and long, braided down her back. She was the first who noticed Sand come in.

"Hello! Are you lost?" she asked, her voice still the same. Amicable, friendly. She could have been teasing him.

"Hi, Mom," Sand said, his voice barely audible. His father and sister turned to look at him, but his mother was already looking out the window again.

"Where were you?" His sister spoke quickly, biting her words like hard crackers. "We waited for you at school and you never showed up. You told me you finished at one."

"No. I finished at two-fifteen today."

"That's not what you told me this morning. God, you're so irresponsible, can't you just—"

"I did too tell you this morning! I told you that tomorrow I finish at one—"

"Can you not fight, please?" Sand's father's voice was resonant and filled the room. The siblings closed their mouths with the same deliberate folding-up of their lips. "Thank you. We're here, Sand's here, everything's fine. Right?" On this last word he turned to his wife. She looked at him, a little bemused, but nodded with a now-familiar vacant smile.

"Right," she said. "Look at the bees in the window box. Did you know that bees can't—shouldn't be able to—oh, what is it, I just had it." Her face collapsed, and the crow's feet near her eyes smoothed over as the smile disappeared and her brow furrowed instead. "Damn it, what is that word? I just had it! Bees are too heavy to. To."

"Fly?" Sand went to join her at the window.

"Yes!" The smile reappeared, hitching itself up automatically like a fat man pulling up his pants. "Thank you. You're a nice boy, Charlie. I always loved you, Charlie. You know that, right?"

Sand caught his mother's hand and whispered, "Yes. Yes. I love you, too."

His sister rolled her eyes and got up. "He's not Charlie, Mom! He's Sand. Saaaand. Your son, remember? Jesus Christ, this is a fucking farce. I'm going to go wait in the car."

"She seems like a very angry young woman, doesn't she?" Sand's mother said, and turning back to the window to watch the bees, she clasped her hands together in her lap again.

Sand and his father didn't look at each other. There were days when it was easier. They were becoming increasingly few and far between.

The room hummed softly around them as the central-heating unit clicked on. Sand removed his shoes and took the empty place on the bed where his sister had sat. The spot was still warm. He peeled his socks off and threw them onto the floor. His father heaved a sigh and scratched his head. The long afternoon was just beginning.

Winners of StoryQuarterly's 2016 Nonfiction Prize

Judged by Meghan Daum

Wendy Call
Apothecarium
Winner

J.L. Cooper
The Sages of West 47th Street
First Runner-up

Sarah McColl
How Sad, How Lovely
Second Runner-up

Wendy Call

Apothecarium

Audacious

> <u>*To stop blood*</u>*: Rub oil of Turpentine and the white of an Egg to make a paste. Put it on pledgets of Muskrat fir and apply it to the body part.*

The year before I was born, my mother, a math teacher, was called into her principal's office for piercing her ears. Her high school students had come to class with inflamed and putrid earlobes, after pushing needles through them, DIY. Still, other girls wanted to follow their painful lead. My mother marched those girls down to the school nurse's office, where the nurse passed a needle through a flame, then an alcohol swab, and then through their flesh and into half a raw potato. My mother wanted to be fashionable, too, so she sat for her own hot-needle-raw-potato treatment.

The principal gave my mother a warning: Those girls could do as they wished, but she was a teacher and a married woman and should not engage in such behavior.

Bandaged

> <u>*For Contusion or Laceration*</u>*: Take Meadow moss and fry it in Acetum and put it on, as hot as can be borne.*

In many photographs of my mother as a girl, a skinned knee grins between her cuffed socks and pleated skirt. In spite of my grandmother's attempts to raise a good German-American-Lutheran daughter, my mother hurtled forward through childhood, often landing on her knees.

I, on the other hand, worried my way through childhood, flying through life only via the words of Alcott, Blume, Keene, and Ingalls Wilder. I lay for hours on itchy sofa upholstery or cool beanbag plastic, the world spinning forward without me.

One afternoon as I lay in the living room clutching a Nancy Drew mystery, the front wheel of my brother's three-speed hit a rock and pitched him forward over the handlebars. A metal brake handle skewered his inner thigh. He dragged himself to the nearest cement front stoop; the neighbor called my mother and told her to come and get the bleeding nine-year-old from her front porch, on the far side of her closed front door.

Mom dressed my brother's weeping wound every day with careful, muscled fingers, while I watched, fascinated. My brother could not bear even to glance at it.

Concealed

> Canker Quinsey: *Take Garlicks, Cloves, Breast Milk. Simmer them together and let the Patient take half a Spoonful.*

Mom won Michigan's statewide flute-playing championships for a dozen years, then got married and put her flute in its blue velvet-lined case. It stayed there for a decade.

When she discovered she was pregnant with me, in the winter of 1968, she knew enough to hide it from her school's principal. At that Kentucky public high school, to be a married teacher was marginally acceptable, to be a mother was not. Loose dresses carried her to the end of the school year, five months along.

She noticed one of her students wearing loose dresses, too, and one afternoon, five years before Roe v. Wade, two pregnant women—one 26 and married, one 16 and not—faced each other across a desk. Neither said anything, just shared a long gaze. A few weeks later, another teacher would whisper to my mother that the janitor had found a newborn baby, several hours dead, in the girls' bathroom garbage can.

Diuretic

> *Juniper: In a Dose, 1 or 2 purges. 6 or 8 Stimulates. Is good in pains from the Gravel or Stone. Forcibly Deterges the Urinary Passages.*

In the summer of 1987, I came home one afternoon from my summer job as a day-camp counselor and found a note from Mom on the kitchen counter. She was driving herself to a hospital in Washington, DC., two hours away, to have kidney stones lasered out of her belly. My brother was too young to drive and I had not yet learned. My father was working on a military base one thousand miles away. The next day, I stood in the day camp's stuffy office trailer with the phone to my ear, listening to Mom's soothing voice, slightly hollow in her hospital room. I don't remember regretting that I could not go and visit Mom, nor worrying what would happen if she didn't return in two days, as she'd promised.

I had good parents graced with good luck. That is to say, I felt confident that everything would be fine, because everything always was.

Ease

> *For Canker or Thrush: Take Borax, Botanical Armenian, Saffron, fresh Butter & mix it well. Then give the bigness of a small Bean. Assidously.*

To hear my mother tell it, her two children came exactly when she wanted them, exactly as she had hoped: one skinny blue-eyed girl and one pudgy brown-eyed boy, less than two years apart. But I know that I arrived after a bitter twenty-hour labor, through the night and into the following afternoon: a fearful baby who refused to sleep, cried too much, and screamed for her father while he was away at work.

My mother and father went on a picnic in Fairmont Park to celebrate Dad's second Father's Day, on a Sunday summer solstice in 1970. Dad read the newspaper aloud to me while Mom grilled chicken. Our family of three finished up the picnic and Mom's labor pains began. We drove to the military hospital and shortly before midnight became a family of four.

Faith

> *<u>Lockyers Pills</u>: Rx Take Antimon & Sal. Niter & one ounce Charcoal. Pulverize then put it into a red hot Crucible then turn into a brass Vessel. Put it into Water Nine Days then dry it in the Sun + make it into Pills.*

One Sunday during Mom's senior year of high school, her Lutheran minister preached from the pulpit that a vote for Richard Nixon was what God wanted. My mother slunk low in her pew. Five years later, in that same church, she would marry a Free Methodist preacher's grandson, a soon-to-be-military man. With that, she divorced the Missouri Synod. She taught Sunday School every week until I was twelve, when she began to suspect that she might not believe everything that she was teaching. Her spirit slipped out of her body, along with her beliefs. For weeks, she spent much of each day in bed. I knew that something was wrong when Mom's flute returned to its case.

Gimpy

> *Take Virgins wax & Olive Oil & 4 ounces of Mercury. Boil them in a New glazen Earthen Vessel one Hour + stir it all the Time. This is good for old sore Legs that have been sore a long time.*

My father is a runner; I am a walker; my brother, a driver; and my mother, a sitter. Growing up, Mom had been a baton twirler, marching band member, actor, and jitterbug dancer. Then she got married, had two babies, and took a seat. She played her flute in half a dozen community orchestras, stitched a hundred quilts, played the dulcimer in countless duets, sewed all our clothes, made curtains for half a dozen military-base houses. Her hands moved constantly but the rest of her body stayed still.

She complained of the bone spurs in her feet, the stiffness in her back, and most of all the arthritis in her hands. In the throes of menopause, a doctor gave her a massive cortisone shot to the spine. Oh, how wonderful it was to move without the burning, pulsing pain. But there was a strict lifetime limit to those injections, so they stopped. With her cancer diagnosis, Mom suddenly had an uninterrupted lifetime supply.

Hopeful

> *To the calous apply a Toad once in two hours until five have been applied then wash the Calous with a dilution of Indigo Root steeped in Cyder.*

Perhaps there was something in that chemotherapy elixir that would help some people. But we came to understand that Mom's tumor was far beyond such a medieval solution. Still, my mother's oncologist tried to convince us that this was a sound equation:

Take a four-to-six-month life expectancy. Add weekly Gemcitabine and Tarceva chemo drip, which adds four days per week of crushing nausea and fatigue. That adds two months to lifespan.

Mom's oncologist must have been one of those students who mastered biology without ever quite mastering arithmetic. Mom, a retired math teacher, knew better.

Invisible

> <u>*Rustica*</u>*: Stimulant, Antiarthritic, Diuretic... An Infusion taken in a large Draught of warm Water proves Emetic.*

It was a simple problem, a straightforward blockage, and yet it seemed to have no solution. A loop of tumor squeezed shut my mother's small intestine and so everything became emetic. Nothing could pass; she vomited everything.

Jaundiced

> <u>*For the Jaundice*</u>*: Take Juniper Bark & Boil it in Water sufficient to make it a strong Tea. Add Rum. Let the Patient take of it verry freely.*

When I was in junior high school in the nadir of the 1980s, rushing with all my friends toward feathered hair and checkered Vans, my mother rushed with all of her friends toward the book *Color Me Beautiful*. It was one of the few fads (along with yellow-ribbon-pins for the U.S. hostages in Iran and double-pierced ears) that Mom and I both adopted during my pre-teen years. She and I excitedly flipped past the book's anomalously ugly cover to learn that Mom was an autumn and I, a summer. I was to wear sage green and Mom, olive. I was to wear bubble gum and Mom, coral. My tone bowed toward pink and hers tilted to yellow. (No one ever thought to wonder about my brother's season, but I suspect he's an autumn, like Mom.)

A quarter-century after Mom and I colored ourselves beautiful, we sat in her oncologist's office. The doctor turned to me and said, "Your mother isn't yellow." From the first hints of her cancer, when brown urine was traced back to a bile duct pinched shut, to the later stages, with raging diabetes, the doctors and nurses said to Mom, over and over, "But, you aren't yellow."

Had she been yellower sooner, might something have been done?

Karmic

> *For the Diabetes: Take Hogs hoofs Torrified and Pulverize them and put it into Rum and Molasses. One or two spoonfuls at a time, as the patient can bear it.*

As my mother grew weaker, I grew more hesitant to leave her alone. My brother and father continued to work fulltime, their jobs sometimes taking them far from home. A friend who lived thirty miles from my parents invited me over for Moroccan tagine and French wine, insisting that I needed time away from Mom's sickbed. At my friend's table, in a haze of saffron and cinnamon, worry melted from my mind.

I pulled my mother's Camry back into my parents' garage more than an hour after I'd promised to be home, cursing myself. I paused at my parents' bedroom door and heard my mother's even breathing. Moved on. I reached my own bedroom door and found a note in Mom's careful script: "Please bring me ginger ale. Blood sugar is low. I cannot walk out there."

Tremors of shame and fear and something else—an emotion I could not then name, but would later come to think of as the anticipation of grief—filled me. The next moment I remember was bending over her bed, a fizzing dixie cup in my hand.

"Mom?" I touched her shoulder lightly.

"Hi, sweetheart," she said. I had mistaken her even breathing for sleep because she was so thinly conscious.

My hand trembled as I passed the cold Vernor's to her.

Luck

> *Billious Pills: Rx Take five Parts Ipeacac, one Part Calomet, Gum Arabic Sufficient for pills.*

Mom married at twenty-two; Dad was the third to propose to her. They had met on the steps of the Big Rapids, Michigan post office. She was leaving just as he arrived with a letter for his girlfriend in Reed City. I can imagine the scene, though no photograph records it: My mother clutching her books, her petticoated skirt flouncing at her knees, long curly ponytail bouncing down her back. My father looking up from farther down the stairs, his pants ironed but shiny from wear. He stares at her from behind thick eyeglasses, his face square and earnest, a love letter to someone else clutched in one hand. Within a week, he had asked Mom on a date.

Matriarchal

> *Sal Absinthii: A Solution drunk in Bed is Sudorific + by walking in the air it is Diuretic. It is a gentle Cathartic.*

Kidney stones struck my brother during a Navy Reserve duty weekend. The doctors said he needed an emergency appendectomy, but they were wrong. With the second attack, and the third and the fourth and the fifth, he knew exactly what to expect: three days of excruciating pain and a five-thousand-dollar medical bill.

Kidney stones struck me on Christmas morning while I was living in a small Mexican town. I called a friend and told him I might be dying, because I couldn't think of any other way to describe how I felt. He told me to walk around the corner to a doctor's home office. I found the doctor playing on the floor with his two young children. He calmly escorted me into the examination room just off his living room and I vomited into a waste basket. His wife emptied a syringe of morphine into my arm and he gave me an ultrasound. He explained the gravel lodged in my kidney's calyx, then handed me a prescription for Cipro and a bill for twenty dollars. The friend I had called brought over a recipe for medicinal tea: cornsilk and horsetail and honey. I slept off the morphine in my front-yard hammock.

Neurotic

> *Small Pox and Scarlet Fever: 1 grain Sulfate of Zinc and 1 grain of Foxglove and ½ teaspoonful Sugar. Mix with Water. Take a spoonful every hour.*

During the months that my mother was ill—or, I should say, during the months that we knew my mother was ill—I sometimes felt that if I were to lose my grip (on the steering wheel, or the kitchen counter, or my mother's shoulder) I would pitch forward or backward out of my world and into some parallel universe. In that other dimension, I would not be able to negotiate reality, but only witness its cruelties. Be acted upon, without offering an equal and opposite resistance.

I thought of this parallel universe as a physical manifestation of the inevitable; I found it calming. I now understand that I was confusing my realization of inevitability with my acceptance of it. It was no such thing.

Oblivious

> *To kill a bad Humor: Take Lye and Wheat Bran. Boil them together. It is very Sweating.*

My mother's illness advanced far faster than did anyone's understanding of it. Some friends and family never came to visit; others came quite late. My brother's long-since ex-girlfriend, whom my parents still adored, visited only after my mother was confined to bed. Mom turned to face her, eyes and mouth blank and round. Black bile welled at the corner of her lips, dripping down her cheek. The ex-girlfriend rose from her bedside chair, eyes stormy with horror.

For two thousand years we believed our bodies to contain four humors, or liquids, in balance: yellow bile, black bile, blood, and phlegm. "Melancholic plethora," a serious illness, was an excess of dryness, of black bile, of the humor of autumn.

Palliative

> *For the Dropsy: Take yellow Hemlock buds, twigs, or Bark that grows on high gravelly knolls. Boil it in Water so as to make a strong Tea. Let the Patient take of it freely.*

The last time we visited my mother's general practitioner, she informed us that Mom was badly dehydrated, wrote out a prescription for rehydration fluids, and walked away. None of the phlebotomists or nurses could pop a needle into Mom's dry veins. Too much black bile; too little blood.

We waited. We were ignored. Eventually, we were sent home with instructions for Mom to drink as much Gatorade as she could stand.

Quixotic

> *Take live Mads and apply them till they are dead, then take them off + repeat until the pain is released.*

What we crave from pain is release. Escape. To free oneself from its clutches, wriggle out from its talons' vise-grip. Even terrible solutions—the buzz of biting flies, the slice of a knife—seem far preferable.

My mother accepted her diagnosis of metastatic cancer with German-American fortitude. She kept notes from her doctor's appointments neatly organized in a three-ring notebook, lined up medications on the counter, made a list of craft and home-repair projects to finish. I quit my job and moved cross-country to my parents' home in North Carolina. My brother drove the four miles from his house to Mom and Dad's once or twice a week, bringing pots of soup and bags of fruit.

Ravaged

> *Take half a Pint of Lemon Juice & put into it one new laid hens Egg shell and let it stand untill the Egg is consumed. Add Loaf Sugar. This is for Cough & Fever.*

Nearly every week, my mother and I attended a support group meeting for cancer patients and their caregivers. My father attended once. Most of the male cancer patients attended with their wives or daughters. Most of the female cancer patients attended alone. My mother was fierce about being there, even when she had to go the bathroom to throw up first. Even when she had to keep a kidney-shaped emesis basin in her handbag.

Soothing

> *For sore Mouth: Take Rose leaves and steep them in Spring Water & then put in Sugar of Lead & Armenian botanical. This is good for little children or adults if they have sore Mouth or the like.*

At the support group meetings, patients casually mentioned major abdominal surgery that snipped out several feet of intestine and calmly debated whether their eventual casket should be open or closed. They joked about the excruciating boredom of vomiting all day long. But their most bitter and loudest complaint was how much their mouths hurt. They compared brands of lozenges and baby-teething cream.

Chemotherapy attacks fast-dividing cells, whether they are in a tumor or the inner cheek. The latter are definitely doomed. The former? We can only hope.

One of the last things I did for my mother, when she could no longer talk, or stand up, or swallow food, or bend over the toilet to vomit, was swab water inside her mouth with a tiny pink sponge on a stick.

Terminal

> *Gum. Tracamahac: Used as Plasters to any part of the Body for Pains of any kind, it is Subtle + dissolves Tumours. In fumigation it is for Hysterical Fits.*

The doctors could point to Mom's tumor on CT scans, locate it precisely, biopsy and measure and image and map its source and boundaries. Yet nothing could be done. It was both vibratingly obvious and entirely mysterious. Or maybe not. Mystery implies continuance—the luxury of wonder.

Scratch that. There was no mystery.

Ulterior

> *For Uterine Hemorage: Sauchar Saturn Mastic & a Tbsp Good Brandy.*

My mother believed her hysterectomy killed her, it just took a while. After years of heavy periods that lasted for weeks, she had her uterus removed at a military teaching hospital. During her surgery more than a dozen aspiring doctors filed through the operating room, gazing deep into my mother's abdomen, her organs bared and splayed for their inspection. Perhaps someone, on his or her earnest path to doctorhood, bruised one silent, angry organ. My mother, entirely calm, explained her hypothesis to me as we sat in the oncology waiting room on a beautiful summer day.

Vitriolic

> *For a Breeding sore: Take Terebinth and Chamberlee. Simmer them together and thicken it up with Rye Meal.*

I complained to my mother that my brother wasn't helping us enough. He rarely visited. He wouldn't go to the hospital, sending his wife instead. Mom reminded me that Alan had a fulltime job. I reminded her that I'd had a job, too, but I'd quit it three days after her diagnosis. I was an asshole to point this out, I know. I think back to those moments standing by my mother's side, those moments that we already knew were ticking away to zero. I mourn those I wasted. Or worse, filled with breeding bitterness.

Wishful

> *Take Quicksilver, one part. Nitrous acid, two parts. Hog's Lard, twelve parts. Stir them together in a marble Mortar.*

After just one Gemcitabine-Tarceva chemo session, my mother waved off bags and needles in favor of hospice. My father pushed the hospice brochures to the far corner of the coffee table and spent days at the computer and on the phone, searching for clinical trials.

Two days before my mother died, my brother went to an ice hockey game. Mom hadn't left her bed in a week; her breathing had taken on the tone and cadence that I would later learn is called "the death rattle."

X Chromosomal

> *Take Ens Veneris one Part, Gum Myrrh two Parts, gram Opium. Febrifies Cramp of the Uterus.*

My mom and a hospice social worker sat in the living room one day, autumn sun sprawled on the plush carpeting. It was the social worker's first visit; she cheerfully asked about Mom's life. I sat in the next room, tired of these interviews.

No, my mother replied to one question, no grandchildren. The young social worker expressed some mild, regretful surprise and my mother said, carefully, "I have made my peace with that."

Neither my brother nor I had any interest in having children. Neither of us believes this has any connection to our own childhoods; we are both grateful for our freedom to choose. Several months after my mother's funeral, my sister-in-law told my brother and me that our mother had once asked her: Did her children not want children because she had been a bad mother? My mother gave us the freedom to disappoint her.

Yearning

> *Doc[t] Hank's Rheumatism Physic: Rx Take Butter Nut Bark and White Ash, put into two quarts of water, boil it down to one pint, add Brandy and Loaf Sugar. Let it stand.*

One day, deep into Mom's illness, I came home from some errand. I stepped to the front door and heard my mother playing her dulcimer. It stopped me, one foot on the top step, one hand on the screen-door handle. The sound of home.

Mom had always worried that her rheumatism would eventually make it impossible for her to play her flute and dulcimer. Cancer and cortisone injections cured that worry. Still, she rarely played after her diagnosis. Perhaps it was more difficult to imagine the loss of music than loss of life. How could her tone-deaf husband and children possibly understand?

Zenith

> *For a Cancer: Take the juice of Cocum Leaves, Sweet Cecily Roots and ginseng Roots & put it on a plate & Set it in the Sun till it evaporates to the consistency of a Plaister. Then put on a Plaster just big enough to cover the Cancer & keep it on & in a few days the Cancer will come out by the Roots.*

I once saw this epitaph on a nineteenth-century North Carolina headstone: *How little we appreciate a mother's love while living.* The stone was so weather-worn that the word "mother" had become "moth."

*

Each of the twenty-six parts of this essay begins with a recipe (sometimes abbreviated, but not edited) that I transcribed from a mid-nineteenth century apothecary's notebook.

J.L. Cooper

The Sages of West 47th Street

I had no category, no summation for what I felt in the presence of Jerome. My unsettled thoughts flowed to him unfiltered, and returned in a gentle rain. He'd offer an irony or a kindness to anyone around. The effect was to invite us fellow taxi drivers to breathe a little slower, look up at the sky, and smile at our confusion.

It was 1974, in Manhattan, when cabbies were killed for a pocketful of cash or less. Most of the veteran drivers were depleted, refused to work the nights, and locked themselves in a vault of untold stories. Their faces were etched with trenches, like they couldn't use their faces anymore to register expressions, even if they felt one coming on.

I was among the new drivers. A black leather jacket might have helped me look the part, but I didn't own one. California was stamped across my presence: longhaired blond kid, wearing tennis shoes in February. Blending was a futile thought that never made it to a full thought anyway, since the main persuasion was hunger for the night to come and take away the shadows. We gathered outside the garage at shape-up in late afternoon, on West 47th Street, waiting for our yellow cabs to be assigned.

Jerome had a thick brown jacket and deep brown eyes to match. I never saw the top of his head since he always wore a Greek fisherman's cap. He never told his past, so I made one up: escapee from a cult, and before that another escape from a family that expected too much. In between, maybe a bit of graduate school. Theology, I thought, or physics. He balanced curiosity with calmness and the mixture spilled easily to the world, but the quality I remember most was his ability to speak directly to the anxiety in a person.

On a shivering day, after witnessing a string of inhumanities on the streets, I told him I couldn't tell the difference between the dread stirred up by the wind or the urgency of sirens all around.

"Is it me, or is the city falling?" I asked. He seemed to know me from another realm.

"If I were you, and maybe I am, I'd remind myself of the good in my intentions. We start out thinking we're just driving a person where they want to go. But it's not that simple. Half the time we take them to a place of resignation, where they're trapped but don't know it, or flat out sad in the going. Passengers think they're unseen, but we see them if we look. We think we're faceless to them, but they can see us too if they look. I used to worry about what to say. I think the better question is what version of myself to bring. Then I'll know what to say. I hope you make fifty bucks in tips tonight. Be safe." I wished him the same and more.

A few words from Jerome could break our isolation. Being in the enclosed space of a car, with dozens of people in random succession is completely unpredictable: one minute a jitterbug, the next minute Brahms. Jerome was a lingering benevolence, concrete at the same time, a chain smoker and a regular guy. We all feared being shot or robbed, but some of us feared futility. Jerome fought it by playing his boom box on low volume, ballads from the South, blues or Bach, or dance music. He'd close his eyes and go right where he wanted. You can't teach that.

A few weeks after I came on the scene, a fellow named Richard joined us: tall sphinx with wild hair and a trademark scarf. It was debatable how much of him was there. He'd listen to our stories of the night before and fix himself to talk, but hesitation got to him and he cocked his head to somewhere far. Like me, he was still a little bewildered. None of us asked how our life paths led to driving a cab. It didn't seem important. We were an assortment, marbles in a jar.

I suppose I told my story out of need for acceptance, how I ended up driving a cab within a week of arriving in the city, all because nobody stopped me. I covered up my ignorance by asking customers what route they would like to take if the trip wasn't a straight shot. It's not like anyone said, *thanks for asking, but you really ought to know that.* It worked surprisingly well.

I'd hitchhiked from California and stayed with a college friend on the Upper West Side, pausing on an eastward drift toward Europe. The city had a taste I couldn't name, a gritty, crumbling persistence, nothing like my homes in Southern California and San Francisco. Trains blew a hot gale through choking tunnels. Some of the subway clocks were broken, but folks didn't look up to notice. Except for bits of space in parks, and the grey surrounding waters, New York City was a vertical cacophony, grinding in shrill collisions, like brakes wearing out on a city bus that nobody planned to fix.

I had no preconception, was running out of money, then an idea came to me the way hands bring water to the face. I'll drive a taxi and become an anonymous seeker. It was time I read *Moby Dick* again, a time to find the *Ishmael* in me, sign up on *The Pequod*, so to speak. All my cars could be like ships, and all my rides and mates would fix themselves to turning pages. The city could be *The Whale*, appearing then submerging. I could be hidden and exposed, folding and unfolding in a surreal Kabuki Theatre.

But I found there's no such thing as anonymous, since part of myself was aware.

And thoughts are only kindling, bringing a small glow before the real fire comes. I didn't know cabbies were being killed with shocking frequency, or a vicious crime wave was strangling the city. I'd driven a cab for extra money during college in suburbs of Southern California, into the barrios and bad parts of Santa Ana, Huntington Beach, Garden Grove; places where cops didn't want to go. But New York City was electric, with constant rising pressure.

I was grateful my friend offered a mat and sleeping bag in a corner of his living room. Friends of his gypsy-like roommate came and went, including a petite pale woman, an artist, when bangs were in, and jeans were rarely washed. I had interest in her, can't say why, maybe her remoteness, then she clarified her two loves were barbiturates and art. She had a premonition she would die in the middle of a painting before the age of thirty. It was something close to a wish. She wouldn't let anyone see her work.

"Why not finish the painting first?" I asked, "then you can see if it's worth dying for, and keep on painting until one image begs for another." I was the optimist, I'm sure, but her romance was with despair and she locked herself in there.

"Don't try to save me. I'm never going to be your type, surf boy."

"Saving wasn't on my mind, but with eyes like yours, the sea isn't far behind." I had no idea why I said that to her.

"Fair enough," she said, making me briefly visible, and we made a deal of distance, the sum of our connection being a few long walks. We never kissed or spoke of darkness. I picked up smaller leaves from our path and placed them on a stump or bench. I don't know if she noticed. It was my way of being around her. Once, she pulled her hair back and let the winter sun come find her. It never seemed a good idea to tell her I was drawn to her quietness.

I had to let her go when I couldn't find a home in the dullness of her eyes, for she started adding alcohol to barbs. I wondered if I mattered to her in some unknowable way, or if her painting told. She went back to her studio across town, and wouldn't give me her number. I went off to drive a cab.

The graffiti outside was menacing and mocking, with saturated reds, black outlines, distorted faces with screaming tongues, defiance in a nest of locusts, a savage bouquet on a subway car. It was not the graffiti of the sixties, not the birth of a new age. Still, the art of the streets felt honest, a response to the decay.

Getting a hack license was an unexpected breeze. I got a NY driver's license, and went to a garage, where a grizzly bear, disguised as a man, handed me a form. One thing you learn in college is how to fill out a form. They were hard-up for drivers; there would be no interview. I took a written exam showing I had memorized locations of a few hospitals, train stations, airports, and had to pass their five-minute physical. Suddenly I had a sponsor, Chase Maintenance Corporation: a fleet to call my own. Nobody trained me or asked if I'd ever seen Grand Central Station, which I hadn't. I pulled out of the garage, made two inexplicable right turns, and opened my life to chance.

My brethren shared similar ironies. Even Richard offered a rare elaboration.

"I like people who stare out the window. If I'm alert, they'll sense it and say something important. It's amazing what people tell. Sometimes I think I'm not even a person to them, and they suddenly say they're going to take a trip, place a bet, change a relationship, or stop drinking. They need to say it out loud. I guess they want approval, or just a little recognition." He was the most careful driver of us all, fresh from Kansas City. It was easier to be gay in Manhattan.

Then there was Rico, who never said where he was originally from, except Jamaica was one of his stops. He drove like a maniac but he was the most skillful maniac I ever saw. Behind the wheel, he looked flat out mean, but he wasn't mean around us. He had a goal of speed, making it his personal challenge to get people to their destination in the shortest time possible.

"If you don't fill a space with where you're going, somebody else will." It was Rico's philosophy. He told of an altercation. "A guy hailed me and I got there first. Yeah, I cut across a few lanes. It's what we do. Shit man, I almost got killed for it. This guy got out of his cab and broke my window. What's wrong with this town?"

None of us wanted to remind him it's the one thing you don't do to a fellow driver, cut in front when you can see he's zeroing in on a fare. There's a backlog of rage waiting to be triggered. Some of it lives in cabbies. Nobody's immune.

Richard surprised us, summoning an oblique response. "If you drive too fast, your rider isn't going to tell."

"Tell what?" asked Rico.

"Tell their world. I collect worlds. They're always checking you out in the mirror, wondering if you're the guy to tell. They're surprised at what they say, and I'm surprised at what I say back. That's why I'm not in a hurry."

Rico debated the matter, "Fucking no money in that, but I get your point. I guess we're different. I want them to admire my skill."

"I want to see if I'm the one," said Richard. There was always a haiku brewing in him.

I, myself, never flipped anybody off driving a taxi, too afraid of the occasional madman, remembering newspaper stories about regular people getting murdered for far less on L.A. freeways, sometimes for driving too slow. Jerome didn't flip people off either, but his belief didn't come from fear. He had elevated awareness.

"In another life, you could be the guy smashing up windows, and no matter what damage you cause, you're going to be alone in that anger." He believed consciousness is recycled. You could say he took the long view. Nobody made us pause like Jerome.

But Marcos, fresh from Argentina, came close. He was just learning English, and all of us helped him along. "I don't like scare people," he added, pointing to his own chest. He could have meant it either way, or both ways, since everything Marcos said was like a mirror.

"Jesus tells me when I'm upset. I don't know it myself. Jesus helps me." At first I fancied him in the wrong profession, and thought he'd be great teaching children to nurture a garden. A person that humble can be chewed up by this job. Maybe not, maybe he was the best of us and could transform common rage into compassion. He made us want to protect him, the way he kept touching his chest, as if to anchor his heart to a tentative hope that others had a heart too. "I like drive," he said, putting his hands in the air at ten o'clock and two.

Jerome reassured him, "Good man." It was the perfect thing to say to Marcos, again and again. All of us nodded in agreement.

Emmanuel, from Nigeria, declared that driving a taxi was the best job on Earth. He had a new baby, proved it with pictures, and said his wife was proud of him. His health was excellent, his humor broad, his affection genuine, without a hint of cynicism. The rest of us had a bit of envy. He wondered why people complain about anything, like his customer who vented for twenty blocks about being passed over for promotion. Emmanuel shook his head, saying the guy gave a lousy tip.

"Your punishment for not agreeing with him," said Jerome. Emmanuel didn't understand the concept and went on.

"He had no idea how he sounded to me. I came from dirt floors, but my mother loved me. I'll bet he came from a rich family, but nobody wanted him. That's why he's poor inside." Jerome took the matter under consideration using two hands to make an imaginary cup.

"Emmanuel, old soul, you know you hold the world together. You've known it for a hundred incarnations. Sometimes it's a burden. You'll be fine if you don't spill the water."

But we didn't know, not exactly. Jerome had us all figured in a vast cycle of reincarnation, but he never said he was Buddhist. He borrowed from all the great traditions. He must have escaped a hundred prisons. Nothing was coincidence; we were given tasks of compassion, fated to live in each other's skin and the hardest part is to hold back judgment. Besides, what is there to judge about the infinite? His boom box was as sacred as any other material thing to him, temporary, like the cars we were assigned. He said our stories were ancient.

My Maggie's Gone

Two weeks into the job, around midnight, a prostitute flagged me down west of Times Square, and informed me of a kindred link between her kind and mine. "How about a ride home, no meter, for a quick hand job. I just got ripped off. I'm broke. The asshole even stole my coat." I thought of my previous customer, his unexpected tip, and the life lesson only minutes before. Poor guy was in a daze, wandering a few blocks from a hospital. The air around him was grave, for his wife of thirty years had died within the hour. In the sacred moment, I was all of humanity to him.

"She's gone, she's gone, my Maggie's gone." I could see him crying in my mirror, and sat with him in the snow. I was sorry he had to do the practical thing and tell me where he wanted to go. I was thinking he needed a church or a friend. The simple became the impossible. He wasn't sure at first, then asked me to take him home, like I should have known the address. He had to reach for it in his mind and it hurt him to say the numbers.

I drove with no quickness, no sharp turns, respectful. But he didn't want to arrive.

"Don't pull over, not yet, just go around the block a few times. I'm not ready to go inside."

"Of course, I understand," but it was too much to understand, and I summoned the kind of silence I learned during long hitchhiking rides across the Midwest, usually from a trucker wanting company, but that didn't always mean a conversation. It's hard to explain, but it's true that presence can be an unopened book on a table. While driving my man around the block, he used the trembling voice you can only show a stranger, telling me about Maggie as he stroked her bag of clothes in a heartbreaking way, like the bag was a treasured cat who knew he was there and purred. He asked me to take the bag of clothes to a charity.

At first I said I'd be honored, but reminded him he might regret that, and to wait a little while before relinquishing anything. He had no strength to argue. I had no Plexiglas barrier in the car that night, no barrier of any kind when he reached to shake my hand. After he was inside, I warmed my hands on the car heater, turning it up full blast. Sometimes the heaters worked.

So when the prostitute was center stage, I was full of other sorrows. She needed to go fifteen blocks, not a small distance in heels. Call me a sucker, but I used the meter to keep out of trouble, and paid for her short ride. "This one's on me," I said, "I don't need any payment." Strangers helped me in a jam many times before, and Maggie was my guide.

It's true, people barf or make love in the back seat of cabs, or pull a note from their purse and read it over and over, then leave it on the seat as if it belongs to someone else. People ignore you or make you vital, resolving, dissolving, opening and shutting the door in a thousand different ways. Jerome was like an attending physician and we were eager interns, so I ventured unanswerable questions.

"Hey Jerome, what do you do when a couple is screaming at each other in the back seat and the woman tells you to let her out of the cab, but you're going fifty miles an hour over the Triborough Bridge in a storm?" By then, I valued Jerome as my mentor, a kind of a preview for psychotherapy training, only better.

He said he'd give the couple another awareness, such as, "Look, you two, my mother is dying in Baltimore. I need to think about what I want to say to her tomorrow. I see you both have a lot of passion, so I'm sure you can help me out. What should I say to comfort her before she crosses over? I'm going to miss her terribly." Jerome said it's true his mother was ill, and the couple might see beyond their destruction if he suggested a taste of loss. I needed more of his wisdom, a template, and an approach.

"Jerome, I'm sorry to hear about your mother. I imagine you by her side, tender beyond words. When the time comes, I'm sure you'll know, maybe thank her for all she's given you, and touch her so she's not alone."

He got a distant smile going, then asked what I thought of his hypothetical response to my couple.

"It's amazing the way you invited the couple to see their existential trap. So what do you do when a woman in your cab is really drunk and seductive, giving you bedroom eyes in the mirror while singing *Someday My Prince Will Come?*"

"That happened to you, didn't it?"

"Last night, both scenarios. Kind of a typical night. Also, it seems every night I have at least one fare that runs down the street without paying, usually a young man, but sometimes a young couple."

"Never chase a runner. Let Karma handle it. Not worth a bullet, plus if you leave your car for even ten seconds, someone will steal it."

"I know. I chalk it up to desperate times and cowards. With the fighting couple, I tried the direct approach, asked them to take it down a notch, and continue their fight later, as I was concentrating on the storm, the one outside. It worked, sort of. At least I got them home. But I wonder if I should have said something different."

"You're the driver, it was good you decided it was time to be seen by them."

"The singing woman had a strange sadness. I was drawn to her perfume. I could have taken advantage, but it's not me. I started to compliment her beautiful singing but when I turned around, she'd passed out in the back. Good thing the doorman helped her in. One of her shoes was missing. Why do I remember that image the most?"

"Because it's central to her novel, a *Cinderella* perversion. Not so unusual. James, you don't need to question how you're handling everything. You're decent. Look for small signs. Listen for your heartbeat. If you stop thinking so hard, you might be a psychologist someday."

Richard chimed in. "Wait a minute, you mean the woman who lives on 77th near West End Avenue? She's famous among cabbies. Perfume is Heaven Sent. I've driven her home too. Everyone knows about her, always stuffs the one shoe under the driver's seat so the cops can prove she was in your car. Always drunk, but cunning. You can be sure she took your hack license number down. Don't ever touch her. She's dangerous, has rape charges pending on at least three drivers I know about. Probably more. Cabbies call her *Poison*."

"My God," I said, "looks like I dodged a bullet."

"You are dangerously green, my friend," said Rico, "don't go up in Harlem for a while, thrill kill of a cabbie last night. By the way, have you ever driven *Chester the Gimp*? He dresses like he's down-and-out, and you never know where he's going to show up. Could be Queens or Brooklyn. Always rushes out in the middle of the street with his big sloppy basset hound, Wilber. He's testing us. If you ask the dog's name, he'll give you a twenty-dollar tip. If you grumble about Wilber, who smells really bad, Chester will signal him to pee in your cab. Then you're done for the night. I've heard he's a millionaire who started a mutual fund and shot himself in the leg after a bad day on the market. That's why we call him *The Gimp*."

Marcos was taking all this in and had something important to say.

"I pick up man John and he came up close and ask, *are you honest person*? And I said, *I think so, I try to be,* and he sat back in the seat all quiet. When I let him out, a gun dropped out of his coat. He got it back. That was all."

Jerome thought it was a sign. "Good man, Marcos," but it wasn't such a good world.

I only saw a few women who drove cabs, and had my lone accident with a gal in Greenwich Village, where I didn't know the slanting streets. It was a small collision, in a no-fault glancing way. We were both from out of state, which explained our polite exchange of information. I liked her instantly, the way she said, "shit happens," without a trace of anger, and I swear she almost winked. I offered to take her to dinner and trade stories in a no-fault glancing way. She said her girlfriend wouldn't understand, but I was glad that she was tempted.

Appearances

On days off, I'd walk for hours, and saw some beautiful portraits on smaller SoHo walls. I wanted them to be the work of the petite pale artist who disappeared. I kept twisting the world that way, and saved a single leaf from being trampled, holding it up the to sun. Later in the day, when I stumbled onto Washington Square Park, all the chess players were deep in contemplation. It heartened me to watch a genius kid playing a very old man, punching the timer and waiting. They had such great respect. Nearby was the stink of trash that had been on the streets for days, piled on the curb or high against buildings. There were pockets of ongoing strikes, gearing up for something big. Services were unreliable. If a fire truck was stuck in traffic, siren blaring, nobody pulled to the side.

Back on the job, a man had collapsed in the middle of Broadway and 108th, with pedestrians walking right past. I was locked in traffic in the opposite direction, watching cars honking, as if they would have been fine with the closest driver running over him: a man in a grey jacket, face on the asphalt, you or I. Everyone was furious at the inconvenience. This world can be dark and you can't un-see it. Apparently he'd been hit and the driver sped off. The streets were paralyzed, the city howled. Finally, a person crouched to check on him. Someone yelled to the owner of a store, but most just honked their horns in a hideous song of idiots.

Two trips later, I found myself in the Bowery and stopped for a tall black man in a dusty black hat, with a beagle in his coat, so I knew it wasn't *Chester the Gimp*. Two cabs in front of me passed him by, probably because he looked penniless. He must have seen my guard was up, and offered kind assurance.

"Don't worry, I'm going to surprise you." He pulled out a wad of one dollar bills and asked me to drive up and down the street while he got out and gave a dollar to each homeless person he saw, then he saved a few for me. Everybody seemed to know him. He left with a tip of his hat. This world has a pocket of gems. Jerome wasn't around to tell, but would have raised an imaginary glass. I saw it in my mind.

I told my recent stories to the tribe, and learned that Rico broke his record getting from LaGuardia to Times Square. He clarified that he only sped on certain occasions, and I wondered if Richard had a strange effect on Rico's urgency, like he started measuring something he never noticed before. Richard said he got a stock tip from a fare and vowed to start looking toward the future for the first time in his life. He also found a new lover, and considered acting school. Marcos was improving his English at an astonishing rate, and got a second job teaching Argentine Tango. We were shocked and so was he. He thought he had no talent, but when he went to take a lesson, women loved his calm, sweet guidance, and wanted him as their teacher. Emmanuel had another baby on the way, hoping for a girl. He was happier than ever, and didn't think of another job. He might still be driving. I was saving money to press on to Europe.

Jerome hadn't been around for a while. We assumed his mother had passed, but I wondered if all that was metaphor. We missed him, missed his mysterious wisdom, but kept the gift of his nature, regretting we never exchanged phone numbers.

I got pretty good at left-footed braking, backward U-turns, and made peace using the horn to survive. On freeways in L.A., you could be shot for using your horn. No kidding. In California, the art was to drive as fast as possible about three feet between cars. You've got to know your territory. I still think of the man down on Broadway, can't shake the image, never will.

Heading east one evening in midtown, I stopped for a huge full moon. It was rising right in front of me, orange between the buildings, hailing me from the end of the block, and for a little while, there were no other cars around. The city stopped and disappeared, leaving me right there in the road, thinking I could touch the moon.

SARAH MCCOLL

HOW SAD, HOW LOVELY

I. The Song

The music subscription service, Spotify, algorithmically generates a thirty-song playlist for its listeners each Monday based on their individual musical preferences. I was driving to school on a bright, snowless winter morning listening to mine while the traffic app Waze directing me down an industrial side street to avoid a snarl on Hamilton Avenue in Brooklyn. It was an hour when technology anticipated my needs. That's when I first heard Connie Converse.

It's an old recording, staticky and quiet. *How 'bout 'Two Tall Mountains,'* a man suggests off-mic. *You can't miss with that.* Then a woman's voice opens up, primly old-fashioned in the Appalachian folk tradition, but with more weight in the hull, like Jean Ritchie after a long night. Two minutes and thirty seconds later, I pressed repeat, and then again, and I listened to the same song until I merged onto the Brooklyn Queens Expressway.

In between two tall mountains
there's a place they call Lonesome
Don't see why they call it Lonesome
I'm never lonesome when I go there

Imagine moving to Lonesome so you could stop feeling it. I wasn't lonesome, either, but in a way that was tenuous enough it bore noting, the kind one might sing about. That evening, when I returned from school, I would roast a Puerto Rican-style pork shoulder for a group of friends and a man of whom I was growing fonder every day. But that was simply social. There was another ache that felt, in some ways, more gnawing and more urgent than the desire to belong among others. It's an artist's ache, one of effort and uncertainty, and of the hope the work itself—without acknowledgment or acclaim—will be enough to sustain you. It's an ache I was only able to identify that morning because I heard it in the breaths Connie takes between the lines.

II. The Story

For nearly a decade, in her apartment on Grove Street and in her pal's kitchen in Hastings-on-Hudson, Connie sang into a Crestwood 404 tape recorder waiting for something to hit, and then when it did, it didn't really. Her big break on Walter Cronkite's "CBS Morning Show" inspired the same reception as playing in her friend's living room. *That was lovely, Connie, thank you.* She'd given up her scholarship at Mount Holyoke for this.

It was 1961. She guessed it was time to quit New York. She packed her coffee percolator and cardigans and unpacked in Ann Arbor. She did what people do when they give up on one life and commit to another, one near a brother and sister-in-law with a nephew to dote on. She reassembled. She took a job at *The Journal of Conflict Resolution*, and after work, in the new living rooms of new friends, she laid her guitar across her lap and warbled through arrangements of Shakespearean sonnets. She kept up the old ways, smoking a little and drinking a lot, but she stopped writing her own songs. At night, she stirred in her cotton bedsheets, and once she stopped stirring, maybe realized it was not entirely honest to say she did not feel lonesome. Was that the word for it? It was some longing. None of it felt right, and a six-month sabbatical to England funded by all those dear new friends couldn't make it so. She returned to Michigan, and everyone saw the same shadows in her eyes. Had she ever been in love, they wondered, or wanted a baby of her own? *The only thing you could get out of her was what she sang*, they said. It was too late. A doctor ordered her uterus out.

It was 1974. She guessed it was time to quit Ann Arbor. She packed her cardigans and her coffee percolator, and she may never have unpacked them. She wrote a stack of letters saying so long: "Human society fascinates me & awes me & fills me with grief & joy; I just can't find my place to plug into it." She dropped them in the mailbox, then waved goodbye from the window of her VW Beetle.

III. Love & Labor

Swallows have built a nest in the space between the window ledge near my writing desk and the air-conditioning unit that hangs from it. They are so close, they sound as if they are inside working beside me. The birdsong outshines the baby-sounds from downstairs and the mother who coos alongside her. I wonder whether it is time to quit New York. Life is easier other places, people always say.

I thought easier meant better until recently, when I watched my favorite couple shuck two dozen oysters. It was Christmas Eve, and the feast had seven fishes. The husband spooned caviar onto tiny homemade blinis and laid chives across the tops like artful pickup sticks. The wife, my best friend, stood over a paella pan the size of a gong, heavy with clams, squid ink, saffron. The husband hauled more champagne up from the basement. It was all so much work. But that's what makes it special, my friend later explained. I held my champagne flute to the light. It was the prettiest color—a pale, warm pink, blushing with gold. *I would like this to to be the color of my next wedding dress*, I said.

But why stop writing songs? Connie's nephew wondered aloud to an interviewer. When did the work stop being its own reward, or had it ever been, really? *She decided she wasn't going to make it*, her brother said, *and in many ways that really hurt her*. If only she had made it, the thinking seems to go, maybe then her story would have ended differently. Only what if she had, and then it hadn't?

IV. We've Been Trying to Be Happy Alone Since Forever, Haven't We?

We lived alone, my house and I.
We had the earth, we had the sky.
I had a lamp against the dark,
and I was happy as a lark.

I had a stove and a window-screen,
I had a table painted green.
Sat on a chair with a broken back,
wearing a pretty potato sack.

I had a rug, upon the floor,
and roses grew around my door.
I had a job; my wants were few.
They were until I wanted you.

And when I set my eyes on you,
nothing else would do, nothing else would do.

V. The Theories

Her new life, her brother Phil thinks, began and ended when Connie's car sailed off a bridge into a river west of Michigan. There was no evidence to serve as punctuation to her story—no waterlogged body, no car lifted by crane draining river water from its seams.

Phil tried to track her down, or at least began to. But the private investigator he hired reminded him, before getting to work, *People have a right to disappear.* There was no search party after all.

Picture this: a woman gunning it, no longer gravity-bound, into the unknown. Compare the rebel rally cry to Connie soldiering on in a midwestern office—using the mimeograph machine, typewriter clacking, rolling her desk chair to the file cabinet across a gray rug. Imagine a life in which her disappointments were so numerous they became indistinct. She could not put her finger where it hurt, could not say *I wish I'd had a baby* or *A record deal would have been nice.* All the potential was together in a jumble, like a necklace knotted at the bottom of a pocketbook.

VI. The Producers, The Radio Hosts, The Critics

In 2004, producer and animator Gene Deitch sat behind a microphone at the WNYC show, "Spinning on Air," sharing some of his rare live recordings of Pete Seeger. He had carried with him from Prague a few old odds-and-ends he thought might interest host and musical historian, David Garland. More than forty years after she quit her music career in New York, Connie was about to get her first radio play.

A couple of guys in Brooklyn heard the show. Entranced, David Herman and Dan Dzula set about collecting Connie's recordings from Deitch and Connie's brother, Phil, who had long kept the tapes she mailed him from New York in 1956 in a filing cabinet in his Ann Arbor home. She had enclosed a card with *Musicks Volumes I* and *II*. "These reels are strewn with minor mishaps," she wrote. "On the other hand, they're not so bad." Connie Converse's 17-song album, *How Sad, How Lovely*, was released in March 2009.

"They are a most peculiar bunch of songs," Robert Forster wrote in Australia's *The Monthly*. "Women weren't writing these kinds of songs in the 1950s. They weren't writing songs so desperate or pure of feeling, or so flippant and wild." *Eerily contemporary*, David Herman said.

Both Deitch and Garland have suggested that long before Joni Mitchell and Joan Baez, Connie was the first to nudge folk music from dust bowl ballads and protest songs into the singer-songwriter's sphere—confiding in the listener. She sings about brawny, tan sailors, about the happiness of empty pockets, about afternoon in saloons playing poker until someone finally takes her home.

"What's known of Converse's life story only makes the songs, which are often meditations on the lives of solitary or independent women, more haunting," Emma Goldhammer wrote on *The Paris Review's* website.

When Connie's album was finally released, the talk was full of unanimous praise and certainty, but there was one piece missing. *She had such promise and such ability*, Deitch said, *but she hadn't put it together somehow*. What might have *somehow* required? The uncomfortable, perhaps—playing publicly in Village coffeehouses or ditching the schoolmarm glasses. But *somehow* may have required the impossible. Maybe if she'd arrived with her guitar on Grove Street ten years later, it would have all worked out. But what would "working out" even mean? In any case, now that Connie's finally had her big break and is, most likely, at the bottom of a river, we can all finally agree: these songs are really good.

VII. My Wants Were Few (And Yet)

When I was twenty-seven, I married the man I loved. A few months later, I had a new job writing Oprah-inspired life advice for a women's website. Since, being twenty-seven, I did not have much wisdom to offer, I researched solutions for the problems I wanted solved in my own life: How to become a morning person, how to create meaningful daily rituals, how to be the heroine of your own life, whatever that means. Each story took about two or three hours, and I generally wrote them from my then-favorite coffee shop down the street, where I sat by the window and watched traffic and dog walkers when I couldn't think of the right word. The pay was good—enough that I could buy organic milk for the first time in my life without thinking of it—and after I filed my story, I could turn to my own writing.

My personal blog, which had gotten me the job, was Oprah-meets-Martha Stewart, on which I used recipes, say, for lentil soup or quinoa salad, to reflect on my emotional life. Put more plainly, I was finding adulthood rather tedious and sad and difficult, at a time when very few sad or difficult things had ever happened to me. But in the morning the light cast long, diffuse beams across the wood floorboards of the living room in a way I found uplifting, and I could eat a nice salad for lunch. Perhaps if I paid closer attention to these things, I thought, I would brighten inside. Toss well, and serve immediately. Is that all there is?

I went to see a therapist. It was not my first time, but at least in high school it had made more sense. She had a basement office on 9th Street near Prospect Park where she folded her long dancer's body in a large black chair. I liked the delicate silver necklaces that glinted at her collarbone, the soft, urging quality of her voice, the tea she drank out of a lopsided earthenware mug made by someone's hands. *I don't understand*, I told her. *I have everything I ever wanted.*

I saw her for six years, following her across the East River to an office near Union Square where we could hear protests march down Broadway during our sessions. She replaced an ugly leather couch with a smart gray one. She pointed one clock at me and one at her. I kept being promoted, until I no longer wrote from the coffee shop in Park Slope but a cubicle on 40th Street near Times Square. Once, to cheer myself up, I rode the carousel in Bryant Park, and often bought chocolate chip cookies the size of salad plates with the same goal in mind. I tried, and failed, to get pregnant. My therapist went half-time in the summers. She adopted one baby, then two. *How is this for you?* she'd ask, and at Christmas, I'd bring her homemade granola or a onesie or branches of winterberry, because how it was was bittersweet.

At our last session, I was thirty-three, and a number of more difficult and sad things had happened to me. I had an ex-husband, a dead mother, and a $22,000 student loan. But I no longer felt I needed to sit in that office on East 11th Street. Some time after that, I stopped taking two little pills—a pink one and a white one—the same ones I had swallowed since high school. A doctor had challenged the continued regimen. *Might you be attributing to these pills work you've actually done yourself?* he asked. A valid point, I thought.

VIII. The Scientists

In studying people who have suffered terrific blows, psychologists have discovered when the worst thing happens, it can actually be good for a person. Of those who lose someone they love, fully 70 to 80 percent report finding benefit to the experience. Often, the ordinary becomes extraordinary. A woman who survived a traumatic plane crash told researchers, "When I got home, the sky was brighter. I paid attention to the texture of sidewalks. It was like being in a movie."

In the months following my mother's death, I thought about writing a book called something like, *The Joy of Death*. This may have been my own unique expression of the denial stage, but it seemed to me there was a stirring beauty in what I then felt as my duty to enjoy life—once for myself, and again for a woman who could not. It was an imperative for pleasure.

Now, I sit at my desk by the window, the nearby birds babbling, and when I can't think of the right word, I look down at the traffic and the yellow lab who suns himself on the sidewalk across the street. I am coming to realize I will do this anywhere, in a craftsman-style bungalow in Los Angeles or in a creaky house in the Massachusetts's hill towns, even here, in Brooklyn, where everything is so hard, they say. But it's not so bad. I go back to tapping at the keys. Sometimes I can hear the man I am falling in love with as he sings country songs and washes the dishes in the next room, but more often than not, I am alone, happy as a lark. *What if it all works out?* I keep saying to myself.

VIII. Alternate Theory

Connie puts it together somehow. She hears her voice inscribed onto vinyl, then listens to it drift, disembodied, out of the dashboard on her way to buy milk. The sound is not at all how she remembers it. It's hollow, somehow. She performs in cities on the prairie, then on both coasts, always in a pool of spotlight. Her fingers keep their calluses and the audience leans in, quiet. She knows it is supposed to feel good, she knows this. Someone who loves her waits in the dark of a hotel room. Connie returns to them, washes off her makeup, steps out of her skirt and unbuttons her blouse. She slips into bed, her cheek at the hollow of an underarm, and her sweetheart stirs, comforted by her sigh, now close at long last. But Connie still feels that same ache, the emptiness inside her, the distance between mountains.

Kisha Lewellyn Schlegel

Dolly

Dolly: *I'll probably look the same when I'm 100, 'cause I look more like a cartoon than anything else. I love to paint and powder. I love the...[trails off]. I have a look, and hopefully it'll always be my look.*
Tom: *Yeah. But I hope to God that you like the way you look when you go home and take it off.*
D: *Oh I do! I'm very comfortable with myself.*
T: *[interrupts] That there's the caricature...*
D: *Oh I'm not that scary.*
T: *[interrupts] ...and there's the real you.*
D: *Yeah!*
T: *No! You're not scary!*
D: *The real me?! [laughs]*
–*Dolly Parton, interviewed on* The Late Late Show with Tom Snyder

Dolly Parton's childhood home is a structure from another time; the tin-roofed cabin has a small, front porch that welcomes strangers without any screens. Inside, dried goods fill the glass mason jars and handmade quilts cover the chairs. There is a single bed that somehow slept the family of two parents and twelve siblings.

Of course, this isn't Dolly's real childhood home. This building is a replica, located in the Dollywood Amusement Park where gas stations and burger joints never aged beyond the 1950s. After the guests make their own candles and visit the blacksmith, they come to the "homeplace." A placard explains that Dolly's mother reproduced the interior. All that's missing is five-year-old Dolly Parton with a head of soft curls looking up at the sunlight to sing the first song she ever wrote about her corncob doll. "Little tiny tassel-top, I love you an awful lot." She stuck a tin can onto a broom handle and shoved the makeshift microphone into a crack in the porch. The dust rose up and glittered in the sun. She stood in that spotlight, dreaming of the woman she would become. That woman was out there. And she was already singing inside.

Along the streets of small town Tennessee, the Parton girls were known for their hourglass figures. They were good girls of course. Not like that woman who walked through town every evening. Her peroxide blond hair was the sun. She wore red high heels and stockings with a seam that ran up the back of her calves. She touched her red lacquered nails to her lips.

"She's beautiful," a young Dolly told her mother.

"She's a tramp," said her mother.

But it was too late. In all the world of faces, Dolly had seen the face she wanted.

The body. Those whipped cream breasts and fairy tale hair. Dolly went home, took a handful of flour from the kitchen cupboard, and spread it across her face. She stuck wet crepe paper onto her eyelids for eye shadow, crushed crayons into blush, and burned matches for eyeliner. She stole her first tube of red lipstick from the general store. She dotted her beauty mark with black so it wouldn't look like "a pimple." She piled her hair onto her head and bleached it bright. She thickened it into glorious waves by attaching more hair to the back of her head. She bought a full wig made of synthetic hair. She bought a wig of real hair. Then another. And another. She never left home without adding hair. She learned to go from shower to show in less than thirty minutes. She lost weight. She had her breasts augmented, her lips lined with collagen, and the crow's feet around her eyes filled with Botox. She had unwanted skin removed, a chin implant, facial fat grafting, and eyelid lifts.

Now, at age 66, even the space between her eyes, that tender plain where tiny lines reveal feeling, does not move. Her face seems placed between where it has been and where it is going. It lacks time's signature. It lacks motion. The permanent pucker of her mouth and taut eyelids erase micro-expressions, those flashes of feeling just 1/15 of a second long, which happen uncontrollably and almost imperceptibly when a person speaks or sings.

"I'm a doll," she tells one interviewer. He looks at her like a doll. She might be real. He leans forward, looking at her with the heightened awareness that stems from disbelief. He looks at her the way convalescing patients in Japan looked at a strange new nurse, introduced to them to help them through their healing. This nurse folded her hands like regular hands, but something was off in the finger's movement. Something was off as well about the click of her blink and the stillness of the skin near her nose. She wore a bobby pin to keep her hair out of her eyes, but those eyes did not seem to smile when she smiled. Her face froze in some places and in others it repeated motion like the pendulum of a clock, a movement that resembles life but isn't quite alive. Her name was Sara. She was an Android. She was made to make patients more comfortable as they healed. She would help them feel less alone. Her silicon skin and cameras for retinas seemed to follow those who were close to her, and when she opened her mouth to speak you could see her back teeth. She was so close to human and so not, residing in a space the Japanese roboticist Masahiro Mori called the "Uncanny Valley," the land of ghosts and zombies and all physical creatures that are familiar and lifelike but never quite alive.

"I'm real," Dolly says. "So I don't mind telling you I've had cosmetic surgery."

"What have you had done?" the interviewer asks, and it is a question that gets as close as he can get to the real question that bubbles up inside: What is it like to change yourself this way? What is it that makes us care? "Why do we humans have such a feeling of strangeness?" Masahiro Mori wondered. "Is this necessary?" Really, who cares if her skin looks like bread? It's *her* face! Why do we care what she does with it? Or her hair? Her boobies or waist, cinched in with a lacquered belt? What if she is only turning her body into *her* body? What if her attempt at preservation only confirms what our bodies will become. Ghosts. The ghosts we are and will become. *Everything remains to be said on the subject of the Ghost and the ambiguity of the Return, for what renders it intolerable is not so much that it is an announcement of death nor even the proof that death exists, since this Ghost announces and proves nothing more than his return. What is intolerable is the Ghost erases the limit which exists between two states, neither alive nor dead.* [Hélène Cixous]

Dolly laughs. Lists procedures. The interviewer relaxes. Dolly smiles and makes another aphoristic quip in the style of Southern girls who know how to direct your attention away from the very thing you want to know. "I'd rather die on the operating table than from my own bad looks." She laughs. "I look at my boobs like they're show horses or show dogs. You've got to keep them groomed." Dolly bubbles onward, floating somewhere between a down-home country song and that figment of timelessness called fame. She stays a comfort *and* so strange, ours *and* not ours, hers *and* not hers. "I'll never graduate from collagen," she says. Pop. Blink. Dimple. The uncanny Dolly closes her lips again.

By 2012, when Dolly smiles, her skin snaps into place like a coffin lid for a beloved who has not been freed from the bonds of adoration. Life has stayed still and is nowhere. The world seems to slip out of time. Interviewers still ask her more about her face than her music, her artistry, the craft of her life.

"You keep a wig by your bed in case there's an emergency..." Ellen DeGeneres informs her talkshow crowd. The comedian turned host, turns to her guest. "...do you ever *not* wear makeup?"

"Well I do. But I would never go outside of the house [...] Especially when I'm in California with all the earthquakes. I always leave my makeup on at night [audience breaks into wild applause], and I *DO*! I leave a wig on a lamppost or somewhere nearby in case I have to be rushed out in the street and the news people are there..."

"How long does it take you?"

"Not long..."

[interrupts] "Or do you have it down to a science."

"Yeah...it's...I'm down to a science."

"Well, I feel like... you could be writing five songs in the time it takes..."

"No. Not really. I'm pretty quick..."

[interrupts] "Ya know. I'm gonna help you out. I'm gonna give you a gift so you don't have to waste time anymore."

Ellen pulls a latex mask with long eyelashes and perfect makeup from a bag. The blond wig is already attached.

They start laughing and the audience joins in, but it's Dolly who laughs the loudest. Her voice reaches up, all the way up, to that highest octave, that most beautifully eerie pitch of the human voice.

"I've already got mine," Dolly says. "You put it on!"

Ellen puts on the mask and pushes her breasts together and the preserved image seems as if it will last forever. Dolly reaches for the face as she always has. "Oh! You look great," she yells. "I love it! I love it!" Dolly runs her fingers along the smooth latex. Her voice is barely audible as she says, "That's what I want." The crowd cheers, and all together they gorge on the image. They refuse to sing its elegy.

Back at the homeplace, the tea kettle waits to boil. The hearth is clean and empty. The table set for six. How comfortable it all seems at first, to be in this house made to look like a home. And yet, the chairs aren't made to sit in. The table is set, but no one is cooking. No one will use that butter churn again. No one will eat the dried beans in the Mason jar. The plates won't hold hot soup. Everything waits as if something is about to begin, but it's already over. We've been invited to a meal no one is preparing. *The uncanny sends us home to the discovery that "home" is not what or where we think it is and that we, by extension, are not who or what we think we are.* [Patricia Wald]

Welcome, says the home, but there is no voice. No one lives in here. There aren't even ghosts because there was never any life. This is the house nostalgia made. Strangeness fills you as you approach the table and see the dust on every spoon. You are consumed by a nostalgia that isn't even yours. You are young again. You too dream of the woman you might be. You sat cross-legged in the clover, feeling all of the strangeness of being alive only to die.

If you had asked her, she would not have said her girlhood dream was to be a "singer," or, "star," but it was a glittering dream just the same. It always involved a kind of love.

Now the girl in you is grown; there's no way to touch the person you thought you would be. There's no way to find her, other than to think of the long-gone girl, dreaming of the future woman that isn't you. This desire to return to another time is just the desire to return to that dream—the moment when you imagined the person you might become—and who never really came alive. So much *nostalgia is the very face of human misery, so blinded and wasted by its exhausting effort to ascend to the source of joy and innocence.* [Camus]

Why not let the girl go. Let the dream die. Let the void fill up the lack.

The flesh is about to fall off anyway. *The wind full of space wears out our faces.* [Rilke] Even the preserved and siliconed body will break down. The chest will collapse and the magpies are already gathering in the corner of the yard, waiting for our yummy bodies. The magpies take the shiny things and the meat. The bellbottom pantsuit and the rhinestone belt. The lavender eye shadow that shimmers and the eyes that see. Time reveals the boundlessness of flesh. *In the end, death is never anything more than the disturbance of the limits.* [Cixous] In death there is no preservation and yet don't we still expect that in this moment, our lives will flash before us like a good spotlight. Life will move through us as we move out of it. Without any hope of preservation, we preserve the hope that we will experience life as a whole. The whole of life. All time. Nothing cut away.

The rocking chair moves as the tea kettle begins boiling while the sparkling girl sings her song on the front porch, "Tiny Tassle Top, I love you an awful lot," and the sun forms a single bleached spotlight over all the stages where the bellbottomed woman and the rhinestone woman and the 66-year-old woman and the woman on her 2016 "Pure and Simple" tour, sings the song, "Jolene. Jolene." 1973. 1995. 2016. There is a repetition. The guitar notes staccato as if thumped rather than strummed. The robust bass disappears beneath the violins that take a couple of repeated higher notes. Except that now, when she sings it in public, the crowd joins in. She lowers her voice a touch so they can. "I'm begging of you please don't take my man. Your beauty is beyond compare. Your smile is like a breath of spring. Your voice is soft like summer rain." Dolly's voice is a honey she knows how to pour. She hits those warble notes with all the history of her ability to Appalachia yodel. She sings without anger. "I could never love again."

On the rare occasion that she was asked about her music (1973) by a man who leaned so close to her she must have smelled his breath, she called the rhythm a "heavier up-to-date beat."

Her hips bounce with this quick and bluesy beat—a beat measured in a $2/2$ cut time signature that tells a singer how long to hold a note. She did not write this song in $4/4$, "common time" that is denoted by a broken circle, a C that means *tempus perfectum* or perfect time. She wrote this song in $2/2$ time, noted with a symbol that has a line down its face: 𝄵. It is a time signature that means *tempus imperfectum diminutum*, diminished, imperfect time. Cut time.

It is in this cut, diminished, imperfect time that Dolly sings to the image of another woman with ivory skin and flaming hair and eyes of emerald green. "Jolene, I'm beggin' of you..." She sings her way deep into the threat of this beauty. She sings in awe of the danger of such beauty. "Jolene, Jolene..." She sings Rilke's elegy for herself, knowing that, *beauty is nothing but the beginning of terror, that we are still able to bear, and we revere it so, because it calmly disdains to destroy us.* She sings into that bright hole. *It enraptures us. Comforts. And helps.* [Rilke]

Emma Bolden

Up a Steep and Very Narrow Stairway

I used to sing.

Sometimes I say it just like that—*I used to sing*—so it sounds like a real and actual thing that I really and actually used to do.

I didn't really sing. Not in a real way, in a me-and-my-lungs-spinning-air-into-tapestries-of-sound kind of way, in an in-front-of-an-actual-audience-of-ears kind of way.

I sang with my fifth grade classmates on the bleachers, belting out the alphabetical states song from Alabama to Conneticut-ettiquette to Wy-ohhhhh-ming.

I sang on the risers beside the altar with the middle school choir, climbing the chords of "Dona Nobis Pacem" in the pitch-imperfect soprano section.

I sang in the bathroom, with the water running, so that I could watch my own mouth O and O in the mirror without my mother yelling that I had a damn bed to make.

But I didn't really sing, not in any actual or beautiful way. I was too afraid of people listening to me, too afraid that they would hear the things that, without my intention or approval, my voice always seemed to do.

*

I was a first soprano because I refused to sing anything but the soprano parts. All of the good parts belonged to sopranos, and all of the good girls were sopranos. All of the beautiful, if helpless, girls were all sopranos. I had not yet realized that transcending helplessness was its own kind of beauty. I had only realized that Christine Daaé in *The Phantom of the Opera,* a soprano, was so helplessly beautiful and beautifully helpless that she was loved, and obsessively, by every man who heard the notes climbing out of her beautiful and helpless mouth. She was loved by the hideous but tortured-enough-to-be-fascinating Phantom, whose tortured passion in turn made her seem fascinating, and she was loved by Raoul, her childhood friend and suitor who was totally boring but transformed into fascinating by his fascination with her.

The mezzo-sopranos and altos were not fascinating. They were not helpless, and they were not beautiful. They were the best friends, the dance teachers, the costume makers, the Spanish Ladies. They were the chorus girls, the ball guests, the on-stage-audience members. Their real roles were to make the harmonies that polished each note the soprano sang into a gem, gleaming before a backdrop of what was essentially silence.

*

The highest note I'd ever actually heard and believed in as possible was the high E at the end of "The Phantom of the Opera," a startled and startling sound that beautifully reflected Christine's startled and beautiful nature. I was obsessed. I was determined: I would stretch my voice upward until I startled myself by entering that note's fragile and beautiful space. I spent seven hoarse and sore-throated months reaching upward, chugging chamomile tea and shower steam and peppermint oil then reaching again and again. I pictured my throat as a stairway and the note as a small silver light floating upwards, upwards and into that high E.

I hit it, perhaps, only once, and in my own bathroom while I was home alone, where no one else could hear.

I spent at least twice as much time trying not to acknowledge my chest voice and its lower tones. I imagined each note as a flash lighting its way through my sinuses, my nostrils. I imagined each note, high as a halo.

*

I gave up on Christine Daaé and her high E in sixth grade, after my body had traveled so far into puberty it felt like my mind would never catch up. I became obsessed with *A Chorus Line* instead. It seemed like the right thing to do, especially after I learned that one of the songs was called "Tits and Ass." We weren't even allowed to hum most of the songs in show choir practice at Our Lady of Sorrows Catholic School, but Laura Whitman—the cruelest and prettiest and therefore the most popular girl—was allowed to sing "Nothing" at our fall recital as long as she sang that "this whole thing," and not "this bullshit," was absurd. And even though—or perhaps because—the lyrics came from Laura's mouth, the same mouth that called me brace-face and four-eyes and invented the nickname "Emily Boulder Butt Bolden," I felt something when I heard "Nothing." I felt the same singular sensation, the same not-ness, the same lostness I felt when I peered out of my cornered and cowering spot of the choir loft to see a swarm of other sixth grade girls angling their bodies and beauties towards the boys, as if they lived inside a space I could see only from the outside.

*

The 1985 film adaptation of *A Chorus Line* was rated PG-13. At twelve, I was allowed to watch it with my mother, who fast-forwarded through "I Can Do That" and "Hello 12, Hello 13." Later, I figured out that she fast-forwarded "I Can Do That" because it was boring, even though it was about a boy wanting to do something girls usually do. I could tell from the fast-forwarded choreography that "Hello 12, Hello 13" wasn't boring, because it was about things that boys and girls want to do with each other. I just didn't understand what, exactly, was scandalous.

Thank God for my friend Margie.

Thank God for my friend Margie's parents, who didn't expressly forbid her from seeing and/or hearing about the scandalous things that boys and girls want to do with each other. Margie sang the alto parts in show choir and she wasn't ashamed. We were both excruciatingly proud to have landed, as lowly sixth graders, solo lines in "Who Will Buy" from the musical *Oliver:* I trilled my sales pitch for ripe strawberries, ripe; she, in persuasively sad low notes, offered sweet red roses, two blooms for a penny. At lunch one day, she slipped her cassette tape of *A Chorus Line* into my backpack, keeping the case for herself in case my mother came across it.

That night, I slid the tape very carefully into my Walkman and checked very carefully to make sure that the headphones fit snugly against my ears. I downed the volume to its lowest audible level then fast-forwarded to "Hello 12, Hello 13," my heart bass-booming, my body sweating through a Laura Ashley nightgown.

I listened.

When the tape whirled into the silence that marked the end of the song, I hit stop.

I sat still.

I looked at the Walkman, thinking *what.* Just like that, with no question mark. It was too confusing to be a question. All of it—the song and its words and the bodies it described—was too confusing. I had already said hello to twelve and I didn't understand a single lyric, except that their faces broke out and everything seemed like a mess. The only changes, oh, down below that I knew about a.) happened only to boys, or b.) involved the menstrual cycle, which I felt was nothing to sing about. Neither was the idea of seeing someone else's down below, which seemed pointless and humiliating, even if you were playing doctor.

I didn't understand getting hard or going down or feeling up.

I didn't understand why anyone would want to be felt up, or kiss or neck or get anyone's pants. I felt as strangely, lostly blank as the moment that letters shacked up with numbers in pre-algebra, and suddenly my own age, my own body, became an equation I didn't even know I had to solve.

*

By the time I started seventh grade, my classmates had at least started to start puberty, which, at first, seemed promising. I'd gotten hips and a waist at eight; at nine, I'd gotten acne and breasts and the desire to only wear black and to never smile. I got my period in the blue stretch of summer between fourth and fifth grade, and my down-there hair had been down there longer than I could remember. When the girls in the seventh grade were confused about their down-theres, about all the hair and pain and blood, I pushed my lips together and crossed my legs, just like the teachers did while they sipped their Diet Cokes and watched to make sure no one threw baloney across the lunchroom. I was like them, the teachers: in matters of pubic hair and menstruation, I was the leader, the high priestess of the female body and all of its pains and peculiarities.

But when my classmates went through puberty, whatever power I'd earned through my body vanished. Like all power based on pain, it couldn't last long.

*

I accidentally became an alto one after-school afternoon otherwise indistinguishable from other after-school afternoons. My mother went across the street to drink pink wine with our neighbor, who smoked into the oven vent and ashed in the kitchen sink. I'd already flipped through all her romance novels, reading passively about members and throbbing and bosoms and wondering why the books left me completely without the up-in-the-bosom and down-in-the-skirts feelings that the heroines always felt. I felt inexplicably angry and slammed all of the doors, which was satisfying, and so I decided to listen to *A Chorus Line,* full-blast-loudly, in rebellion.

I fast-forwarded to the circling storm of minor notes that swirled around the start of "At the Ballet." I sang along with Sheila about life not being a picnic. I sang along with Bebe about our mothers' promises that we'd be attractive when we grew up, when we grew up. I spoke along with Maggie's lines about having a fantastic fantasy life, about dancing around in the living room, letting the wish that we could be someone else take the lead. I followed her into singing and as she proclaimed the everything-beautifulness of the ballet, I proclaimed along with her, singing "at the ballet, at the ballet"—and it happened. My voice, freed from the diaphragm, up-up-upped from my chest and into my mouth, into the air, and it wasn't me and it was me, all at once, I was someone different from myself, I was a deep voice belting about beauty, I was a self that neither I nor anyone else ever knew.

I stopped singing.

I sat on the living room floor. I listened to the next song, "Sing!" I hated it and its exclamation point, and I hated that Al finished all of his wife's sentences, that I could never remember her name, that they both believed that power could make up for pitch, that I now understood the whole point of the song to be that if your singing didn't sound like you thought it should, you shouldn't sing at all.

The following Monday, I quit show choir.

*

If there were show choirs in 16th century Italian Catholic schools, the highest notes wouldn't have been sung by women. No notes would have been sung by women, as women were forbidden to sing. Saint Paul said so, after God's light shrieked through him on his stroll to Damascus. "Let women keep silent in church," he ordered the Corinthians, and so the church banned women from singing the notes their throats were made to sing. Instead, these notes were sung by the castrati, who were castrated as boys before puberty made them men, who therefore lacked the androgens necessary to push their bodies up through puberty and their voices down to baritone or bass. They lived and sang outside of sexuality, with voices suspended in pre-adolescence like a crystal suspended on a silver chain, clear and holy as any light.

*

I experienced puberty in 1990. My classmates began to experience puberty in 1991. My classmates began to experience sexual feelings in 1992. I realized that I was not experiencing sexual feelings in 1993.

All of this was awkward.

All of this was especially awkward because I didn't have the language for it, didn't have the right words to explain.

Here is how it happened: some of the girls started looking at boys and some of the boys started looking at girls, and they felt something, a whoosh-whoosh down in their down-theres. And some of the girls started looking at girls and some of the boys started looking at boys and they also felt something in their down-theres. Whoosh, whoosh.

I looked at the boys. I looked at the girls. And I felt—nothing.

*

I first heard the word "asexuality" in 2013 when a student said to me, "I am asexual and no one understands it."

I nodded.

I said, "I understand." And I did understand, though I didn't fully know it or know why. I waited until I got home to Google "asexuality." I was afraid to use my computer at work. I don't know if I was afraid of someone finding out that I suspected I might be asexual or if I was afraid of myself finding out that I suspected I might be asexual.

I learned from Wikipedia that an asexual is someone who experiences "the lack of sexual attraction to anyone or low or absent interest in sexual activity." I learned from the Asexual Visibility and Education Network that an asexual is "someone who does not experience sexual attraction." Asexuality, I read, is not a choice but a sexual orientation. I read both definitions again. I sat still. I looked at the computer screen for a little while, thinking *what.* Just like that, with no question mark. There weren't any more questions.

*

Decades after show choir, after I'd found myself in my thirties and far enough from the first awkward disappointments about what my body didn't feel that I no longer tried to force myself to feel it, a friend and I went to a conference. From our separate beds in our together hotel room, we talked about our post-sexual lives. We talked about relief. We said we missed the companionship of romantic relationships, the camaraderie. We missed the good morning coffee, the good night decaf. We missed the romance, of course, but that's like missing the fjords, or missing the midnight sunset, or missing our long and celebrated Broadway careers, or any of the thousand other nouns and verbs we never had. We did not miss the pressure, metaphorical or literal, of our sexual lives. And I was happy talking, happy chatting, happy offering halves of Diet Cokes and chocolate walnut cookies, and I was happy watching television when a commercial for *Les Miserables* came on, and then I was happy singing and she was happy singing about stars, there, out in the darkness. It was her favorite song from *Les Mis*, she said, her favorite favorite one, and because I was happy I said it was mine too, and I happy sang and she happy sang, *Keeping watch in the night, keeping watch in the night.*

*

In most productions of *The Phantom of the Opera,* the high E you hear doesn't come from the actress' mouth in that moment. The actress who plays Christine is actually only required to ascend into that high E once: in the recording studio, where the note is captured on tape to be replayed on stage.

*

"Stars" is, of course, not my favorite favorite, or even my favorite, song from *Les Mis.* My favorite song, my favorite favorite, is and always has been "I Dreamed a Dream," which Fauntine sings from the floor of the stage in a tattered dress patterned with the same Laura Ashley roses as my childhood bedspread. Fauntine sings about a time when world and song were exciting, a time before it all went wrong. It seemed so true, even when I was a child. It always seemed as if it, whatever it was, had already gone or soon would go wrong. In bathrooms, at sleepovers, at choir practice, I couldn't help but sing every tiger and killed dream of it, every and even the lowest note of it.

*

There are, of course, synonyms for the word *asexual*, all of which hit a different note.

There's *celibacy*, the choice to not have sex.

There's *low sex drive*, a term that implies its opposite–*high sex drive*–and therefore describes desire as an impulse that may wax but can wane again.

There's *frigidity*, a word that's also a punishment, a slur that freezes women with the dangerous implication that if a woman denies a man sex, that woman is doing something wrong–or, at least, that there is something wrong with her.

There's *Hypoactive Sexual Desire Disorder (HSDD),* also known as *Inhibited Sexual Desire Disorder*. Both, according to *The Diagnostic and Statistical Manual of Mental Disorders,* are mental illnesses. According to the Mayo Clinic, they are physical and/or mental illnesses.

*

A year after we sang about stars and fugitives running and falling from God, falling from grace, the conference friend and I were no longer very good friends. It was the kind of sad thing that always seems to happen, at least when two people are close enough to sing and split chocolate cookies in their hotel rooms, so I tried to not be very sad about it. She went to another conference where she shared a different hotel room with a different conference friend. She called me the next week, while she shopped for bananas and I Cloroxed my kitchen counters. The conference, my friend said, was beautiful and infuriating. In the lobby she'd seen a sign that said ASEXUAL MEET AND GREET, which she found infuriating and not beautiful. "They were all just *standing* there," she told me over the phone, "in their–you know how they dress–in their futuristic clothing–"

"Like *Hunger Games* clothing?" I asked.

"Yes, like District 13 clothing."

"Like my clothing, then."

"Yes," she said, and I nodded at the Clorox bottle, as if we had both just received confirmation of everything we had expected. "They were just *standing* there, in their District 13 clothing, drinking coffee."

"Did you talk to them," I said, not because I wanted to know but because it felt important to engage in the conversation.

"No, I didn't," she said. "I don't get the whole thing anyway. How is a person *asexual*? What does that even mean, *asexual*?"

"Well," I said to the phone and the Clorox and the cabinets and me, "it means they don't have sex."

"But what does that mean?"

"Well," I said again, "it means that they don't want to have sex. That they don't have that kind of instinct."

"Right, right, but what does that even *mean*? How do you not have that kind of instinct? What are they even *doing*?" She said it in that fast way, and I knew, by instinct, that she had found the bananas and was rushing to the check-out, and suddenly I felt very sad because I knew that, and because I knew her, and because I would probably never again be on the phone with her and know that she had found the bananas. "It just feels like a betrayal," she was saying. "It just feels like they're betraying us all, don't you think?"

"Yes," I said to her and the Clorox and the bananas, "it feels like a betrayal. Agreed."

*

On the Asexual Visibility and Education Network's website, one will find, under the heading "Arousal," the following caveat to the very concept of asexuality:

> <u>Note:</u> *People do not need sexual arousal to be healthy, but in a minority of cases a lack of arousal can be the symptom of a more serious medical*

condition. If you do not experience sexual arousal or if you suddenly lose interest in sex you should probably check with a doctor just to be safe.

*

Because the castrati grew up in bodies without post-pubescent hormones, their bodies grew up differently. Without a surge in androgens, their larynxes stayed small, the folds of their vocal cords remained thin and able to produce those suspended crystals of soprano notes. Without the onslaught of testosterone, the ends of a castrato's long bones did not harden and instead grew longer, their arms and legs reaching far up and far down, their rib cage stretching and circling around more and more air, as if their very bodies were nothing other than a voice.

*

It is entirely possible that *The Diagnostic and Statistical Manual of Mental Disorders* and the Mayo Clinic and the Asexual Visibility and Education Network and my conference friend and her bananas are all correct, when it comes to me, that asexuality is not a sexuality but a medical condition. When I started my period, I started experiencing symptoms of polycystic ovarian syndrome, which caused my ovaries to make more androgens than they're supposed to make, which in turn made my female body trend slightly more towards the male, sprouting facial hair and body hair and zits. I also started experiencing symptoms of endometriosis, including cramps and bleeding which soon became so paralyzingly bad that I was faced with a choice: take hormones to prevent ovulation and menstruation or fail out of school before I even got to eighth grade. This, of course, was not a choice.

I wonder: how many things are?

*

The week after I talked to my conference friend and her bananas and my Clorox, I finally bought my own copy of the soundtrack to *A Chorus Line.* I listened to it on every car ride from home to my campus office to home, filling my hatchback Toyota with my half-cracked soprano notes. Halfway through the week, I switched to my chest voice, wide-mouthing the words to

"What I Did for Love" and "Nothing" and even if the sorority sister in the monogrammed SUV next to me stared, I kept singing. I kept singing about love never being gone, about trying to melt, about feeling nothing except the feeling that this bullshit was absurd. I felt loud and messy and satisfied. I felt freed from my body, like I was only a voice, like I was a voice only I could hear.

*

I wonder: were I to audition for show choir today, would I be a soprano? Would I be an alto? Would I be ripe strawberries ripe or sweet red roses? Or would I instead be something else, a nothing, always in between all of the notes I was given to sing?

*

I don't know how to talk about myself, sexually. I don't know if that sentence should read, "I don't know how to talk about myself, sexually" or "I don't know how to talk about my sexuality." I don't know what terms to use, if there are terms to use, if terms do anything other than offer an easy name for the difficulties of living inside a human body. With one friend, I use the word *celibate*. With another, I use the term *post-sexual*. I use it in a sentence. I say, "If I wasn't *post-sexual*, I totally would have flirted with him." She uses it in a sentence back: "Well, when you stop being *post-sexual* and start being *sexual-sexual*, you can flirt with him." She changes the definition, and I want to change it back, to tell her that there wasn't a before and there probably won't be an again, but it's too clumsy and bothersome a thing to pass over the tongue.

With my mother, I am too embarrassed to use terms, so I say, "Maybe I should have been a nun." With my physician, I say, "I have not engaged in sexual intercourse for a very long time." She says, "Like, several months?" I say, "No, like several years." She checks a box on her chart. I know there is a word there, a term she is using to define me. I don't ask her what it is.

*

The thing about trying to sing in harmony with a group of people is that you often are not in harmony. Sometimes they sing the wrong notes. Sometimes you sing the wrong notes. Sometimes you are all singing the wrong notes but in different ways, in sharp ways and flat ways and just-wrong ways. Sometimes you are stubborn and insist upon singing the soprano notes whether or not you can actually hit them. It becomes complicated. It becomes even more complicated because no one can stop singing and say *hey, you're singing the wrong notes,* or *hey, am I singing the wrong notes?*

In show choir, we held hands all the time we stood together. If your neighbor's note was sharp, you moved their hand to the front. If it was flat, you moved it to the back. And every time I did so, it felt like the first in a very long series of times that I had actually told anyone how I felt. The silence, the anonymity, the shared purpose of song made me safe.

*

For a musical so consumed with the ways in which sexuality consumes the body, the finale in *A Chorus Line* is refreshingly asexual. No one falls in love. No one kisses for the first time or makes love for the first time. No one walks out of a church in a tuxedo and no one walks out of a church in white. There's no thrown rice, no lit candles, no mood music and no bodies moving like the shadows of the bodies their owners knew as their own. The auditionees aren't there to make love with each other: they're there to work. They're there to dance. They're there to make their bodies move in beautiful ways for their art, because their art is their beloved. Zach, the director, has one final question for the dancers: he wants to know what will happen to them when their bodies no longer behave, no longer dance. The auditionees answer with "What I Did for Love": they will move on, and without regret.

Only eight auditionees are cast in Zach's future production, but in the final scene of *A Chorus Line*, every dancer gets a chance. Their bodies vanish into a gold smear of other bodies. It is then that we see the roles that they will ultimately play: not leading ladies or romantic interests or love-sick ingénues. Instead, they move inside a space where the body has a different kind of meaning, where sex is not the only way to express passion, love, joy. And they are beautiful. They are glimmeringly, goldly beautiful.

Mimi Kawahara

Listen If You Can

I.

"Remember when my spring cleaning unearthed a family of killers?" I said, trying to sound lighthearted.

"Remember when you forgot that life is like a box of chocolates?" Vernie replied offhandedly, between sips of tea.

"Remember when you showed appalling insensitivity and lack of imagination by using a stale simile to compare my staggering discovery to a bonbon with an unexpected filling?"

"How do you know the stories didn't spring from great-grandpa Yves' imagination?"[1]

---

[1]Yves, who came of age in a medieval village on a lavender-speckled hillside in 19th century France, though endowed with a fertile imagination, did not invent a family of executioners. On the contrary, he fervently wished to uninvent them. But his father presided with pride over the guillotine, as had his grandfather. A sensitive boy with keener interest in his mother's parsley than his father's post, Yves dreamed of becoming a gardener or a chef, though he knew he was destined to replace his father.

As the time neared for him to take over, Yves began staring inappropriately, sprinkling his conversation with non-sequiturs, and talking to an invisible interlocutor. After a long, disheartening winter, his family despairingly accepted the public consensus that he had lost his mind. To escape the constant pressure to perform his new role, he took up residence in the basement of an abandoned building on the edge of town. Thus he became the village "fou," secure in the knowledge that a madman would never be entrusted with the national razor.

At first he was ecstatic. He was free. He was relieved of a crushing burden that had oppressed him for as long as he could remember. He could look forward to quieter sleep, to dreams with fewer angry heads hovering over him, shouting and dripping blood on his pillow. Soon, though, he was overwhelmed by his isolation. People who had known him all his life passed him quickly by, as if his condition were contagious. He began talking to himself, and cooking elaborate meals of the sort he had previously made for his family, both seen as further evidence of his lunacy. He took up writing to ease the boredom. He reminded himself that executioners were subject to extensive public scorn; indeed, some parents went so far as to send their children away to school, lying about their background, to spare them the ridicule. But at moments of overwhelming loneliness his fate seemed worse even than that. One day he was a capable strapping youth, the next a useless eunuch, with nothing ahead but time to count his dwindling days of tedium. Maybe it would be better to do his

"Because many appear in books I found at the library."

Multilingual snippets from nearby tables punctuated the silence of my voluble friend. The restaurant's neon sign blinked "Happy Lot," the "us" dark, dead like my relatives' victims.

"Remember when you were speechless for the first time in your life?" I teased her.

"I'm contemplating your family's hand in history."

"Apparently there's no shortage of roles for the banality of evil."

"Why so judgmental? It's more interesting than a succession of doctors."

"Who knew you would warm to the news that I may have a knack for decapitation?"

"Mike says I must like murderers." Her adversary in court, Mike was her partner in carnal crime. She was repelled by his politics–she tried to save people from the capital punishment he sought for them–but the sex was sensational.

"Mr. Hot Prosecutor might have a point." Our waiter delivered Vernie's sesame chicken and my Singapore noodles with a self-effacing smile, then hastened away.

"Remember that every topic, like a chamber pot, has two handles."

"My electronic bidet has fifteen settings, but not one cleanses dirty hands. What old tome are you into now?" No matter her caseload, she had recreational reading at hand, partly, I think, so she wouldn't be swallowed by the work.

"By happy coincidence, it's called *On Murder Considered as One of the Fine Arts*."

"I've got it."

"You do?" she asked, surprised, as I usually relied on her to recommend books.

"Not the book, the other handle. Murdering the murderers must be an even finer art–is that your point?"

---

duty; at least he would have family and friends; he could marry a daughter of one of his father's colleagues, and have a son. But he too would be destined to spend his days putting people to death. That thought always brought him back to his present predicament, which, however bleak, was preferable to the prospect of subjecting his progeny to the hideous future that he had escaped only at this preposterous cost.

"If I had a point," she answered with a hint of impatience, "it would be that most people do their jobs, whatever they happen to be."

I took the hint and changed the subject. "How'd the hearing go this morning?"

"Hard to say. It may depend on the mood of the judge's wife tonight."

"Has my crusader for justice turned cynical?"

"Only when I end the day by losing a final appeal."

"I'm sorry, V. Why didn't you didn't tell me?" I replied, more a show of sympathy than a question, as I understood that she had ceded center stage to my rude awakening.

"You had your own news."

"Why does everything seem to be about death lately?"

"Maybe it always was, only we're just noticing." She stared into her teacup as if reading the leaves, though there were none, and in any case she was not conversant with the hermeneutics of moist biomass.

"You're taking this one hard. Do you want to talk about it?"

"Not really. I'd rather hear more about what you learned at the library."

"In 1829, when his father died, a seven-year-old was forced to assume his post as executioner, presiding over an adult 'assistant' who carried out the sentences."

"I don't know if that makes me feel better or worse."

"Apart from cases like that, it was customary to hide the family profession from the children. One boy learned of it when his school friends began to shun him for no apparent reason, until someone handed him a drawing of a guillotine with his family name underneath. He stopped going to school, remarking that further study would be superfluous for his career."

"So much for the fine art approach," she said, welcoming the diversion from her reality. "What happened when Yves got here?"[2]

---

[2]One afternoon as Yves sat in his dank cellar hunched over his notebook, a little girl came scampering down the stone steps that ran past his open door and peered at him, her blond curls and azure eyes glinting in the sun. He smiled at her, then stiffened in self-consciousness, hoping his deliberately disheveled appearance wouldn't scare her away. With a puckish curtsey she announced, "I am Madeleine Ribière," adding gaily, "Will you play with me?"

They whiled away hours with a whimsical cast of characters. A sulking spoon sought sympathy, moaning about the merciless pestering of the temperamental pepper mill, who held her responsible for the mysterious disappearance of his partner, the

"He got a job in a restaurant and ended up marrying the owner's daughter. They had my Grandma Maddy, named after the girl who inspired him to emigrate, and she was the first in the family to become a doctor. You know, the immigrant story with the happy ending."

"Seems like that used to happen more. Most immigrants I meet are more like the street vendor outside my office, who was an economist in Bangladesh. Now he's out there serving coffee and donuts, somehow with a smile."

"I know what you mean, but how about the man at the register over there. He could be the proprietor. This might be a big step up from tending rice paddies."

"Careful with your crosscultural speculation," she cautioned, turning to look at him. "He's not exactly brimming with beatitude." She reconfigured

---

salt bowl. Such nonsense she had never heard and could no longer endure; she hadn't slept for days. Madeleine comforted the spoon by eating a bowl of soup au pistou, which made the spoon feel warm and useful, and Madeleine hoped the exertion of ferrying a full load from bowl to mouth would induce sleep. Another day she encountered spoon-fish frolicking in a basin, who remarked how disagreeable it must be to breathe air, only to be berated by an egotistical cork who had managed to offend everyone within minutes of his liberation from a bottle of Bordeaux.

She told Yves about her father's adventures at sea, and about a miraculous land across the ocean where he was saving up to send for her and her mother. Yves filed these stories in the little girl fantasy section, the prospect of losing her more than he could bear. Their friendship generated much talk among village residents, many of whom worried for Madeleine's safety; Yves' mother insisted that he would never hurt anyone–whatever his eccentricities–and certainly not a child. It was inconceivable even to the least suspicious that Madeleine would remember her time with him as the happiest of her childhood. That she would save Yves from irrevocable disengagement from the world occurred to no one because they assumed that was already a fait accompli.

Shortly after Madeleine's seventh birthday, which she spent mostly with Yves, her mother decided it was time to bring an end to this attachment. Madeleine never had a keen interest in her peers, preferring the company of an imaginary companion called Ponette, but now she spent no time at all with other children, and Ponette, she announced about a month after she began visiting Yves, had gone with her mother to the paradise where they would soon join Papa. Madame Ribière, who had worried about Madeleine's devotion to this fictional friend, was unable to find satisfaction in its replacement with a flesh and blood lunatic.

Again bereft, only more so for having known the boundless love of a lonely girl, Yves could no longer abide his barren existence in Charix. So, with the clothes on his back and a few personal effects in a sac, he set out to find Madeleine's land of dreams come true.

her face to match his weary frown. I smiled at her adroit mimicry, but felt sorry for the chubby Chinese man.

"Maybe he just learned that his grandfather played a key role in the Cultural Revolution."

"Hey, imagine how much more inadequate you'd feel if you came from a family of saints."

"Maybe. But even after Yves had done well for himself and his family, he was dogged by the feeling that he was a disappointment."

"Sometimes I think those are the people who do the most good."

"Or the most bad. Like bullies. Like Hitler."

"Your relatives weren't Nazis."

"I bet some were."

"Last time I checked, we didn't believe in hereditary guilt. Besides, they don't sound like bad men to me."

"Since when are you so kindly disposed toward the death penalty?"

"Maybe since I learned that it led to my best friend's birth," she said with an impish smile.

"Ugh, I hate that way of looking at it." But I was glad she seemed to feel better.

"It's the twisted beauty of contingency—we might as well enjoy it."

"Easy to say—as long as your head remains attached to your body."

"Is that a threat?"

"Maybe my ancestral spirits are speaking through me."

"Now you sound like you'd fit right into Yves' stories."

"Exactly. The one who wasn't a killer was a kook who animated spoons."

"Not such a far cry from puppets," she averred.

"I beg to differ. Puppetry is an art, arguably a fine one. Anyway, no one expects Niko to be a model of mental health after growing up in a war zone. His physical prowess is incredible, though, especially considering his modest endowment." After I had corroborated the disorienting claims in my great-grandfather's journal, I met Niko on the library steps, his puppets stepping lively around him. Before I could say "My mother taught me not to canoodle with performing mendicants," he was animating my nipples in the shower, then on his knees, his tongue reducing me to a marionette undulating in waves of pleasure.

"I think if it was my family, you would be more forgiving," Vernie said.

"And you would be less."

"Probably."

"I can understand executioners hiding their identity, but my parents, generations later—why?" The moment we put down our chopsticks, a busboy came to clear our plates, moving at warp speed, making a clatter.

"We don't know that they knew. They might never have had the key to that antique box, and decided not to ruin it by forcing it open the way you did."

"You think so? I can't fathom not finding out what was inside."

"You always want to know everything. Not everyone is like that."

"I don't understand not wanting to know."

"Let's crack that nut later. I've got to prepare Cory's appeal." She pulled the tray with the check and fortune cookies toward her. From one she extracted the talismanic slip of paper. "Here's yours: 'All people are your relatives, therefore expect only trouble from them.'"

"It does not say that."

"Yes, it does, look."

"What's the opposite of serendipity—when you make an unfortunate discovery by accident?"

"That's just bad luck."

"And that's the bracing candor I count on. Let's hear yours."

She cracked it open. "'A bird does not sing because it has an answer. It sings because it has a song.'"

"It sings because it doesn't have any human relatives." I was trying to make a joke, but it came out sounding like Niko on a dark day.

"It sings because 'joy and woe are woven fine.'"

"Who is that?"

"Blake," she said, her encyclopedic memory at the ready.

"Someone should put that in a fortune cookie."

II.

I never liked white men. Romantically, I mean. All else equal, I preferred chocolate to vanilla, and nothing else was equal, so, as a self-respecting black woman in the United States, my aversion was overdetermined.

But Niko was different. Though he fulminated against a rival Caucasian sect from his consonant-laden homeland with whom his people had been at war for years, he had no animus toward African-Americans. He also had no appreciation for our struggle, but the combination of his background and foreplay enabled me to overlook that shortcoming.

Before Adele introduced us outside my office, I had noticed the puppeteer on the library steps, but barely. Then, after we met, we kept running into each other. It wasn't long before I agreed, innocently I thought, to have a drink with him after work. And I wasn't long into my mojito when I realized he had amorous intentions and to my astonishment, I was beginning to share them. (Not only was he lacking in eumelanin, I knew that his pale cock was a fraction of the size to which I was accustomed.)

Thank goodness Adele and I didn't generally gravitate toward the same men; it would be nice to think our friendship would survive any rift, but one never knows. She usually favored the cerebral type, but they put me to sleep, the pasty ones with the wire-rimmed glasses who learn more about life from books than their own experience. My guys wouldn't have kicked her out of bed, but she wouldn't have given them the time of day.

Niko was well-read, without any of the affectations of literacy. To him it was just another tool for making his way in the world. He knew that having a gun at the right moment can matter more than a lifetime of learning. When the war in his country pitted friends and family members against one another, his erudite father was told one day by his neighbor of twenty years, whose children were like siblings to Niko and his sisters, that he would be killed if he didn't leave town. He would not flee his own home and could not believe his friend would carry out such a threat. The next day he answered the door for the last time. Soon thereafter, Niko's mother brought the kids here.

He had a roguish charm that defies recounting as surely as it seduced those later at a loss to explain it, but when he was training it on you, it was irresistible, even if he was redeploying lines he'd debuted on my dearest friend. I know that sounds ridiculous; he may have been ridiculous, but he felt sublime. He brought to mind a remark by Victor Hugo: Reason is intelligence taking exercise; imagination is intelligence with an erection. Niko was in a state of perpetual imaginative arousal, and in his company you felt as if you were the source of all that imagino-libidinal excitement and you could not help but enjoy it. When we argued and he got under my skin, the sex was even better.

Adele claimed that she cared more about the quality of her time with a man than his fidelity, and I half believed her, but I didn't tell her about Niko. I thought she'd talk to him about it, and he'd lose interest in both of us. One might ask why I would have a stake in a guy like that. A shrink would say I was looking for my father, who purportedly possessed that kind of charm, (my mother says he had her at "Hey"), that the men I dated were all versions of my idealized image of him—except Niko was white, like the man who killed my father. Apparently pheromones are color-blind.

I felt awful lying to her. But I wasn't ready to give up Niko—he was my comfort and comic relief while I tried to save Cory from lethal injection, and I was confident that whenever I told her, she might be miffed, but she would forgive me. Not my finest moment, but Niko's touch was transporting—more so than his post-coital conversation.

"Consider policeman's job. He cannot do job if he is dead, and he will be dead if he does not protect himself," Niko averred, lighting a cigarette, mulling over my father's final encounter.

"Maybe you should sign up. I'm sure they could use some puppet police." I opened the window to let out the smoke, wondering at the fault lines that emerged when we were more than six inches apart, when all the differences that had melted in the heat of our bodies solidified in the cool air, turning the space between us into hazardous terrain.

"I do not deserve insult, so you may apologize." Among his oral talents, he could blow heart-shaped smoke rings, which he sent floating toward me as a peace offering, but I was in high dudgeon.

"My father didn't deserve to die, but no one is apologizing to him." Mistaken for a drug dealer, running while black had been his only crime.

"Like someone in almost every family in my country," he replied sotto voce, suddenly somber.

With shame I remembered the circumstances of his father's death. "I'm sorry, I know."

"Maybe now you remember we are not so different, you hear me better. Police have difficult job."

"The thing is, if you knew what it's like to be black in this country, you might have less fraternal feeling for the police."

"I tire of hearing I cannot comprehend life of black people."

"But this is the first time I've mentioned it."

"Americans think foreigner cannot understand."

"It might be the kind of thing you have to see from the inside."

"I prefer to see you from inside."

"Niko, I'm serious."

"Also I am serious. Vlad shot my father with same color of skin." He paused, extinguishing his cigarette with deft swirls in the saucer-cum-ashtray. "Tell me, would you be his lawyer? Why you defend killers?"

"Leaving aside your presumption of guilt, are you saying poor people don't deserve representation?" The cold-blooded murder of his father did seem indefensible, but my client Cory was as prone to violence as Fernando the bull. I wished Niko could see the guileless warmth in Cory's molten chocolate eyes.

"I just want to understand you," he said, softening. He pressed himself against me from behind, with mock desire. "Maybe you are like life for Kierkegaard: you can only be understood backward?"

"A historical perspective on equality might help, now that you mention it." I thought of Cory's mother, Mabel, who worked long hours as a home health aide and didn't make enough to pay her bills, but kept bringing me gifts. After I beseeched her to stop spending money on me, she knit me a cozy beige blanket with a cowrie shell border.

"Americans have culture of deep inequality with devout belief in equality. In nature there is no equality."

I turned to face him. "So we should go back to the jungle?"

"Why not, we climb into Rousseau's Dream. There is no war there." His gaze gravitated to my cleavage; I half-wished I minded.

"And no Bach or Beyonce or books." I fancied myself holding some conceptual high ground, despite having surrendered my netherparts without hesitation.

"We drift from our subject. I mean to say, always there will be poor people."

"There will always be death, but still we do our best to fight it."

"And we all die."

"But most of us live longer than before."

"You win, Mama Teresa. You devote to downtrodden and I devote to you. Now I need nap after dawn meeting with very hungry, very professional mosquito."

For a moment I thought I must be loony to betray Adele for such silliness. Then he enveloped me in his arms and I lost my discernment in his dreamy scent. Typically, I went for men one misstep away from becoming my client, with plenty of promise and no opportunity, like my father, which didn't stop my mother from calling them hoodlums. But if I'd presented my other romantic deviation, Mike the prosecutor, as my beau, she'd have run to the bathroom to be sick. Niko would have raised an eyebrow, but she wouldn't have taken him seriously. Then again, neither did I. It wasn't part of the two-timing-on-your-best-friend-since-fifth-grade deal.

*

Throughout middle school, we were inseparable: Adele, the petite It girl with golden locks and allowance galore, and me, the 38DD scholarship girl from the ghetto. Occasionally she came to my apartment, but mostly I went to her house; it was closer to school and it was grand—all the space and privacy and light I didn't have at home, the plush silence afforded by white privilege, her own phone line in her room (in the pre-cellular era), her closet nearly the size of my bedroom, and what I coveted most, her own bathroom. On sleepovers I would doze off pretending we were sisters, or, when she had annoyed me, she was my guest and would be sent away in the morning instead of me.

Her sensitivity to our contrasting circumstances made our friendship possible, along with our shared linguaphilia and congruent senses of humor, but nevertheless we lived on opposite sides of the pearly gates. When we were arrested for shoplifting in eighth grade, my mother blamed the pernicious influences (aka Adele) at the fancy private school she had chosen "for my betterment," which she decided would arise instead with my own kind at a public school in our neighborhood. Thus did I endure the consequences of our transgression, cast out of Adele's domain, demoted to the company of kids more adept with weapons than words, while Adele carried on as usual. Not her fault, world not of her making, but still...when she was upset that her ancestors were executioners, I couldn't help thinking, so what? My ancestors were slaves. Look at where you are now, at your father the pediatric oncologist, and mine, the dead drug dealer.

I understood that it was unsettling to discover a hidden past, though what she learned from her ancestor's diary was fascinating. When I said that to her at Happy Lotus, she took me to task, pointing out that I wouldn't say it's fascinating that my father was murdered by a cop, or that it would be fascinating to learn that her father was that cop, to see my father's death from his perspective.

"True, I wouldn't use that word," I replied, "but we do have to try to understand him if we want to change him or prevent others from becoming like him."

"In my case, we don't have to worry about that," she said with undue solemnity.

"That's actually a non-trivial difference. Your ancestors seem bound by the norms of their time in a way that racist police in the post-civil rights era do not, so they seem less culpable." A new waiter brought our water glasses with a splash, followed by frantic wiping up and a profusion of sorries.

"But, until Yves, they were still wrong not to follow their conscience."

"And who among us can claim a clear conscience?" I heard myself say.

"Remember when you had a change of heart about capital punishment and became a staunch defender of executioners?"

"Yes, and then you didn't want to be my friend anymore."

"Was that a question?" She decided to lighten up, thank goodness.

"Are we playing now?" I cradled my teacup, warming my hands.

"Isn't it obvious?"

"Couldn't you have told me?" My scallion pancake arrived, along with chopsticks, which Adele twiddled nimbly, awaiting her lo mein.

"Did I tell you that French aristocrats sliced bread at the dinner table with mini-guillotines?"

"Did they blindfold the bread?" She introduced the topic, so I thought it was fair play.

"Do you think that's funny?"

For once, I couldn't tell if she was serious. "Is that indignation faux or real?"

"Is that question faux or real?" she parried.

"Isn't that repetition?" The waiter placed our dinner unceremoniously on the table, hurrying away to serve the additional plates balanced on his forearms.

"Isn't that changing the subject?" she persisted.

"Since when is that prohibited?"

"Weren't you worried I was offended by your joke?" Sometimes she knew me too well.

"Did your ancestors play psychic in their spare time?" A fast eater, she was already making a dent in her heaping pile of noodles.

"Are you trying to be obnoxious or is it effortless?" She was laughing now, so I knew she wasn't upset. She didn't paper over things; she excavated them. Then it occurred to me that maybe I *was* trying to be obnoxious, to make her angry at me without telling her why she should be.

"Do you think Tom Stoppard imagined that people would play this game?" I waited on tenterhooks to see if she would join me on easier ground.

"Do you think people are playing it?" she replied sportingly. I breathed a silent sigh of relief. She was too busy devouring her food to notice.

"What are we, chicken liver?"

"Was that rhetoric?"

"Have you always been such a pedant?"

"Have you always bent the rules of the game to accommodate your own slow-wittedness?"

"Do you think your brother made you so competitive?"

"Do you think I should tell him?"

"Do you think it's fair to ask me that now?"

"Okay, time out. You know he bought into the doctor tradition way more than I did. I think he'd be pretty upset, but it feels wrong not to tell him."

"Would he want to know?"

"If you were to ask him, he'd say yes, but I think he'd really rather not. But who am I to say?"

"I guess I think he has a right to know," I answered, setting a new personal best in hypocrisy.

Adele put her Amex on the check and cracked open the cookie closer to me, which tradition decreed was mine.

"No horse can wear two saddles," she read.

"I plan to remain bareback," I said, thinking that if I had a superstitious cell in my body this kind of coincidence might send me over the edge. When I bedded Niko, I had not bargained for a reproach from a fortune cookie. Or perhaps it referred not to my betrayal of Adele, but to my simultaneous dalliance with two men. I usually rode them though, not to put too literal a point on the metaphor.

"Here's mine: Wisdom is a comb which nature gives to men when they are bald."

Eyeing her flaxen ringlets, I kidded, "Then you have a long way to go, but we knew that already." And notwithstanding my closely cropped afro, that comb lay even further from my reach.

III.

"Remember when I gave your eulogy and no one got our jokes?" Adele said. Vernie's lung cancer had settled the long-running debate as to who would deliver whose eulogy. Adele sat on the side of the hospital bed that had been installed in Vernie's room.

"Remember when I laughed my ass off listening from the afterlife?" Vernie retorted.

"Remember when you had a deathbed conversion?" Adele did her best to hold up her side of their banter, all the while wondering how she would carry on without her friend. She couldn't burden Vernie with that; she couldn't burden her with anything anymore.

"No, but I do recall when you mistook my fantasy of the postmortem motel for religiosity you know is alien to me." Lately Vernie spent most of her time alone lost in reverie or attended by aides with no interest in her conversation; Adele's visits brought her back to a semblance of her old self. She relished these resurgences, though they exhausted her.

Belatedly understanding that Vernie was referring to a fictional afterlife about which they had both read, where people remain until their name is spoken for the last time, discharging them into oblivion, Adele said, "Even while dying, you outwit me." She marveled at Vernie's equanimity, wished she would fight for more time, but Vernie had chosen hospice, wanting optimal quality of life in however many days she had left.

"I've been daydreaming of the people I would see there–Asha, holding hands with my mother, who's probably chatting up Rosa Parks, and Cory, with his mother." She paused to cough and adjust the nasal cannula that supplemented her oxygen and irritated her nostrils. "Even Niko, who I picture seducing everyone with inspired quips about his death erection."

Asha, Vernie's only child, had drowned in coastal flooding that nearly took Vernie too. Sick with grief and self-recrimination, Vernie had contemplated suicide, but when she imagined Asha asking, as she so often had, "Why, Mommy?" Vernie found no satisfactory answer, so instead she distributed her surplusage of maternal love among her clients and allowed herself the consolation of cigarettes.

Niko had returned to his country, become mayor of his hometown, and been killed in ethnic strife. Adele, who saw no value in revisiting Vernie's long mourning at this juncture, wondered if her recollection of Niko's magical fingers (manipulating puppets or pudenda) and entrancing tongue (employed for linguistic or sexual feats) had been embellished by the ensuing years of mediocre sex.

"You know, I wouldn't have felt this way at the time, but I'm glad you slept with him. Otherwise you would never have believed such ecstasy was feasible with such a phallus. He was phenomenal, wasn't he?"

"Yes, my small scoop of vanilla had stupendous flavor." Vernie said, playfully licking her parched lips.

Struck by the incongruity of this gesture on Vernie's skeletal face, Adele overflowed with love for her friend, who managed to remain fully alive while her body shut down, never complaining, still making jokes, still the same indomitable Vernie. Adele would have succumbed to the disease, her identity reduced to blood counts and bedsores, like a shadow losing itself in the absence of sun.

"Speaking of flavor, how about some sesame chicken?"

"Thanks, but no." Vernie had lost her appetite and her voluptuousness. Her skin hung slack on a bony frame. As she lay there, days and nights merged into one stream of semi-consciousness; people from her past appeared unbidden, their presence as vivid and alive as Adele's. She saw Cory at their last meeting, his hulking softness rising from the threadbare cot to greet her, his face opening to a wide smile, puffy cheeks dimpled, eyes beaming childlike devotion. She couldn't bear his gratitude for her faith in him; he would soon die for a crime he had not committed; she had failed him, the system had failed him from the day he was born to an impoverished, single black mother. After his execution, she had stopped seeing Mike and Niko, had no interest in sex or food or pleasure of any kind for months—until she met Xavier, Asha's father, whose easy laugh and dry wit inspired an intensive investigation of what else lay under his hoody and fatigues. She had fallen hard for him, envisaging a shared future for the first and only time in her life, but the prospect of a baby sent him in search of less encumbered company.

"And speaking of back in the day when I was worked up about my ancestors, why didn't you tell me I was making much ado about ancient spilt blood?"

Adele's question reached her as if through a wormhole, but time travel was second nature to her now, past and present revolving in variegated permutations in her mnemonic kaleidoscope. "Your brother took care of that for me."

"Did you know he would?" Adele asked, reflecting that Vernie had received the comb of wisdom long before the chemo left her bald.

"I thought he might," Vernie said absently, her thoughts drifting back to Asha and the ineffable joy it would be to hold her again, to hear her laugh, to smell her butterscotchy breath. One month after the fatal flood, Vernie had been pressing her nose to the belly of Asha's stuffed bunny, inhaling deeply for a whiff of her, when Xavier showed up. Since Asha's first birthday he had returned at erratic intervals, like a rich uncle but without the money, as if he himself were a gift, expecting Asha to run to him, which she never did. He was about to ask after her when he discerned the answer in Vernie's face. Though they hadn't touched in years, he wrapped his arms around her, and held her in loving silence. Undone by this unexpected tenderness, she sobbed into his shoulder. She wasn't surprised, or even sorry, that he never came back, but she had sometimes wished for another hug like that.

Her father never had a chance to show up. She considered whether his name had already been spoken for the last time or whether she might meet him at last. He had not known that her mother was pregnant when he died. Surely she had told him by now.

Then she caught herself, indulging in what her mother would have called poppycock, even her secular mind seeking a tunnel of escape from eternal nonexistence. She sensed Adele watching her.

"Remember when the game was over?" Vernie asked, her eyes incandescent, titian nebulae radiating light of bygone worlds.

Adele thought: And we both lost. But she couldn't say that. "Maybe we'll have another round in the motel, you never know."

"We say that, but we do know."

This brought Adele up short. She wasn't ready for this conversation. Vernie saw her terror.

"It's okay. Just stay with me." She closed her eyes. Adele had to refrain from begging Vernie to stay with *her*, idiotic and selfish as she knew that was. She sat there clueless and afraid, listening to the choppy rise and fall of Vernie's breath. After a while she noticed Vernie's head listing to the right, her wig off-kilter. Adele stood up and leaned over to straighten the wig and adjust the pillow. Bloodstains on the sheet brought to mind her great-grandfather Yves' nightmares of freshly sliced heads hovering above his bed, spouting epithets and blood. No man-made machinery of death here, just Mother Nature and Father Time doing their bloody duty, she mused as she sat down, accidentally kicking the bag of Chinese food.

Adele had no appetite either, but she took out the fortune cookies, comforted by the familiar crinkle of the cellophane wrapper. Remembering that hearing is said to be the last sense to go, she decided she would read them aloud, as they had always done.

"Okay, we can skip lunch, but not our just desserts. Here's yours: A candle lights others and consumes itself." She reread it silently, unnerved. "V, did you hear that?"

Vernie was unresponsive, breath no longer audible, the irregular red squiggle of her heartbeat on the monitor the only sign of life.

They didn't believe in these manufactured prophecies, Adele reminded herself. Yet she couldn't help concluding that Vernie had been her candle, and that she would now be in the dark, like the "us" in Happy Lotus, not a happy lot at all.

It occurred to her that at another time she might have said: Would you care to shed some light on this? Instead, she fought back tears and opened the other cookie. "And here's mine: Water drunk together is sweet." She looked at Vernie, mouth agape, cheeks hollow, eyes lashless and sunken—the silhouette of a skull.

"With you, it was sweet, even when it had a hint of bitter. I know you're ready to go, V. You're right, it's okay, I'll be okay." She stopped to collect herself. She would not break down now. "Just so you know, the eulogy will be a showstopper, so listen if you can."

Stephen Dixon

Drankwater's

He sees her again. He was with his daughters the first time. Now he's alone. Came into this soup and salad and sandwich place for a small container of one of their soups and a coffee. A slice of bread comes with the soup. If you ask for a heel, they'll give you that instead. He was planning to take the soup home and eat it there and start drinking the coffee in the car. He gave his order at the counter and paid for it with his credit card. Most times when he comes in here to take home some food or a loaf of bread, sliced, and always a container of coffee, he brings a book with him to read a page or two till his order's ready. But he'd just finished a book while he was on an exercise bike at the Y and didn't have another book in the car. So he looked around, there she was. Same table she was at the last time, and again with what he thought could be her seven- or eight-year-old granddaughter, when he felt he'd made a fool of himself by going over to her, as he and his daughters were leaving, and saying "Excuse me, but do we know each other from someplace? I know it's a stupid old line, and I'm really reluctant to use it, but it's because of the way you were looking at me while I was having lunch with my daughters, and you do look familiar." "No," she said, "I'm sure we don't. You must be thinking of someone else." "Sorry; my mistake," he said, and left. He was so embarrassed, after—though his daughters said he did the right thing; he thought he might have known her and was being polite—that he promised himself never to do it again unless he was certain he knew her from someplace but couldn't remember where. That time he wasn't. And he wondered if he'd only said it because he was attracted to her and used her glancing at him a few times as an excuse to get to know her.

She's sipping her mug of coffee or tea, starts to look in his direction over the rim of the mug, and he quickly looks away. Good. She didn't catch him looking at her. Don't look at her again.

"Phil?" the woman at the counter says.

His order's ready. "That's me," he says, and takes the small bag with his soup and slice of bread in it, and his coffee in his other hand—café au lait; he likes the way they make it here—and heads for the door.

"Sir? Philip?" someone says behind him. He turns around. It's the woman, standing next to him. "You are Philip, aren't you, or am I mistaken?"

"Don't tell me," he says. "So we do know each other? I mean, more than from the last time here, when I thought I'd made a terrific fool of myself by going over to your table and saying, or just thought it a possibility, we did?"

No such luck. He pushes open the door. Nobody called out his name or said "Sir?" or anything like that to him since the woman at the counter did to give him his order. He turns around, does a quick look at her. She's not looking at him. He thought she might. Maybe curious, if she recognized him, why he didn't say something to her this time. Probably not. The little girl is talking to her and she's listening intently. He still finds her very attractive. He goes outside, gets in his car, puts the coffee container in the cup holder, sets the bag of food on the seat next to his, carefully so it doesn't fall over, presses the towel he used at the Y around it so it'll stay upright against the back of the seat, and picks up the coffee container and starts drinking.

Someone raps on his window. He looks out. It's the woman. She's making a motion with her hand for him to roll down the window. The windows don't work like that. They're power windows and the ignition has to be on for them to go up and down. He doesn't want to turn on the ignition. That might scare her. He holds up his hand, motions for her to step back, and opens the door. "Yes?" he says.

Wouldn't he love for that to happen. He drives home. He finishes half the coffee by the time he gets there. He takes the coffee container and his sweaty shirt from the Y and the book he finished and the bag of food into the house. He drops the shirt into the washing machine in the kitchen. He doesn't like eating soup out of the container—he always seems to make more of a mess that way than out of a regular bowl—so he empties it into a soup bowl. He gets a tablespoon out of the utensil holder in the dishrack—he also doesn't like using the plastic spoon that comes with the soup if he doesn't have to, though he will use the paper napkin that also comes with it—and brings the napkin, soup and spoon to the dining room table. He gets the tub of soy butter out of the refrigerator, butters the slice of bread, puts it on a plate and brings that to the table with the coffee, which he doesn't mind drinking out of a container. But he should have toasted the bread. It wasn't a heel and would have fit in the toaster. He likes his bread and bagels toasted—even his bread in sandwiches at restaurants—though not rolls, but too late for that. He starts eating the soup, hoping it's still hot. It is. He's about to bite into the bread, when the phone rings. He goes into his wife's study, which is on the other side of the kitchen, and picks up the phone. "Hello?"

"It's me," a woman says. "Big surprise, right?"

"Excuse me. Are you sure you dialed the right number? This is four-ten, eight two-five–"

"You were just at Drankwater's. You came in for some take-out. It wasn't hard getting your number. They gave me your name, I figured you lived around here, and looked it up on my smartphone. The woman with the little girl."

And so on. Wouldn't that be nice. He eats the soup, drinks the rest of the coffee, eats the bread. He's still hungry. He puts the dishes and spoon into the sink, the two containers into the trash can, and opens the refrigerator and looks inside. Nothing much there. Plenty of vegetables, but that won't satisfy his hunger, and the only fruit he has is a grapefruit and banana in the fruit bowl on the dining room table. He doesn't keep the refrigerator stocked the way he used to when his wife was alive. Nor the fruit bowl full. He opens the deli tray in the refrigerator, though he knows what's inside. A garlic bulb and a few wrapped slices of processed cheese. He keeps the cheese for the woman who cleans his house every other week. For lunch she likes a single slice on an onion roll with lettuce and mayonnaise and a couple of thin slices of smoked or barbecue-flavored turkey he buys a quarter-pound of a day or two before she comes to the house. Also a bottle or can of Diet Coke, which he puts in the refrigerator the day before she comes. There's food in the freezer–soups and lentil and millet patties he's made and several onion rolls–but any of that would take time to thaw and none of it is something he wants now. Maybe he should go back to Drankwater's and get a sandwich to take home and another café au lait. The one he had before was even better than usual. And the grilled Portobello sandwich, which was on the menu today, is delicious. Or the chicken salad sandwich, which they have every day. He loves their chicken salad. Or something from the breakfast-all-day choices on the menu. He knows which one he'd get. The same one he always gets. The cheese omelet, which comes with hash browns and two slices of buttered toast of any one of their breads. He'd get the flax seed bread and ask for the butter to be on the side. He'd also ask for some Dijon mustard for the hash browns. And while he's there, he'd get a loaf of bread and have it sliced, because the bread he has in his refrigerator is getting a little old. Their seeded rye is very good, and if they don't have it, then the whole wheat boule. And he wouldn't be going back there to see the woman. She'd probably be gone by then, anyway. If she wasn't, it'd seem odd his being there twice in about forty minutes. But he wouldn't look over to where she's sitting. He'd act as if it was the most natural thing in the world for him to be ordering food twice in so short a time. The first could have been for someone else, the second for him, or the reverse. But if he was going to order the omelet, he'd have to sit down there to eat it. Suppose she was still there and the only available two-table—he certainly wasn't to sit by himself at a larger table—was next to or near hers? So no omelet. And actually, it's a bit too much food. Just the Portobello sandwich. If they're out of it, which has happened a couple of times—it seems to be a very popular dish—then the chicken salad sandwich. And not half of one but whole. If he only eats half of it when he gets home, then he'll have the other half tonight. It could be his dinner. Maybe with their field green salad. Comes with all sorts of things: pecans, pickled daikon, crumbled goat cheese. All this is going to cost. But he's been so cheap with himself since his wife died, he can be a sport for a change. He was pretty cheap with himself before she died too, though he wasn't cheap with anything she wanted, especially her last few years.

So he goes back to Drankwater's. It's closed. No it's not, but for a few seconds from the car it seemed to be dark inside. He opens the door. Coming out are the woman and child. He steps back and keeps the door open for them. She says "Thank you." He says "You're welcome." She smiles and goes past him.

"Don't we know that man?" the girl says.

"I don't believe so," she says.

He goes to the counter. Quickly looks back through the door and sees them approaching some parked cars and the headlights of one flashing on and off, as if she just pressed the whatever-you-call-it gadget that unlocks the driver's door. It's the same car he has, a Prius, but the new model and a color he likes a lot better than his.

He orders a grilled Portobello sandwich and field green salad and small café au lait to go, and pays for them. Damn, he thinks, he forgot to bring a book with him again. While he's waiting for his order, he thinks he really should have got the omelet. He's that hungry, and he just sees himself eating and enjoying it.

"Excuse me," he says to the man who took his order. "I'm not canceling my order, just adding to it. I'll still have the sandwich and salad to go, but a cheese omelet and the coffee here."

"Why not sit at a table and tell your server what you want. I'll have her bring over your sandwich and salad and your coffee."

"In a mug, please? And sorry for being such a bother."

He sits at a two-table. A server comes over with his café au lait in a mug and a bag with his sandwich and salad in it. He orders the omelet, toasted flax seed bread, butter on the side, and a small portion of Dijon mustard. "No water, please. And could you also put on my bill a loaf of rye bread, sliced?"

"Will do," she says.

The omelet plate comes. He eats, asks for the check, pays up, goes home with the bag of food and another of the bread. Now he has a dinner tonight he'll like and enough bread for the next week and a half, though he'll freeze some. The sandwich he'll wrap in aluminum foil and warm up in the oven a little before he eats it.

Half an hour after he's home, someone's at his door. This time he's not kidding. Someone's there. It's Roland, his next-door neighbor. "I'm mowing today," Roland says, "and thought you might like me to mow the grass along the road in front of your house."

"You mean the weeds," he says. "I should do it."

"It's nothing for me. I'm on my tractor. Take me a minute."

"Yes, then; thanks. I don't know anything I can do in exchange, but if there is something, let me know."

"Don't worry. I like doing things for people, especially neighbors as nice as you."

"Oh, if you only knew," he says.

"What do you mean?"

"Just joking with you. I've always got to say something."

All this said through the kitchen screen door. He should have opened it to talk to him. Even invited him in. Would have been friendlier. Next time he'll remember to do it.

He goes into his bedroom to lie down for a nap. All that food must have made him tired. Or maybe he's just tired. He shuts his eyes. That cat's still outside. That's all right. There's plenty of light left. A minute later he hears the mower going. It's not a sound, at least from here, he dislikes. The phone rings. He gets off the bed to answer it. "You were right," the woman says. "My little granddaughter said something that reminded me where we first met." No, he's done that. Just rest.

Hannah Dela Cruz Abrams

Three Myths from the Northern Mariana Islands

Creation Myth

The Chamorro people say Puntan and Fu'una. Puntan the brother, caretaker of emptiness. Fu'una the sister, caretaker of nothing. They say the brother died and the sister plucked out his eyes and flung them high, sun and moon. She pushed his heavy breast until it arched, became the heavy sky. They say the brother's heart drummed and they say the drumming is time. The sister Fu'una rested the brother's back on the bottom of the nothing, laid it down gently on the nothing. They say she pounded and tilled the brother's back into earth and Taro grew and Pandanus grew and bees unfolded from the coconut trees. The sister smiled and cried, they say. Swam with sharks and followed whales, and in the sea near Guahan, became a rock that broke apart. They say every stone is a people. Some are not good. Some fish, muddy streams, are tender, and at the end of the day when everything is slow and the light is full of dust they say, "Come near you young children, and listen."

Myth of the Ancients

The Chamorro people say: We came here for many reasons. We came here because we don't know why. Because there were too many people in the other place, because there was famine. In the other place, there were tribal wars. We can't remember the other place. Because there was fighting over god and earth, that's why. A catastrophe, a disaster. A volcanic eruption. We came because we felt the ocean was our mother and the stars were our father. The night before we left, we ate a good dinner, some of us danced and drank fermented coconut milk and fell asleep on the sand. And in the dark, before the sun was up, we pushed our sakmans into the water and raised the masts. We waved goodbye to those standing small on the vanishing shore, and then for years we drifted, listening to the swells. We drifted for many years, watching our own faces change, hearing our sounds change. When we came, we were a different people, a new people. And all we brought with us were slingstones and rice.

The Myth of the Lourdes Spring

The Chamorro people say they did not want the war. They did not care about the war. The Japanese were nice, they say. The American soldiers were good, had medicine, and fine tobacco. They say that when the beaches caught fire, and the sky was like fireworks, they gathered their bags of potatoes, their pots and pans and crosses and children, and headed for the hills. For the dark caves full of bats in the hills. They say it lasted too long. That the food ran out. The birds flew away. From the caves, they could see the gray ships in the water and the planes in the sky. They say the Japanese farmers ran off the cliffs. With their small children, hand in hand, off the cliffs. At night, the sky was bright and loud, the ocean red. At night, they prayed. On hands and knees, they prayed. On the rocky cave floor, their fingers moving the rosary beads. Fresh water bubbled from the ground, they say. They carried the water in their cupped hands to the sick. Held it to the lips of the dying and felt death go away. The spring they called Lourdes, and left their idols there.

Matthew Vollmer

Supermoon

They had just finished eating—the man and woman and their son—at their favorite Mexican restaurant, where, even though they hadn't quite cleaned their plates, they complained that they'd eaten too much, which was a signal for the man to say, as he always did, "Time to visit the vomitorium." Though the man knew that feasting was an important part of high culture in ancient Rome and that the wealthy enjoyed slathering wild boar and venison with fermented fish intestines, he also knew, because he'd consulted his phone during a previous visit to this same restaurant, that feasters did not excuse themselves, waving away slaves who'd been enlisted to brush crumbs and bits of bones from their faces, in order to visit a system of tureens reserved especially for regurgitating food, thereby allowing vomiters to return with vigor to their indulgences. The man knew that the word "vomitorium" actually described the entryways of ancient Roman amphitheaters. But because "vomitorium" was a word that made both his wife and son shake their heads and laugh despite themselves, he said it, and the trio took it as their cue to leave.

On the way home the woman suggested that they should all go for a walk; after all, the dog had been left inside all day and could use some fresh air, and as good as it might sound to lie down, the family might better aid their digestion by perambulating the neighborhood. This sounded like a good idea to the man, but once he parked the car in the driveway, the boy slung open the door and scampered toward the house, and by the time his parents made it inside, he had already resumed the playing of whatever video game he'd most recently downloaded to his tablet computer, the one that required him to tap and swipe the screen of the device with the relentless tenacity of a madman. The woman shrugged. The man hooked the dog's collar to a leash. And, because they had recently agreed that twelve was an appropriate age to leave the boy alone in a house for short periods of time, they told him they'd be back in a little while, and left without him.

At first, the man and woman walked without talking, and this, the man thought, was fine. Nice, even. The man had always enjoyed taking walks with the woman, and she with him. Though the two were different in many ways, and though she was half an inch taller and her legs were longer, the couple walked at the same brisk pace—the woman often noted that they shared a similar stride—and so walking together, though they never held hands, as this had the tendency to introduce an awkwardness that impeded their gait, felt completely natural.

At the crest of the hill, the woman sighed heavily, and when the man asked what was wrong, she said she was in a funk.

Instead of asking her to talk more about this funk, the man said something like, "Me too" or, in a way that suggested he was in the same boat, "Tell me about it." It would be easy to imagine that the man had good intentions for claiming a funk of his own, and that by commiserating with his wife, he might have been curating a little funk-sharing space, one they might inhabit together and thereby lift one another's spirits, but the truth was, the man had gotten temporarily caught up—as he sometimes did—in a kind of playful but ultimately self-serving brand of spousal antagonism. After all, it was beyond ludicrous to think that even if he did have a funk to call his own that it could compare to hers, which was a funk that happened to be six months in the making, a funk that, were it a human baby, would soon have the strength and wherewithal to crawl around on its own. This funk had been born, more or less, at the end of the previous winter, when the man and woman went to a local breast imaging center and sat in a waiting room where a bald, goateed man in overalls and a satin Harley Davidson jacket held a little girl on his knee while the old woman next to him—head wrapped in a scarf, eyebrow-less face forcibly placid—drank Styrofoam cup after Styrofoam cup of medicine.

At this point, the woman squeezed the man's hand. He squeezed back and said, "It's going to be okay," and then a nurse called the woman's name and she left the room. Two days later, the woman received a call from the radiologist, who said everything was fine, that there were some calcifications in both breasts, nothing major, but something to keep an eye on, which was something of a relief, at least for the next 48 hours, until the woman got another call, and the same guy said that he'd been having some second thoughts, and that he'd given the mammogram to another radiologist, one who had a bit more experience, and this radiologist had said something like, "Well, fifty percent of doctors who know what they're looking at would tell you that it looks like you might wanna biopsy, and the other fifty percent would be content to watch and wait" and "If it were me, I'd biopsy," and so a week or so later the doctors removed tissue from one of the breasts and sent it to a lab, where it tested positive for a certain kind of non-invasive breast cancer, specifically a kind that begins in the milk ducts.

Before the woman had learned of this new development, she had decided—because it was the most conservative and therefore safest approach—that if the news were bad she would elect to undergo a double mastectomy with reconstruction, a process that subsequently involved visits to a number of doctors, including a family physician, an oncologist, a breast surgeon, a plastic surgeon, and a radiation oncologist, and a regular oncologist, who, after learning that the wife had suffered four miscarriages, surmised that the flood of estrogen of a full-blown pregnancy might have been just the thing to cause the cells in those milk ducts to spread. Other doctors wrote on white boards, drawing normal looking cells and cells that had mutated. They suggested books for the woman to read. They asked the same questions that nurses had just asked. They made inquiries about family history and medications. During exactly zero of these visits had the woman explained that she'd been writing a book about the rhetoric of breast cancer survivors, a project whose origins could likely be traced back to the fact that the woman's mother had died when she was only 46 years of age, and that the woman had been 14 at the time, and that this event had shaped her life to a profound degree, since, for years afterward, she privately grieved for her mother, filling journals with writing, notebooks upon notebooks she still kept but never read and never showed anyone. It goes without saying, then, that the woman's diagnosis had been devastating—she had lain for a long time in the middle of the day on the bed with the man, crying and dabbing her eyes and saying things like, maybe there's a silver lining to all this, because they'd discovered it before it had become invasive, and then thinking of a world in which her son didn't have a mom, and crying some more, and the man remembered a story his wife had told him long ago about sitting alone on the floor of her living room not long after her mother had died, watching cartoons with tears streaming down her face, while eating an ice cream pie that had been delivered by her father's new girlfriend. So yes, the news had been devastating. The procedure itself had also been painful—the first surgery involved not only the removal of breast tissue but the insertion of expanders to stretch her pectoral muscles—and exhausting—the woman had to sleep in a recliner for four weeks—and messy—tubes draining blood and liquid from wounds into little squeeze bottles that had to be emptied twice a day—and boring—it turned out a person could only watch so much TV before you felt like you were going insane—and frustrating—she longed to exercise, but couldn't run for a month, and then, once she'd returned to her previous form, the second surgery, during which the expanders would be replaced with gel packs, she'd had to give up running again. This, more or less, was the extent of the woman's funk, which, it is perhaps plain to see, the man was foolish to have equated with his own, even—and perhaps especially if—he was joking.

The couple continued to walk in silence. This silence, though, it wasn't like before. It wasn't comfortable. At least not for the man. Did the woman now resent his presence? Did she wish she'd stayed at the house—or that he hadn't come along? He couldn't be sure. The only thing he could say with absolute certainty was that the evening through which they were walking was, without question, incredibly beautiful. In the distance, unseen children were laughing and screaming happily—the man imagined a game of chase or hide and seek while the children's parents sipped cocktails or stood over flaming grills. Fireflies pulsed in the air: little intermittent flashes of green. One might even say—as the man couldn't help but think—that they were walking right through the middle of a quintessential summer evening, as if the night itself was pulling out all the stops to put on the performance of the season. The man and woman turned a corner. A soft breeze rustled the leaves of a tree, which diffused a yellow glow. Past the tree, they could see, in the sky, a low full moon: a bright and impossibly huge sphere hovering above the neighborhood, illuminating the algae-blanketed pond across the street, riming the dark green fields beyond. The man pointed skyward. The woman said, "Wow." The fact that they had both been rendered speechless gave the man hope; maybe, he thought, the beauty they'd encountered during this little stroll would erase the memory of his ineptitude. He kept quiet, so as not to infringe on an unspoken truce. He thought about taking a picture and instinctively patted his pockets to locate his phone, which he remembered having left in the bedroom to charge. And that was okay. It wasn't possible to take a good picture of the moon, anyway—at least not with his phone.

As the couple approached their house, a light in the living room snapped on, followed shortly by another light downstairs. Initially, the man figured the appearance of a sequence of lights in their house could be easily explained: his son likely wandering through rooms, looking for a cord so he could charge the dying battery of the tablet computer. Then again, the man thought, it could've been anybody. For years, they'd left the front door unlocked: they would leave the house for a few minutes or a few hours or an entire day and though they would certainly shut they rarely locked their front door, placing full trust in their neighbors and anyone who might wander into their cul-de-sac (proselytizers and lawn care specialists and meter readers and pizzeria employees placing hang-tags on doorknobs) that they would have the good sense not to enter a home that wasn't theirs.

They heard the screams as they approached the front door. It was the boy, screaming—in a way that seemed desperate—their names, as if through force of sheer will—and volume—the man and woman might materialize. The man figured that the boy had somehow injured himself—and remembered once when he was a kid at a church camp and how he'd ducked out of playing baseball, because he hated baseball, and returned to his room, where he'd cut himself playing with a pocket knife, and started screaming bloody murder for help, and how a neighbor had appeared and said, after inspecting the injury, which turned out to be rather slight, "I thought somebody had cut their leg off." The boy, however, was not injured. He was, as he attempted to explain, between exhausted sobs, *scared*; he hadn't known where his parents were. He'd tried to call his mother's phone and she hadn't answered, and he'd tried to call the father's phone, and he hadn't answered either, and because both of them had never *not* answered their phones, the boy had become afraid, and began to entertain worst-case scenarios. It was here that the man was overcome with empathy for his son; he could remember having this exact feeling as a kid, and how terrible it had been to not know where your parents were and then imagining that something horrible had happened to them and the more time passed without them showing up, the more real the imagined scenario became, until it had solidified itself in reality and become the only viable explanation: this was it, they were never coming back, they were gone forever. But the man and woman *had* returned. They were not gone forever. And so the woman hugged the boy and then the man hugged him too and then the man said I want to show you something. He took the boy's hand and led him outside, knowing that the boy was probably wondering what in the world was he doing, taking him out into the yard at this hour, *at night*, and then in the space between the houses across the street, the man pointed, and the boy looked into the sky and saw the big bright moon.

For the most part, the couple had kept their son in the dark about the particulars of his mother's surgery. He didn't know that the entirety of his mother's breast tissue had been removed. He didn't know that a surgeon had placed expanders under her pectoral muscles and that she'd had to visit the surgeon every two weeks to receive injections that would gradually enlarge them. He'd never seen the drains where red fluid sloshed. He didn't know that the expanders had been replaced with gel packs. He didn't know that his mother would be returning to the operating room in December to remove her fallopian tubes, because that was, doctors had discovered, where ovarian cancer likely started. The boy had only known that doctors had found something in her breasts that could turn into cancer if they didn't remove it. He didn't ask any follow-ups. He was more concerned about the recliner the woman had to sleep in. Once she was done with it, she'd promised it would be his.

The man didn't explain that the moon wasn't really bigger, that its apparent enormity was merely an optical illusion. Instead, he let his son bask in the brightness, hoping that the sight of it would act like a commemorative stamp on his memory, and that someday the man would say, "Hey, remember that time when you thought we were gone and I showed you the moon," and the boy would say, "Yeah," and then the man would tell him about how he and the boy's mother had walked together, each of them carrying silent burdens the boy had known nothing about, and the boy would remember the time when his father, who could not always be depended upon to do or say the right thing, had shepherded him into the yard and pointed to the huge round rock in the sky that was reflecting the light of the nearest star, and how the boy had wiped away his tears to see it.

About the Contributors

Hannah Dela Cruz Abrams received the 2013 Whiting Award for her novella *The Man Who Danced with Dolls* and her memoir-in-progress *The Following Sea*. Her work has most recently appeared in, or is forthcoming from, *Oxford American*, *Carolina Quarterly*, and *Mayday Magazine*, among others.

Ellery Akers is the author of two poetry books, *Practicing the Truth* and *Knocking on the Earth*. She has won thirteen national writing awards, including the Poetry International Prize, the John Masefield Award, and *Sierra* magazine's Nature Writing Award. Her poetry has been featured on National Public Radio and in *The New York Times Magazine*, *Poetry*, and *The Sun*.

Ron A. Austin serves as a senior editor for *december* and is a 2016 Regional Arts Commission Fellow. His stories have been placed in *Ninth Letter*, *Black Warrior Review*, *The Masters Review*, *Midwestern Gothic*, *Natural Bridge*, and other journals. He has taught creative writing at the Pierre Laclede Honors College, and he is now finishing his collection of stories, *Avery Colt Is A Snake, A Thief, A Liar*.

Emma Bolden is author of the poetry collections *Maleficae* and *medi(t)ations*, the poetry chapbooks *How to Recognize a Lady*, *The Mariner's Wife*, *The Sad Epistles*, and *This Is Our Hollywood*, and the nonfiction chapbook *Geography V*. Her poetry and prose has appeared in such journals as *The Rumpus*, *Prairie Schooner*, *Conduit*, *the Indiana Review*, *the Greensboro Review*, *Redivider*, *Verse*, *Feminist Studies*, *The Journal*, and *Guernica*, and her work has been anthologized in *Best American Poetry 2015* and *The Best Small Fictions 2015*. She is the recipient of a 2017 NEA Fellowship.

Richard Burgin's newest book is the short story collection *Don't Think*. His stories have won five Pushcart Prizes and have been anthologized in *The Ecco Anthology of Contemporary American Short Fiction*, *The Best American Mystery Stories*, and *New Jersey Noir*. His other books include *Hide Island: A Novella and Nine Stories*, the novels *Rivers Last Longer* and *Ghost Quartet*, and eight collections of short fiction.

WENDY CALL is co-editor of *Telling True Stories: A Nonfiction Writers' Guide* (Penguin, 2007) and author of *No Word for Welcome: The Mexican Village Faces the Global Economy* (Nebraska, 2011), winner of the Grub Street National Book Prize for Nonfiction. She teaches creative writing and environmental studies at Pacific Lutheran University. "Apothecarium" was made possible by a 2010 Creative Artists Fellowship from the American Antiquarian Society, where the apothecary's notebook is in their collection. "Apothecarium" was originally commissioned by Hugo House in Seattle, for their 2014 Literary Series.

ALEXANDER CHEE is the author of the novels *Edinburgh* and *The Queen of the Night*. He is a contributing editor at *The New Republic*, and an editor at large at *VQR*. His essays and stories have appeared in *The New York Times Book Review, Tin House, Slate, Guernica, National Public Radio* and *Out*, among others. He is winner of a 2003 Whiting Award, a 2004 NEA Fellowship in prose and a 2010 MCCA Fellowship, and he has taught writing at Wesleyan University, Amherst College, the University of Iowa Writers' Workshop, Columbia University, Sarah Lawrence College and the University of Texas–Austin.

LISA CHEN is the author of a book of poems, *Mouth* (Kaya Press), winner of the 2009 Writing Award from the Association of Asian American Studies. She was a 2015-16 Emerging Writers Fellow at the Center for Fiction. She is currently writing a novel about MSG mines and a colony of rogue snow monkeys in upstate New York. She was born in Taiwan and lives in Brooklyn.

J.L COOPER is a writer and psychologist in Sacramento, California. Awards include *The Tupelo Quarterly* Prose Open Prize, TQ9, First Place in Short Fiction in *New Millenium Writings*, 2013, and Second Place in Essay in *Literal Latte*, 2014. His short stories, poetry, and a craft piece have appeared in *The Manhattan Review, Oberon Poetry Magazine, Hippocampus, Structo (U.K.), The Tishman Review, Gold Man Review, The Sonder Review, The Leveler, The Sun* (readers write), and in other journals and anthologies. A full length collection of poetry is forthcoming from WordTech.

MEGHAN DAUM'S most recent book is the essay collection *The Unspeakable: And Other Subjects of Discussion*, which won the 2015 PEN Center USA Award for creative nonfiction. Her other books include the essay collection *My Misspent Youth*, the novel *The Quality of Life Report*, and *Life Would Be Perfect If I Lived In That House*, a memoir. She is the recipient of a 2015 Guggenheim Fellowship and a 2016 National Endowment for the Arts fellowship and is an adjunct associate professor in the MFA Writing Program at Columbia University's School of the Arts.

STEPHEN DIXON has published 16 story collections and 16 novels since 1976, and about 600 short stories. His most recent books include the novella *Beatrice*, the novel *Letters to Kevin*, and the story collection *Late Stories*, all published in 2016. He lives in Ruxton, Maryland.

DARROW FARR is from Philadelphia and and now lives in Austin, where she is an MFA candidate at the Michener Center for Writers. Her work can be found in the *Saints and Sinners 2016* anthology.

AH-REUM HAN received her MFA from George Mason University, where she was the 2014-2015 fiction fellow. Her work has appeared or is forthcoming in *Okey-Panky, Blunderbuss, Fiction International, Flyway* (winner of the Notes from the Field contest), and *Fugue* (runner-up for the prose contest), among others. Her work has also been shortlisted for the *Masters Review* and received Honorable Mention in *Glimmer Train*, and she was a finalist for *Indiana Review's* fiction prize.

JAC JEMC is the author of *The Grip of It*, forthcoming from FSG Originals in 2017. Her first novel, *My Only Wife* (Dzanc Books), was a finalist for the 2013 PEN/Robert W. Bingham Prize for Debut Fiction and winner of the Paula Anderson Book Award, and her collection of stories, *A Different Bed Every Time* (Dzanc Books), was named one of Amazon's best story collections of 2014.

BETH UZNIS JOHNSON is a graduate of the MFA program at Queens University of Charlotte and a contributor at the Sewanee, Tin House and Bread Loaf Writers Workshops. Her work has appeared in the *Bear River Review, Delphi*

Quarterly and the *Rumpus* Readers Report and is forthcoming in *Southwest Review*. She is the editor and senior writer of *Thrive*, the patient magazine of the University of Michigan Comprehensive Cancer Center.

A story based on a chapter of MIMI KAWAHARA's first novel, *The Cicada's Song*, appears in the Fall 2016 issue of *Washington Square Review*. A Roman-born Japanese Jewish bibliophile, Mimi is seeking an agent while working on a memoir and a collection of stories about her experience with hospice patients. She can be reached at mkawahara29@gmail.com.

MATTHEW LANSBURGH's fiction has been published in *The Florida Review*, *Michigan Quarterly Review*, *Columbia*, *Guernica*, *Hobart*, *Slice*, and *Joyland*. His stories have won *The Florida Review's* 2015 fiction contest and *Columbia's* 2014 fiction contest and have received four Pushcart Prize nominations. His work has received financial support from the Sewanee Writers' Conference and NYU's MFA Program, where he taught as a Veterans Writing Workshop Fellow.

ILANA MASAD is an Israeli-American writer living in NYC. Her work has appeared in *The New Yorker, McSweeney's, Tin House, Printer's Row, Joyland, The Butter, Hypertext Magazine, Split Lip Magazine, Broadly, Dame, The Guardian,* the *Los Angeles Times,* and more. She is also the founder of *The Other Stories*, a podcast that makes it just a little bit easier for writers to get heard.

SARAH MCCOLL received her MFA from Sarah Lawrence College in May 2016, and her writing has appeared in *South Dakota Review, In Context Journal*, and a forthcoming essay anthology from University of Nebraska Press.

JONO NAITO lives in Syracuse, NY and is excavating an MFA and waiting for sunlight. They have been published in *Waxwing, Paper Darts*, and elsewhere, and is an Assistant Editor at *Salt Hill.*

ALIX OHLIN is the author of four books of fiction, and her work has appeared in *Best American Short Stories, Best American Non-Required Reading, Ploughshares, Triquarterly*, and many other places.

WENDY C. ORTIZ is a Los Angeles native. She is the author of *Excavation: A Memoir*, *Hollywood Notebook*, and the dreamoir *Bruja*. Her writing has appeared in *The New York Times*, *Hazlitt*, *Vol. 1 Brooklyn*, *The Nervous Breakdown*, *Fanzine*, and a year-long series appeared at *McSweeney's Internet Tendency*.

TANJIL RASHID is a journalist for the BBC in London. His fiction, poetry, and translations have appeared in literary journals such as *Asymptote* and *Hourglass*, and his criticism and reporting has been widely published in the British press from *The Guardian* to *The Financial Times*. In 2015 he was a runner-up for the Harvil Secker Young Translator's Prize run by Penguin Random House.

KISHA LEWELLYN SCHLEGEL'S essays have been published in *Drunken Boat*, *The Iowa Review*, *Gulf Coast*, and elsewhere. She holds an MFA from the University of Iowa and currently teaches creative writing at Whitman College.

MATTHEW VOLLMER is the author of two collections of stories, *Gateway to Paradise* and *Future Missionaries of America*, as well as a collection of essays, *inscriptions for headstones*. With David Shields, he is the editor of *Fakes: An Anthology of Pseudo-Interviews, Faux-Lectures, Quasi-Letters, "Found" Texts, and Other Fraudulent Artifacts*. He is also the editor of *A Book of Uncommon Prayer*, an anthology of everyday invocations. He directs the undergraduate creative writing program at Virginia Tech.

BRYAN WASHINGTON has written for *The New York Times Magazine*, *The Paris Review*, *American Short Fiction*, and elsewhere. He divides his time between Houston and New Orleans.

CLAIRE VAYE WATKINS' stories and essays have appeared in *Granta*, *Tin House*, *The Paris Review*, *One Story*, *Glimmer Train*, *The New York Times* and many others. She is the author of *Gold Fame Citrus* and *Battleborn*, which won awards including the Story Prize, the Dylan Thomas Prize, and New York Public Library's Young Lions Fiction Award. A Guggenheim Fellow, Claire teaches at the University of Michigan and is co-director of the Mojave School.

WIL WEITZEL'S fiction has appeared in *Conjunctions*, *Kenyon Review*, *Prairie Schooner*, and elsewhere. He received a NYC Emerging Writers Fellowship from the Center for Fiction, won the Washington Square Flash Fiction Award, and was a finalist for the David Nathan Meyerson Prize for Fiction.

ALEX WILSON's short fiction has appeared in the *Southwest Review, Tupelo Quarterly*, and *New Stories from the Southwest*, and one of his stories was recently named runner-up for the *Glimmer Train* Short Story Award for New Writers. His nonfiction has received honorable mention from *The Best American Travel Writing* series and has appeared in *Byliner, Surfer*, and the *San Diego Union Tribune*, among others. He is the deputy editor of *The Surfer's Journal* and has taught creative writing at New School of Architecture and Design.

MARLÉNE ZADIG is a writer in Berkeley, California. Her fiction made *Longform*'s Top 5 list of Best Fiction in 2015 and has appeared or is forthcoming in *Joyland, Green Mountains Review Online, Slice Magazine, Blunderbuss Magazine, The Adirondack Review*, and elsewhere. She is a 2016 *storySouth* Million Writers Award nominee, a 2015 Best of the Net finalist, the runner-up for the 2015 Fulton Prize for Short Fiction, and she blogs for *Carve Magazine*.

Bricolage Source List

Lines culled from

"Three Myths From the Northern Mariana Islands" - Hannah Dela Cruz Abrams
"The Universal Particular" - Alix Ohlin
"A Portrait of the Artist as a Young Imam" - Tanjil Rashid
"Half Dollar" - Jac Jemc
"How Sad, How Lovely" - Sarah McColl
"Sages of West 47th Street" - J.L. Cooper
"Paper Face" - Richard Burgin
"Catch the Snow" - Jono Naito
"Up a Steep and Very Narrow Stairway" - Emma Bolden
"Cauldron" - Ron A. Austin
"Cousin" - Bryan Washington
"Apothecarium" - Wendy Call
"Excerpts from Bruja: A Dreamoir" - Wendy C. Ortiz
"Sand Running" - Ilana Masad
"The Devil is a Lie" - Darrow Farr
"Behind Me" - Beth Uznis Johnson
"Geese" - Wil Weitzel

Lines culled by

Tom Bertrand
Joshua Demaree
Sean Kauffman
Paul Lisicky
Brook McClurg
Alex Rosenfeld
Kevin Smith
Matt Stalnaker
Kymberly Williams